Emergency

Irish Hospitals in Chaos

Marie O'Connor

Gill & Macmillan

Gill & Macmillan Ltd
Hume Avenue, Park West, Dublin 12
with associated companies throughout the world
www.gillmacmillan.ie

© Marie O'Connor 2007
978 07171 4227 9

Typography design by Make Communication
Print origination by Carole Lynch
Printed by ColourBooks Ltd, Dublin

This book is typeset in Linotype Minion and Neue Helvetica.

The paper used in this book comes from the wood pulp of
managed forests. For every tree felled, at least one tree is
planted, thereby renewing natural resources.

A CIP catalogue record for this book is available
from the British Library.

5 4 3 2 1

'Don't you see that the whole aim of Newspeak is to narrow the range of thought? In the end, we shall make thought crime literally impossible, because there will be no words in which to express it'.

GEORGE ORWELL, *NINETEEN EIGHTY-FOUR*

This book is dedicated to my late parents—my mother, who first taught me the meaning of solidarity, and my father, who remained true to his Hippocratic ideals—and to all who struggle to widen the range of thought on health—my friends in Ireland, and elsewhere, who strive to prevent medical hegemony, corporate greed and political complicity from damaging human health.

Contents

Introduction

I have always been interested in hospitals. Although never ill myself, I grew up with hospital patients. My father ran a regional orthopaedic hospital, just outside the village of Croom, Co. Limerick, for many years. My mother was a theatre sister in her day. His three brothers were doctors, her two sisters nurses. Some of my earliest memories are of children who were orthopaedic patients in Croom—in for the long haul. It was a hospital that had a human face, a feature that often seems missing from larger hospitals today.

This book is about hospitals, about what goes on inside them, about the dynamics that drive them. It looks at the services from the point of view of patients, their families, their communities. A nurse, who was a patient in A&E, paints a picture of mayhem in the hospital where she trained; a mother, coerced into submitting to unwanted medical intervention in a labour ward, relives the anguish of her experience of industrialised care.

Many of today's health stories make difficult reading, like the story of an elderly man with MRSA who died in a private nursing home from burns he sustained, having been left sitting too close to a radiator for too long. Or the account of an inquest into the death of a baby born prematurely by Caesarean section, repeated attempts by her mother to get her due dates corrected in her file having failed. Sometimes, it is impossible not to be outraged by the growing injustice of a system that denies care to the less well off; and that now proposes to cut 'golden hour' access from hundreds of thousands of people to anything resembling an acute hospital. By the stark contrast between the gloss of one of the wealthiest countries in the world and the primitive conditions that prevail in so many of our public hospitals. By the chaos and dysfunction of a system that allows hospital bugs to flourish, while denying hospitals what they need to deal effectively with infection. By our Government's obdurate refusal to fund our public health system adequately.

Few engage with what is happening in our health system. There is a lack of critical awareness, of investigative journalism. The failure to interrogate spin, the sustained propaganda about 'taking politics out of health', the art of public lying—or public relations—the dismissal of community interests as 'parochial', the routing of elected representatives from health: all stifles debate.

Behind the rhetoric of our 'world-class' health service lies the reality: the two- and three-day waits in A&E, the four- and five-year waits for public patients to see specialists. The interminable wait for surgery—22,000 operations in public hospitals cancelled at the last count. The rise in deaths from hospital-acquired infections, such as MRSA, clostridium difficile and other highly dangerous bugs.

Noël Browne eradicated tuberculosis in the 1950s at a time when it was almost a pandemic; isolating the 'index case' was key. In straitened times, the Government funded 7,000 new hospital beds: psychiatric hospitals were pressed into service, as well as fever, district and county hospitals. Even a teacher training college was mobilised in the war against TB. Yet today, in an era of unprecedented wealth, when we have another pandemic on our hands that is just as lethal, there are no government plans to implement a 'search and destroy' policy; that MRSA victim could very well be beside you on the next trolley, in the next bed, in intensive care.

There is a chronic shortage of beds, consultants, nurses, midwives, physiotherapists, occupational therapists, speech therapists—the list is endless. Consultants say they cannot get access to theatres to do their work. Some are turning to the private sector in frustration. Others write letters to the newspapers explaining why they are forced to play golf, because the theatre list has been cancelled—yet again— due to the flood of emergency admissions.

Yes, money *is* being poured into the system as never before: €14 billion according to the most recent figure, and rising. And yet the system seems to stagger from one crisis to another, with no visible improvement. We now have a health service administration that has been centralised, that is impervious to scrutiny, presided over by a politburo of six, whose daily overtime rate is more than some households' average monthly income. A health service that logs 1,000 'adverse events' every week, where doctors' decisions cannot be queried by law except through the Medical Council, where grievance machinery, launched in January 2007, has been legislated for that actually *prevents* patients from complaining about anything involving a 'clinical decision'.

The Government has reneged on its commitment to its own health Programme for Government. The stopgap solutions brought forward instead are creating their own vicious circles. Beds reserved for day surgery are now being commandeered for A&E patients, for example, so while the HSE trolley count may look better, scheduled operations have to be cancelled every day. This means longer waits for surgery, and ultimately more public patients queuing in A&E, or in 'transit lounges', for their cancelled operations. (Casualty has long been the quickest route to a hospital bed for public patients, who bear the brunt of an inequitable system.)

Another vicious circle of longer duration is the waltz of medicine with litigation. The more doctors over-treat for fear of litigation, the more adverse outcomes occur; the more people are injured in our hospitals, the more they sue; the more litigation, the more over-treatment. Unnecessary testing, unnecessary procedures—Caesarean section is a very good example—are costing the system an incalculable amount of money every year.

Paradoxically, the current explosion in private health care will ultimately lead to less access, not more. International experience shows that the more private 'providers' there are, the more medical goods and services are consumed; the more consumption, the bigger the insurers' bills; the higher the pay-outs, the more the premiums will rise. In the United States, for example, health insurance now runs at around $2,000 a *month*, putting the cost of family health insurance on a par with the family home mortgage. Could we see such unaffordable premiums in Ireland? A rise of 30 per cent in private health premiums over the next three years or so has been predicted. Whatever the actual rise, the increases are sure to be substantial enough to put private health care out of reach for many.

This book looks at black holes as well as vicious circles. One of the biggest is the public–private mix: taxpayers pay up to 60 per cent of the bill for private medical practice in publicly funded hospitals. The public system subsidises the private, paying publicly employed doctors twice, in the case of private patients, to treat the same people. Speaking of the consultants' 'common' contract, Professor Niamh Brennan said: 'I could not believe that such a contract could exist.' But there is more: the serf taxpayer also foots the bill for malpractice insurance, picking up the tab even for doctors working in private hospitals and clinics over which the state has no control.

This book is not an attack on the medical profession, or on medicine: I write, on the contrary, out of a sense of idealism, a belief in a better world. Day in, day out, hospital staff strive to provide high-quality care despite the irrationality that threatens to engulf the system. Thousands of doctors, nurses, midwives and others do their level best, within a system where solidarity and caring are increasingly forced to give way to corporatism and careerism. But this is a culture that needs to change, where ownership, for example, still rules—where, if you are admitted as an A&E patient, the surgical team on duty will not touch you; where, if you are a private patient and your consultant is unavailable, you will not be seen by another doctor. Where 'collegiality' has endangered patient safety, as it did so spectacularly in the Lourdes hospital.

All professions are not necessarily conspiracies against the public, as George Bernard Shaw once remarked. However, in the case of organised medicine, it is impossible not to question an increasingly elitist, professional project that, more and more, seems to have lost sight of the patient. Not to question a health agenda that prioritises medical ambition over service needs—arrogantly dismissed as 'parochial issues' by HSE chief Brendan Drumm. The proliferation of specialties, sub-specialties and sub-sub-specialties, that are infinitely more suited to a densely populated country, such as England. The craziness of a system that gives publicly unelected and wholly unaccountable private medical bodies—the royal colleges—the power to determine access to life and death services in local communities.

Knowing that rich and poor alike are dying needlessly in our hospitals and outside them for want of appropriate and timely care is intolerable. That people have died needlessly in transit to more remote hospitals, that women have given birth on the side of the road, all casualties of the prevailing agenda to centralise hospital care. That the Government plans to close our smaller public hospitals, while at the same time subsidising the building of even smaller *private* hospitals, co-located on public sites (where they will do maximum damage to the public hospital system). That plans to close up to half the country's maternity units will further dehumanise the services for birth.

There is the added ugliness of a health service that depends on the size of your wallet. Hearing a 39-year-old mother on RTÉ's *Liveline* describe, just a couple of weeks ago, how she now faces a death sentence because she could not buy access to private cancer testing and treatment was a double shock: I have known 'Rosie' for a number of years; I recognised her voice immediately. Will her courage and her anger change anything? Knowing that all of this is being driven by vested interests both within the medical profession and outside it, I wonder.

So much is driven by the naked pursuit of power and money and status. Driven now from behind by a new dynamic, Medicine Inc., the drive towards for-profit medicine, towards corporatised health care, which in turn is being fuelled by another nexus, the banker, the broker, the builder, all of whom stand to make enormous profits in the boom, as new hyper-hospitals are built and prime sites released onto the market for redevelopment.

Many of those working in the health services strongly oppose the current trends of centralisation, privatisation and bureaucratisation. Yet hardly any medical bodies have spoken out against them. The only health union to date to take a strong public position against privatisation, for example, is Impact. There is a sense of fear among health professionals, even among consultants. Few have gone public on conditions in our hospitals, although there are honourable exceptions, whom I shall not embarrass by naming. Sustained efforts made by health bureaucrats in recent years to silence consultants are disturbing. But if medical consultants are reluctant to speak out, where does that leave lesser mortals in the hierarchy?

I have tried in this book to unpick some of the threads of dysfunction, and to do so in a way that is accessible. Opinion polls indicate that, as we approach the 2007 general election, the abysmal state of the health services is one of voters' top priorities. It is not for me to prescribe a comprehensive blueprint for genuine reform: that is the responsibility of political leaders. However, in the final two chapters—setting out more than fifty recommendations—I have proposed an agenda for change that would eliminate the medieval fiefdoms, and, in their place, restore the republic.

Prologue

On 11 December 2002, Denise Livingstone woke at around 3.30 in the morning with crampy abdominal pains. She was six months pregnant with her first child.

As soon as she realised she was in labour, Denise left her home in Emyvale, Co. Monaghan, accompanied by her partner, Barry Kerr, and her sister Tina. Monaghan General Hospital was only six miles away. But Denise's sister, Sharon, had given birth when she was six months pregnant three years previously. They were taking no chances.

Arriving at the hospital at around 5 a.m., they went around to the back to find the doors of the casualty unit closed, even though the hospital was on call for medical and surgical emergencies. They drove around to the front of the hospital. The door was answered by a porter, who told them that they had no maternity doctors and advised them to continue to Cavan Hospital, a fifty-minute journey over bad roads. Barry persisted, and they were finally allowed to enter the hospital.

By then, Denise was very distressed and in severe pain. She was also bleeding. An experienced midwife, who had previously worked in the maternity unit, was on duty in the treatment room at the time, as it happened, together with a staff nurse. Disused incubators and state-of-the-art neonatal resuscitation equipment stood in the hospital's maternity unit, just upstairs from where Denise stood. Closed twenty months earlier, the labour ward was now being used as a storage room and waiting area.

The mother continued to bleed; she complained of feeling a 'gush of fluid'. She was getting contractions every three minutes: she felt certain the baby was coming. Both the midwife and the nurse believed that the mother was on the point of giving birth. A junior hospital doctor in surgery took charge. He suspected a placental abruption, where the afterbirth shears off the wall of the womb, a potentially lethal complication for both mother and baby. Not realising Denise was in labour, he decided to transfer her to Cavan General 25 miles away, and contacted the SHO in obstetrics there to arrange the transfer.

The midwife who had looked after Denise contacted the ambulance base at 5.20 a.m. She asked for a midwife to accompany the patient and said that the hospital had none available. Denise was given 50 mg of pethidine, a drug that dulls the pain of labour and depresses the baby's breathing. At 5.28 a.m., the ambulance arrived. The emergency medical technicians (EMTs) seemed to realise the birth was imminent and requested a midwife to accompany them. They were told that that none was available. Denise was given a second injection of pethidine at 5.35 a.m. At 5.39 a.m., the ambulance left Monaghan General Hospital with Denise, her sister Tina and the EMTs. By then, Denise was on continuous oxygen and IV fluids.

There was no incubator or neonatal resuscitation equipment in the ambulance. No midwife accompanied her, although two midwives were on nursing duty in the hospital at the time and a surplus nurse had been rostered to deal with such emergencies. The midwife had told the EMTs that Denise would not make it to Cavan. About 17 miles into the journey, the ambulance had to pull over at the side of the road: the baby was coming. Twenty minutes after her mother had been turned away from Monaghan General, Bronagh Livingstone was born.

The baby was born in the breech position. Initially flat and unresponsive, she was suctioned and given oxygen via a 'bag and mask'. She cried en route to Cavan. Mother and baby arrived at Cavan at about 7.30, where they were seen and transferred to the maternity ward. Her grandfather later reported that she had 'a good head of black hair'. The little girl weighed 1 lb 10 ounces. Jimmy takes up the story again: 'After a while, they decided to ventilate the baby because she was getting tired. At about 8.30 they came in and said Bronagh had taken a turn for the worse and, at about ten to nine, they said she had died.' He described how his daughter held Bronagh's tiny body in her arms all day and the following day, and how they had to coax her to give the baby up for burial.

Two days later, Denise appeared on the *Late Late Show*, still visibly traumatised by her ordeal.

Subsequent analysis of the placenta revealed a large abruption or clot, showing that Denise had been at significantly increased risk of bleeding during and after the birth. Two lives had been placed at risk.

Up to twenty midwives were then employed at the hospital as general nurses; no plans were in place to ensure their availability in cases such as Denise Livingstone's. The Irish Nurses' Organisation said it had sought a midwifery roster two months earlier; this was denied. Nor were there any arrangements in place to ensure that a midwife could accompany a mother in labour in an ambulance transfer. These arrangements had been discontinued some three months previously, an official inquiry into the death later noted. A consultant obstetrician was still on the payroll; he explained that he could have done nothing for Ms Livingstone as the health board had not allowed him to renew his malpractice insurance.

An emergency drill drawn up after the maternity unit had closed—setting out the 'legal duty of care' owed to patients—said that babies should be delivered at Monaghan General if delivery was 'inevitable prior to transfer' to another hospital. How this might be accomplished was unclear; midwives are the sole specialists in normal birth and the new rules were based on 'the understanding' that there would be no midwives or obstetric staff on site. The protocol had been tested twelve months previously, when a similar emergency had arisen. On that occasion, the mother had been allowed to give birth at the hospital; staff were reportedly rapped on the knuckles and told that the health board was not insured to provide care to women in labour. This was later denied.

An internal review into this 'adverse event' by risk managers found that the decision to transfer Denise was the correct one. But the external inquiry commissioned by the Minister for Health into the baby's death concluded that Ms Livingstone should have been delivered in Monaghan General Hospital and that delivery during transport in an ambulance was 'not optimal'. The *Daly Report* said that the staff and equipment at the hospital were more than adequate to resuscitate and stabilise the infant initially. It criticised the failure to summon the consultant anaesthetist on call. 'The consultant anaesthetist has certification and training in neonatal resuscitation.... There was a sophisticated resuscitaire available in the delivery suite which could have been used to ventilate the baby.... Baby Bronagh could also have been placed in an incubator which was more than adequate to maintain heat.' However, the authors concluded: 'Given Baby Bronagh's birth weight, the fact that she was born at 24 weeks and 6 days, and the fact that the premature labour appears to have been associated with a placental abruption, her chance of survival could be less than 10 per cent. Unfortunately more than 50 per cent of survivors could have significant disability.'

Bronagh Mary Livingstone was buried in Corracrin Cemetery, just outside Emyvale. She was just three hours old when she died.

In the 'risk society', the obligation to look after a patient is in danger of being reduced to a legal requirement or compliance with a protocol. The notion that a professional might have a higher duty of care is becoming obsolete. Have we reached a point where the system matters more than the patient?

I Roots

Fools

Chapter 1
Medical Fiefdoms

Over the past fifty years or so, medicine has become an increasingly dominating force in our lives. The power of the medical profession now stands higher than at any point in human history. Like the church and the monarchy in other cultures and times, medicine presents itself as infallible and omnipotent. Doctors determine where and how we shall be born, and, increasingly, where and how we shall die. Medicine has changed beyond recognition, from community to hospital, from familiar to unfamiliar. Today it has become an empire that costs billions in public monies to maintain. In Ireland, as in other countries, corporations are now a driving force in health care, as is bureaucracy. Both are equally pitiless. In the new Ireland, there is a growing indifference to human suffering, to the pain of others. Compared to the health of hospital finances, the cost of a human life hardly matters. Cost-effectiveness rules.

Health care has changed beyond all recognition. In many communities, the family doctor is no more. Hospitals have once more become places to be feared, as in the nineteenth century, when operations were performed without anaesthesia. As these institutions have grown in size, so doctors have in large measure become divorced from their patients. And as technology has advanced, some consultants have become technocrats, increasingly distant, remote and cut off from their patients. Many hospitals have become severed from their communities. The thread of relationship has broken.

BARBER-SURGEONS

The power of the medical profession has taken over 500 years to consolidate. Ireland's leading medical trade associations, for example, were created by the British monarchy in the late Middle Ages. By then, the healing arts had developed into trades: members of these trades formed guilds. Apothecaries (or chemists), barber-surgeons, and herbalists (or physicians) organised themselves into trade unions, more or less successfully. The barber-surgeons were the very first to be incorporated: Henry vi gave the Dublin Barbers' Guild a charter in 1446. This was the first incorporation of what today in these islands we would call 'medical practitioners'. Barbers were then equated with surgeons: no distinction was made between the two. They were mixed with other trades; the third charter given to barbers, for example, covered wigmakers as well as apothecaries. The barber-surgeons' union lasted for over 300 years. Not until 1702 did freelance surgeons attempt to dissociate themselves from barbers, apothecaries and wigmakers.

Women as well as men were admitted to the guild. This later became a ground for attacking the trade union, which was denounced as 'a refuge for empiricks, impudent quacks, women and other idle persons who quit the trades to which they were bred'. During the eighteenth century, there was free trade in surgery, although barbers were supposed to confine themselves to bleeding patients and pulling teeth. George ii later granted apothecaries their own charter, giving them the power to form their own guild, the Guild of St Luke.

Turf wars erupted as barber-surgeons tried to displace midwives and physicians. Although vast numbers of women must have earned their living from midwifery in Ireland in the sixteenth century, just as they did in England, there seems to be no record of a midwives' trade union; an early attempt by English midwives to form a corporation was foiled by their rivals in the College of Physicians. Following the College's advice, the King refused to incorporate midwives. It was a defining moment.

> *It* [the midwives' petition] *expressed the disconcerting doctrine that what was sauce for the gander was sauce for the goose.*
> The Royal College of Physicians, in 1616, rejecting a demand from midwives to set up their own corporation

The rise of trade unions, such as the guild of barber-surgeons, and the entry of the upper classes into medicine via the universities (as in 'the men of physic') brought men into the birth chamber. This was one area from which they had been barred: female modesty forbade that men should be allowed as much as a glimpse of the female organs. Medieval lithographs depicting the birth chamber show 'man-midwives' standing manfully by the labouring woman's bedside, their hands under the coverlets, groping for the birth canal.

The development, around 1588, of a new technology—the child-birth forceps—gave men in England a new point of entry into the birth chamber. The Chamberlens made a fortune out of their invention, travelling extensively and charging enormous fees—payable in advance—to attend royal and noble mothers. The physicians decided to assert their trading rights: Chamberlen was a member of a rival trade, the guild of barber-surgeons. In 1609, the College of Physicians accused Chamberlen of illicitly practising medicine, and fined him 40 shillings. The College also had the power to imprison those it found guilty of malpractice. In 1612, Chamberlen was jailed in Newgate Prison for dispensing medicine.

Female midwives struggled with male doctors from the seventeenth century. By then, man-midwives were actively seeking to de-skill female midwives by restricting their role to 'attending' rather than 'intervening' in childbirth. Intervention was to be left to men with their technology. Over time, in a division that persists to the present day, labour was divided into 'normal' and 'abnormal'—female midwives for the former, man-midwives for the latter.

BROTHERHOOD

Today's Royal College of Physicians in Dublin's Kildare Street began life as a brotherhood in Trinity College; the College got its first charter in 1667 from Charles II, some seventy years after the university was founded. Physic was then classified as an art, not a science. The aim of the King's charter was to stamp out the 'the daily abuses of ... the art of physic ... by mountebanks and other ignorant and illiterate persons'. The royal charter granted the College of Physicians territorial powers, giving the College a monopoly over the practice of herbalism in Dublin and its environs, within a seven-mile radius of the city. From then on, no one, except a 'fellow' or graduate of the College of Physicians could practise herbalism in Dublin. Meanwhile, in the rest of the country, only those who had a licence to do so from the College of Physicians or those who had graduated from Trinity College, or from Oxford or Cambridge universities, could use herbs to heal. Women healers and herbalists—barred both from the university medical faculties and the medical training bodies on account of their sex—found their herbal practices outside the law.

The new charter also gave the brotherhood power over other trades—apothecaries, barber-surgeons and midwives. Strategically, the College of Physicians declared ownership over the 'science', but not the 'art', of surgery, just as medicine would later claim ownership over midwifery. College members had special privileges: they were exempt from serving on juries, for example, or from doing duty as a constable or a scavenger.

Trinity began to hand out degrees in medicine in 1674. In 1687, the provost and 'senior fellow' of Trinity declared that the university's kitchen garden should be made a physic garden, to be maintained at the expense of the men of physic.

William and Mary gave the brotherhood a further charter in 1692, this time extending its territory to the whole of Ireland. This enabled physicians to operate a closed shop: no more than fourteen Fellowships could be handed out under the 1692 charter.

This charter gave the College of Physicians power to grant licences in medicine and midwifery. A monopoly pact was made: the College agreed to admit no one to its ranks as a fellow except Trinity College medical graduates; the university reciprocated by undertaking to give no one a degree in medicine except those who had passed an examination set by the College of Physicians. These degrees and examinations suggest a modicum of organised teaching, but there was none. Corporate power and control seemed to be the priority, not education. No arrangements were made either by the College or the university to train doctors. Trinity sometimes allowed students who had not been examined by the College to graduate; the College refused to recognise their degrees. From 1692 to 1740, the College issued only four licences to practise midwifery, three of them to men.

WARRING TRADES UNITE

The union between the barbers and the surgeons was dissolved only in 1784, when the Royal College of Surgeons came into being. 'Surgeons', as it became known, owes its existence to His Late Majesty, as the College referred to him in 2003, King George III. (College historians do not record whether the King granted the College its royal charter before or after his descent into madness.) The Dublin college formed a triumvirate with two other colleges in the then British Empire, one in London, the other in Edinburgh. George the Fourth extended the College's considerable privileges in 1828, when its President, Vice-President and what was known as the 'commonality', were incorporated into one 'body politic and corporate'. Nearly 200 years later, this charter continues to form the basis of the College's considerable power in the Republic of Ireland.

Obtaining corpses for dissection was a constant struggle for surgeons. While the King gave the bodies of four executed persons to surgeons every year for dissection, the surgeons considered this too few. An illegal trade in bodies developed; surgeons were willing to pay any price for them. Those who dug up and removed human remains were charged, not with stealing corpses, but with purloining the winding-sheet. Dublin medical students regularly armed themselves with clubs and firearms, plying mourners in the Cabbage Garden Graveyard (near Kevin Street) with whiskey laced with laudanum before stealing the body of their loved one. There was a flourishing export trade to Scotland, with the College of Surgeons being used to warehouse the dead until 1828. Four years later, surgeons arranged that legislation be passed entitling them to as many dead bodies as they needed (the Anatomy Act), unless the deceased person or their next of kin objected.

The frequent wars of the 1700s and early 1800s increased the demand for army and navy surgeons, and the College thrived. Turf wars continued; the surgeons, for example, wanted the apothecaries to be allowed to enter the guild, but physicians, whose practice was closer to that of pharmacists, disagreed.

By the middle of the nineteenth century, physicians, barber-surgeons and apothecaries had joined forces, uneasily uniting their separate trades into a single medical profession. Midwives were excluded, de facto, from the 1858 Medical Registration Act, which empowered the General Medical Council to keep a register of quali-fied medical practitioners. It was another defining moment for the profession. Women were admitted to the ranks of the Royal College of Surgeons in 1885, however, 100 years after the College had staked its claim to midwifery.

EARLY HOSPITALS

The first hospitals in Europe were places of Christian hospitality and rest, halting sites for pilgrims that offered a welcome respite from the rigours of the road. When travellers fell ill, they were cared for until they were well enough to resume their penitential walk or until death intervened. In Ireland, our first hospitals were the leper houses opened by religious orders in the twelfth century. Monks also ran general hospitals until the suppression of the monasteries in 1534.

Private non-profit hospitals, the 'voluntary' hospitals, as they were called in these islands, were set up as early as 1718. Many were in Dublin. When Handel's *Messiah* premiered at the Fishamble Street Theatre in 1722, the proceeds went to Mercer Hospital. Dublin's first hospital for incurables (today Donnybrook's Royal Hospital) was founded in 1744. Many of these institutions, such as the Meath Hospital, were initiated by medical men. They were motivated partly by charitable impulses and partly by self-interest: hospitals were seen as essential to the teaching of medicine. The Dublin Hospital for Poor Lying-in Women (today's Rotunda) was set up in 1745 to care for the 'poor suffering' women in childbirth; it also provided vital 'clinical material' in the form of patients' bodies for student 'man-midwives' to study. Some of these private hospitals were linked, from their very early days, with the royal colleges, and with university medical faculties. Sir Patrick Dun's Hospital, for example, was set up in 1792 to supply clinical material for medical students of the Royal College of Physicians and the School of Physic in Trinity College. Forty years later, professors at the Royal College of Surgeons, 'handicapped by having no beds [bodies] for teaching purposes', founded the Royal City of Dublin Hospital in Baggot Street.

Public hospitals were very slow to develop, beginning with county surgical infirmaries in 1765; lunatic asylums and fever hospitals followed. Workhouses were set up under the 1838 Poor Relief Act; conditions in them were appalling. The infirmaries of these work-houses provided exceedingly basic medical care. Until the founding of the Free State in 1922, these infirmaries—the forerunners of our public hospitals—were the main source of hospital care for most rural areas in Ireland.

Only the poor went willingly to hospital. Until the end of the nine-teenth century, the paying patient who needed surgery stayed at home. Medicine, and particularly surgery, was primitive. Before 1846, for example, surgery in Ireland was performed without an anaesthetic. Opium and whiskey were the only soporifics available, and the patient's bedroom was usually the operating theatre. 'To take three minutes over the amputation of a leg was regarded as dawdling,' a medical historian observed.

The following 150 years saw remarkable advances in medical knowledge and in the development of health care services. Hand in hand with these came the consolidation of those early medical fiefdoms. Medical power grew dramatically, particularly in the last forty years.

Today, the Minister for Health and the medical establishment cherish dreams of a 'world-class' health service. But is world-class chaos closer to the mark?

II Dysfunction

Chapter 2

World-Class Chaos

What works for patients is what works for me.
Nothing more, nothing less. Patients come first.

Minister for Health Mary Harney

One wonders when open-heart surgery will be
performed in the car park.

Dr Paul Carson, writing thirteen months later in
The Irish Times

When we were poorer as a country, we spent more on health. Now that we are richer, we spend less. This may not be the paradox it seems: in the new Ireland, money is all and all is money. Although we are spending billions more on health, it is not enough to bridge the gap between what there is and what there ought to be. Decades of under-investment have left us with huge craters that remain to be filled.

A&E DIARY

12 November 2004: A 66-year-old man who suffered a stroke finally got a bed after two days on a trolley in the A&E department of Dublin's Mater Hospital. His family sat with him through two nights, afraid to leave him on his own; he was paralysed and could not swallow. 'If he was in a ward, at least we'd know there were nurses and doctors around and we could leave him at night,' his son-in-law, Paul Walsh, commented. Care during the first twenty-four hours following a stroke is critical in determining how well or badly the person survives it.

18 November 2004: the Minister for Health produced a €70-million ten-point A&E plan. In it, she promised 300 extra beds in public hospitals; new 'medical assessment units' to bypass the traditional A&E, take referrals directly from GPs and get priority for laboratory and other tests; improved management in public hospitals; additional step-down facilities to allow elderly or otherwise infirm patients to be discharged from those hospitals; and enhanced family doctor services in the community.

Days earlier, Mary Harney had visited an A&E unit in Manhattan, New York City. Was this, perhaps, the Government's vision for A&E in the future? A huge, private Grand Central Station-type facility with no fewer than three Level 1 trauma centres catering for 250,000 patients a year, which charged for its services, while at the same time dealing with 'charity' cases? Eight months after the Minister's visit, St Vincent's, the largest Catholic hospital chain in New York, went into examinership, so that it could continue in business while not having to pay its debts of $1.1 billion.

14 January 2005: An anonymous contributor to *The Irish Times* wrote:

> These [A&E] departments are now highly dysfunctional. People spend days packed sardine-like as trolleys are pushed one against the other. Blood, urine and faeces mix to form an unpleasant and unhygienic environment. Cleaners cannot complete their job and the risk of infection rises. Doctors and nurses have difficulty providing treatment that ordinarily would be administered in the wards of the hospitals. When a patient's condition deteriorates, vital minutes are lost before resuscitation can begin. During periods such as this, A&E departments, rather than offering a safe refuge, become significantly dangerous places for patients.

8 March 2005: 'It was hard to know where to look. I didn't want the man in my direct line of vision with the blood-soaked bandage to think I was staring. Behind him, a man was removing his shirt and having electrodes attached to his chest. The only options were the wall on my direct right or the curtained area on my left, behind which were seriously ill (and often visible) patients.' (Nurse Denise Deegan on bringing her mother to a Dublin A&E.)

4 April 2005: A 61-year-old Mayo man who urgently needed an operation finally got a bed at University College Hospital Galway, having waited for eleven days. A diabetes sufferer, he had been diagnosed with gangrene in his big toe. Had the infection spread because of the delay, the man could have lost his foot. He had previously lost a leg as a result of his condition.

Independent Mayo TD Dr Jerry Cowley commented: 'It is a terrible scandal. Gangrene is so dangerous and can go through a diabetic like lightning. It is an infection in the tissues: the tissue just dies and has to be cut away to prevent it spreading'.

27 April 2005: Annie Talbot recalled how her brother John (67) died having finally got a bed in the Mater Hospital, following three days on oxygen on a trolley and chair, in the vicinity of a patient who was smoking. John Glynn suffered from emphysema.

In April 2005, the Minister announced that 'every action' in her ten-point A&E plan was being implemented. 'If new actions are needed, there will be new actions. If new decisions are needed, new decisions there will be. We want results. And hospitals should be paid for results.'

23 October 2005: 'My mother lay in bed at home crying with pain.... We were forced to watch a lady, with pride and dignity, dying in front of us.' Brought to Cork University Hospital at 9 a.m., the woman had to wait in a waiting room under 'appalling conditions' until she was given a bed, eleven hours later. While staff members were 'outstanding', 'patients were subjected to a distinct smell of urine'.

Despite the fact that this was a 'rapid-transit ward', it took three days for this lady to be transferred to a proper ward.

5 November 2005: 'On the radio, a woman weeps as she tells how her father died on a trolley in a hospital corridor in Dublin. She says her mother had to steal a pillow from another patient when he went to the toilet, in order to make her father comfortable in his last hours. It is this small theft that makes her cry.'

18 January 2006: Tallaght Hospital confirmed that a woman with a clot on her lung was still waiting for a bed having spent eight days on a trolley in the casualty unit, but said that she was receiving all necessary treatment. Bernadette Higgins (43), from Clondalkin, described the A&E as 'awful'. 'The trolleys are end to end. There isn't room to swing a cat. If one trolley moves, they all move and there's only two toilets for all the people.' Getting painkillers was a problem and there was no privacy if you were talking to a doctor. The mother of four praised the staff: 'They're bending over backwards to accommodate people but they can only do so much.'

According to the Irish Nurses' Organisation (INO), there were forty-seven others on trolleys in Tallaght Hospital at the time. Nationwide, the figure was 406. The Health Service Executive disputed the INO trolley figures, claiming that the trolley population was 'down' to 306.

14 February 2006: Overcrowding at Tallaght Hospital's A&E unit scaled new heights, with seventy-five patients waiting for beds. One woman, on a trolley for five days, described the hospital corridor as 'a war zone'. She had been rushed to hospital with a suspected heart attack and had been told that she had a clot in her lung. 'Not even a bed screen is put around the bed when you get an injection,' she said. 'You can't sleep because it's so busy. They are just in and out all the time.' The shower was blocked: 'We call it the Mary Harney suite,' she told a reporter. Edel (27), from Citywest, had also been on a trolley for five days. She, too, had clots. 'This is my fourth time in this hospital in the last 1½ years and I've never got a bed. I've always been on a trolley.' She found them 'horrible': 'I'm 5ft 11in and my feet stick out at the end.' As well as the lack of sleep, there was the lack of dignity: 'I have to have stomach injections twice a day in front of everybody.'

The INO said that a number of the patients at the hospital had spent over eight days on trolleys. The hospital appealed to the public to use the A&E department only in an emergency.

21 February 2006: An *Irish Times* journalist wrote:

> It is 3.30 a.m. on a Sunday in the new Accident and Emergency Unit of St Vincent's Hospital in Dublin. The scene is chaotic. Sick patients on trolleys take up all corridor space. Nurses, porters and the two doctors on duty are rushing around. Many of the patients are elderly, but there are also a half a dozen or so young people. Her [daughter's] trolley, and the one alongside her, are blocking access to a lift door and three fire hoses. I can't help but notice the sign on the wall stating that the fire hoses are to be kept clear at all times, but I say nothing. I am able to hear the medical

history and diagnosis of many patients around me. A lot of detail is personal and embarrassing. If you don't have a relative or friend with you, getting to the toilet or even getting a drink of water is not easy.

The Health and Safety Authority later found a number of hospital fire exits blocked.

8 March 2006: The numbers waiting on trolleys for beds reached new heights—495. The HSE, while disputing the INO trolley count as usual, promptly announced the setting up of 'a dedicated task force'. The Executive blamed the winter vomiting bug and patients—their respiratory problems—for the spike in numbers. Once confined largely to big urban hospitals, overcrowding had now spread to smaller hospitals all over the country. Hospitals in Cavan, Wexford and Letterkenny showed the same high levels of overcrowding as Dublin's St James's, Tallaght and St Vincent's Hospitals.

10 March 2006: An inquest into the death of an elderly woman heard that she had died of a brain haemorrhage whilst on a trolley in the Mater Hospital. Eamonn Brazil, a consultant in emergency medicine at the hospital, told her family that what had happened was 'inexcusable': 'Things like this are happening on a daily basis. It's disgraceful that she wasn't seen [by a doctor] for four hours.' He described the situation in the Mater as 'beyond crisis'. He said that every day there were twenty/thirty people on trolleys for up to three days. 'Standards have dramatically decreased. It's getting worse every year,' he added. Outside the coroner's court, Nancy Lucas's daughter, Frances Holmes, told a reporter: 'My mother had no dignity when she died. We were all cramped into a nurses' tea station with no privacy when she died.'

Patients were being charged €60 per day for the privilege of occupying a hospital trolley.

THE WAITING GAME
Some patients are driven to go to a casualty unit in their quest for a hospital bed, because they cannot wait any longer for a test or a procedure to be performed. Ireland has an entrenched two-tier system where public patients 'may wait years for treatments which private patients may receive within weeks in the same publicly funded hospital'. Those who cannot pay wait months for urgent appointments, such as

mammograms, and years, *literally*, for non-urgent surgery, such as hip replacements.

It is almost ten years since Frank Cunningham, a surgeon at Naas General Hospital, told a consultants' conference that it was 'unacceptable' for patients, after they had seen a consultant, to have to wait 'for one year or two years or more' on a list. 'It would seem that there is now such a thing as an acceptable waiting list'. He told delegates that waiting lists had not dropped below 25,000. General practitioners, 'in desperation', sent patients on waiting lists to A&E 'in the hope' that 'somebody will recognise their problem as serious'.

Janette Byrne brought her problem to the High Court. In 2001, the 39-year-old woman took an action against the State, the Eastern Regional Health Authority and the Mater Hospital to compel them to provide her with chemotherapy after her treatment had been cancelled over and over again at the public hospital, due to lack of beds. 'I felt that, while I was at home waiting for a bed, the tumour was growing again. I had been advised my cancer was treatable, but time was of the essence,' she told the judge. Janette suffered from a form of cancer of the lymph glands, non-Hodgkins lymphoma. A public patient, she had been operated on nearly five months earlier to remove a cancerous tumour. During the hearing, the hospital authorities offered to treat her at the Mater Private; Janette accepted but, the following day, a bed became available in the Mater Private.

In another case, a Dublin woman in her late seventies developed gangrene in both feet. Her GP advised her to go to casualty, saying that she would otherwise have to wait six weeks for a bed. An offer from a charitable organisation, the St Vincent de Paul Society, to pay for her treatment brought swift results; her local hospital found a private bed for her that same afternoon.

Official waiting lists in Ireland were cosmetically enhanced, like prime ministers. Hospital waiting lists were a model of bureaucratic ingenuity: chronic under-reporting was built into the system, skewing figures to the point of worthlessness, particularly in urgent care areas, such as cancer and heart treatment. Maev-Ann Wren, in her detailed, scholarly study of Irish health care, draws attention to the unreality of official waiting lists. Family doctors refer public patients to consultant outpatient clinics in public hospitals; those specialists then refer those patients for in-patient treatment, if necessary. Being referred by your GP does not mean that you will actually get an appointment as an outpatient. 'Public patients may wait years before they get their foot even on this first rung of the ladder,' Wren comments, soberly. In the Dáil, Labour health spokesperson Liz McManus said that she was aware of a person waiting for four years to see an ear, nose and throat specialist, while Jerry Cowley said that people were waiting eight years to see a urologist in the west, and between four and five years to see a rheumatologist. In March 2006, HSE head Brendan Drumm acknowledged that the length of time patients wait to see a specialist was one of the biggest challenges facing the Executive.

Departmental figures have ignored these months and years. In this Alice-in-Wonderland universe, time spent waiting for a specialist outpatient appointment was not time spent waiting at all; only time spent waiting *after* you had seen a consultant counted, and the first three months of waiting did not count at all, or were, in any case, discounted.

There have been deaths on waiting lists as well as deaths on trolleys. Anyone can die on a trolley, but dying on a waiting list is something that happens only to public patients. Private patients are usually given appointments for surgery or treatment; public patients are added to a list. In 2002, for every public hospital in-patient, there were more than two waiting for treatment, one of whom had been waiting for over a year. Not having private health insurance increased your chances of waiting. In September 2002, over 29,000 patients were waiting for treatment in public hospitals.

Not surprisingly, no statistics are kept on those who die waiting. Peter Sheridan was one. A farmer from Tourmakeady, Co. Mayo, he died following a second heart attack, while on the public waiting list, where he had spent six months awaiting a heart bypass, having previously suffered a coronary.

CANCELLED OPERATIONS

In 2004, it emerged that operations were being deferred because hospitals did not have beds to accommodate patients booked for surgery. Apparently operations are being cancelled in their thousands—over 20,000 in 2004, and almost 22,000 in 2005. Some patients will have little quality of life as a result; others will die waiting. Limerick toddler Róisín Ruddle, scheduled to have a heart operation at Our Lady's Hospital for Sick Children, Crumlin, Dublin, died after her operation was cancelled in 2003. The little girl and her parents had waited for three months for the operation, which was cancelled due to a shortage of intensive care nurses at the hospital.

The number of operations cancelled in 2004 was far greater than the number of patients treated by the National Treatment Purchase Fund. In that year, the Fund arranged for 13,627 patients to be treated at a cost of €44 million. A survey of patients in twenty-six hospitals showed that one in every five had had an operation or procedure cancelled and rescheduled at least once; 4 per cent said that theirs had been cancelled twice; while half that number said that their surgery had been rescheduled three times. Fine Gael health spokesperson Dr Liam Twomey referred to one hospital, Wexford General, 'where investigations for cancer and bleeding ulcers have been cancelled every second week for the last 12 months'. The hospital cancelled 815 operations in 2005.

PROTESTS

This represents a catalogue of human misery which nurses can no longer tolerate and which they say is grossly unacceptable in a developed and wealthy country.

Dave Hughes, INO deputy general secretary

Groups campaigning for better services began to emerge. High Court litigant Janette Byrne co-founded Patients Together, a group dedicated to improving A&E services. Her mother had spent five days on a trolley in the Mater Hospital, where she caught the winter vomiting bug and developed bedsores. In November 2004, Patients Together asked the Minister for Health to set A&E targets, so that no patient should have to wait for more than four hours on a trolley, and should have a shorter wait if occupying a chair.

On 17 March 2006, speaking on RTÉ's *Late Late Show*, Brendan Gleeson expressed his outrage at the way many patients were treated in A&E. The actor said that the conditions elderly people had to endure were 'disgusting' and suggested that 'a baboon' could sort the problem out. Brendan Drumm later blamed unspecified 'internal processes' in some hospitals: X-ray departments that closed early; delays in discharging patients; and the absence of out-of-hours GP cover in parts of Dublin. Gerry Lane, emergency consultant at Letterkenny Hospital, said that conditions there were 'awful'. He compared them to war-time in an Iraqi hospital where he had worked twenty years previously: 'It's worse than Baghdad was in the 1980s. I have never, ever had to treat a patient on the floor before. Somebody comes in out of an ambulance, they are really, really sick, [and there are] no trolleys, no chairs. I have to lie them on the floor on a blanket. I've never actually had to do that before. I've had to do it five times in the last year'. Meanwhile, in that same month, the HSE told the Joint Oireachtas Committee that it had balanced its books for 2005 and had underspent its capital allocation by €51 million.

A 'NATIONAL EMERGENCY'
Stung, apparently, by Brendan Gleeson's impassioned contribution to the debate, the Minister for Health said that A&E had to be treated as a 'national emergency'. New beds were to be assigned immediately to A&E departments; patients would be discharged seven days a week. Hospitals would be given targets for maximum waits in A&E; no more than ten patients could wait for admission to a ward. Hospital budgets, the Minister said ominously, would be linked to meeting these targets. Public hospital laboratories would be required to remain open in the evenings and at weekends; if not, the state would 'go' to the private sector.

In April 2005, the Dublin Fire Brigade complained that its ambulances were being held up for several hours: 'You're taking ambulances out of commission by virtue of the fact that they're in a queue,' trade unionist Tony McDonnell of SIPTU said. The ambulance service is seriously under-resourced: the number of ambulances has not increased since 1985, when there were just 20,000 call-outs, one-fifth of what there are today.

> Patients have complained that they cannot raise the attention of staff to get simple things like bed-pans. Some other patients have complained about their property being stolen, odd-looking characters hanging around and drunks falling on top of them.
>
> An A&E patient in a Dublin hospital

The INO mounted a series of protests at hospitals across the country. The union warned that more of its members would resign from A&E if patients continued to be treated on trolleys. Two nurses, according to the INO, had stepped down from their posts since mid-April when the new €10.8 million accident and emergency unit opened at Cork University Hospital.

By 26 October 2005, almost a year after the Minister had announced her ten-point A&E plan, the trolley population had doubled.

On 14 April 2006, nearly 200 people lay down outside the Dáil to protest at overcrowded and unhygienic conditions in hospital A&E departments. Janette Byrne of Patients Together said that she had just been diagnosed with cancer for a second time, and she feared going back to hospital. The last time she had been treated for cancer as an in-patient, patients had lit scented candles to cover the smell of sewage in her ward, she told *The Irish Times*. Accompanying Janette was Vivian Hamilton, of Clonsilla, Dublin; she was wearing a shirt bearing her father's name, Robert Hamilton. He had died three months previously, at the age of 86, having spent seventy-two hours on a trolley. Another protester, Judi Costello, had brought her son, Adam, who had an immune deficiency disorder. Adam once had to wait for a week for an electrocardiogram because there was no paper available for the machine.

On 27 April, the Oireachtas Health Committee was told that over-crowding in Dublin A&E departments could be leading to over 100 deaths a year. James Binchy, emergency medical consultant at University College Hospital Galway, told the politicians that over-crowding could account for up to 30 per cent of 'excess mortality' or needless deaths in hospitals. Hospital and A&E overcrowding were linked to 120 deaths in Perth hospitals, an Australian study had found. Dr Gerry Lane pointed to a second Australian study which had found that one Canberra hospital had about thirteen deaths a year linked to emergency department overcrowding. Keeping patients in over-crowded A&Es over a 'protracted period of time results in added deaths,' he told the Committee. James Binchy said that it was a 'myth' that the demand for A&E services was unpredictable: some 75 per cent of patients came to casualty between 8 a.m. and 8 p.m. He also rejected the Fine Gael thesis that drunks were a major factor in the casualty crisis. Intoxicated people were 'a small percentage of the problem', he said. They were still entitled to treatment and even if they were all removed from the system, elderly people would still be on trolleys. At least 3,000 additional acute beds were needed, he concluded, and this would still not bring us up to the OECD average.

On 24 May, following RTÉ's *Prime Time* documentary exposing the appalling experiences of very ill patients in casualty denied a hospital bed, emergency medicine consultant Aidan Gleeson bemoaned the fact that it had taken covert cameras to focus attention on our A&E services: 'Persistent cries for help from emergency department staff and patient interest groups over the past ten years were repeatedly ignored.' Instead, we got 'years of denials, finger-pointing and some spectacular blame game tactics'.

Ireland has one of the lowest numbers of acute or urgent-care beds per head of population of OECD countries, he pointed out, adding, 'Not only are we failing to meet the needs of patients with emergencies; we are floundering in our ability to deal with our elective workload … This is a "bed access crisis". It is not a crisis of patients presenting to emergency departments who should be with their GP, or of drunks who should be sent to a gulag on Bull Island for the night.'

PIECEMEAL SOLUTIONS

Patient care and patient safety will drive every aspect of reform and investment.

Mary Harney, April 2005

In June 2005, the HSE announced that it had approved the commissioning of a new twenty-five-bed A&E unit at the Mater Hospital. The following week, *The Irish Times* reported that what the Mater was being funded for was a 'transition' ward—an extra deck on the *Titanic*—where patients could wait for an in-patient bed having been seen in A&E. The hospital had previously rejected an offer of Portakabins from wealthy listeners to RTÉ's *Liveline*. Other measures announced included the fitting out of a new casualty department at St James's Hospital and the 'go-ahead' for a new A&E facility at Portlaoise Hospital. The funding, part of a €63 million investment plan, was said to form part of the Government's ten-point plan for A&E services. The HSE also claimed to have commissioned thirty-eight long-stay beds in west Dublin and Kildare, sixteen in Baggot Street hospital and fourteen in Leopardstown Park Hospital, as well as six additional palliative care beds in a Blackrock hospice. Meanwhile, Letterkenny Hospital was to get money for a new A&E unit; Wexford Hospital was to get the nineteen extra beds it had been promised a number of years previously; and Cavan Hospital was to get a twenty-five-bed ward and an operating theatre. It looked as though Santa had decided make the trip in mid-summer.

Other Dublin hospitals earmarked for significant funding were St Vincent's, James Connolly, St James's, Beaumont, the Coombe Women's Hospital, the National Rehabilitation Hospital and Our Lady's Hospital for Sick Children, Crumlin. Outside Dublin, the happy recipients were Cork University Hospital, University College Hospital Galway, Marymount Hospice in Cork and Birr Unit for the Elderly. Smaller hospitals scheduled for funding—despite being scheduled to close on current plans—were Naas, Portlaoise, Mullingar, Clonmel and Castlebar.

Fifteen months later, what had happened to those pots of money that studded the Minister's ten-point plan? Or to previous promises? Take, for example, Ennis General Hospital, slated to get a €20 million extension and refurbishment programme in 2000. All monies were subsequently frozen, pending the results of a value-for-money audit. Yet three months before the A&E funding was announced, no fewer than seven consultants at the hospital had come out publicly, asserting that government neglect was risking patients' lives. Eighteen months later, still stymied by the strategy of the audit, the hospital still had not seen a penny.

By then, an entirely new approach, the stick-and-carrot model, had appeared.

On 11 May 2006, the new plan, flagged in March after Brendan Gleeson's appearance on the *Late Late Show*, was announced: hospitals with casualty units not reaching new A&E targets would be 'docked' 2 per cent of their annual budgets in the second half of 2006. Meanwhile, the HSE said that all thirty-five hospitals would have to ensure that no patient spent more than twenty-four hours in A&E— once a decision had been made to admit them. Later—it was stated— the target would reduce to twelve hours and, by 2006, it would be six hours.

The stick was followed by a carrot, in the form of additional specialists. Up to 100 additional consultant posts were to be funded in high-performing A&E units that met the new ministerial targets. Bigger hospitals, 400-bedders, could get up to seven carrots, over and above those already sanctioned. Instead of trolleys, patients would have to be accommodated in beds in, say, 'admission lounges'; they should be left waiting no longer than six hours to be fully assessed; 25 per cent of A&E patients had to be accommodated within six hours. Hospitals would also have to ensure that elective or non-urgent cases accounted for at least 20 per cent of all admissions. The maximum wait for an outpatient appointment was set at nine months; anyone waiting more than three months for a procedure would have to be referred automatically to the National Treatment Purchase Fund. Not more than 5 per cent of procedures could be cancelled.

That extra deck on the *Titanic* had already swung into view. In May 2006, the HSE announced new overflow areas outside A&E departments to accommodate patients needing a hospital bed. Nine hospitals were chosen for advancement over a six-month period. Patients waiting for beds might wait, but not in A&E. But would new admission lounges and new modular units or Portakabins be sufficient to ensure that the Minister's targets would be met? Or would day case beds be pressed into service?

According to one consultant, these day beds are being used to mask the scale of the problem with bed capacity in the system.

Hospital management condones the practice of admitting patients from A&E to 'beds' in day services units. In this way a hospital with thirty patients on trolleys in the A&E Department can admit twenty of these patients to the day services unit and proudly claim that there are 'only' ten patients awaiting admission. This strategy contributes massively to inefficiencies in day-care. At a time when there is strong world-wide emphasis on performing more and more surgical procedures on an outpatient basis in day services units, these beds are being sacrificed to allow the HSE to claim that the issue of patients on trolleys in A&E Departments is being addressed. Paradoxically, this means that other patients are being admitted overnight for elective procedures which do not require hospital admission and would otherwise be done in day services. This further contributes to the beds crisis and is a good example of problems in one area leading to further inefficiencies elsewhere in the system.

A SHORTAGE OF BEDS

The chaos in our health system has grown over decades. One of the main reasons why conditions in A&E, for example, have been so deplorable is that there are not enough public hospital beds to go around. Our non-capital spend on health actually *fell* as a percentage of GNP from 7.72 per cent in 1980 to 6.23 per cent in 1996, when the boom began. By 2001, we were beginning to spend a little more on health, but it was still not enough to bring us up to an acceptable level, to make up for decades of poverty and parsimony, to ensure that people would not be forced to lie on trolleys in casualty for days on end, waiting for a bed.

Expenditure on health has increased considerably over the past decade, but the real increase is far less than it appears, when price and wage hikes are taken into account. In 2004, less than half the money earmarked for health went to hospitals. And, in any event, Irish figures on health spending need to be taken with a large pinch of salt, as the OECD has recognised. The Department of Health routinely inflates them by 25 per cent, to include a *guesstimate* of monies spent by private health insurers, private hospitals and private health care agencies, as well as families and individuals. National health expenditure figures are further boosted by monies spent on social services: this expenditure accounts for as much as 20 per cent of the total 'health' spend, because a vast range of personal social services are delivered as part of health. These include: care of the elderly, medical cards, occupational therapy, physiotherapy, speech and language and disability. Extraordinary as it may sound, we simply do not have an accurate, reliable set of national health accounts. So our ratings in international tables cannot be relied upon. In 2003, economists Dale Tussing and Maev-Ann Wren calculated that, in real terms, Irish current expenditure on health per head was less than 90 per cent of the EU average. This was not enough to compensate for those decades from 1970 to 1996 when, year in, year out, we spent 63 per cent of the EU average on health.

The gaping craters left by those decades pose a threat to patient safety today. Deputy General Secretary of the INO, Dave Hughes, has said that the bed crisis in hospitals and the numbers waiting on trolleys are far worse now than they were ten years ago. He described nurses as 'battled and bewildered from the gruelling daily experience of working in overcrowded and unsafe emergency departments'. Cystic fibrosis sufferers, for example, whose immune systems are heavily compromised, are often obliged to admit themselves to hospital as in-patients; they complain of being put into large, multi-bedded wards where they are at increased risk of catching infectious diseases, including MRSA.

The resource issue surfaces again and again. In January 2006, for example, in an effort to ease pressure on the city's A&E departments, the Minister announced cuts in the numbers of non-Dublin patients to be accepted for non-urgent treatment in Dublin hospitals—the aim being to re-route them to hospitals in the provinces. Consultant physician Seán Murphy, who works at Mullingar General Hospital, was dismissive. Describing the announcement as a 'rabbit out of a hat', he said that his hospital could not cope with a substantial increase in patients without additional resources. The swingeing cuts of the 1980s and early 1990s are still with us, as everyone who has ever waited for an operation or sat in an A&E unit knows.

An external analysis of A&E departments in ten hospitals later confirmed this. The *Triba Secta* report found that, while work and operational practices were a contributing factor, A&E difficulties often reflected the legacy of these cutbacks. Not only did they reduce capacity, the report said, but they also eroded the traditional general practitioner–consultant relationship. This was probably a reference to the fact that, many moons ago, GPs could ring a hospital to get a patient admitted. (Today, that kind of direct communication is being rediscovered, impelled by new 'pilot' initiatives.)

Many factors feed into the A&E funnel; lack of resources is not the only one. Delays in seeing consultants were also identified as contributing to A&E problems. *Triba Secta* looked at a small group of ten patients with chronic obstructive pulmonary disease, and found that five of them had waited in hospital for two–six days before seeing a consultant.

The problem is multi-layered: lack of capacity in one department creates bottlenecks in another, seemingly unrelated, area. A consultant anaesthetist underlines the lack of capacity in our endoscopy units, which reduces bed availability by creating another involuntary group of 'bed blockers'.

> Another example of a crisis in one area impacting on bed availability concerns endoscopic investigations (using a camera to inspect parts of the body such as the stomach or large bowel). In-patient endoscopies often involve a delay of three–four days. Waiting lists for outpatient endoscopies, on the other hand, are often six months or more. Frustrated clinicians regularly keep their patients in hospital for the extra three–four days to ensure that the test is performed as quickly as possible—with obvious implications for bed occupancy.

Productivity, or, rather the lack of it, may be another reason. From 1997 to 2004, the funding, in real terms, of acute or short-stay hospitals rose by 72 per cent, yet the number of patients treated by doctors increased by only 44 per cent.

Bureaucracy can be counterproductive. In one hospital, during the first six months of 2005, delays in discharging patients resulted in the loss of 2,286 bed days. *Triba Secta* found that Cork University Hospital (CUH) had been experiencing increasing difficulty in discharging elderly, frail patients into the community or elsewhere. 'Much delay is attributable to the significant amount of bureaucracy associated with subvention application and response,' the report said. CUH reported six- to eight-month waits for rehabilitation beds for young people. The external consultants also found that elective surgery frequently had to be cancelled at the hospital because medical patients were occupying beds on the day ward in order to prevent trolley waits in A&E.

Ireland's ratio of what are called 'acute' or short-stay hospitals falls hugely short of international standards. Despite being one of the wealthiest countries in the world, we can manage only a measly nine general hospitals per million people, and this in a country with a very scattered population. (The Government now plans to slash this number in the guise of health 'reform', and this is a topic we will return to in Chapter 9.)

The number of acute beds hardly increased at all during the 1990s. Add to this the substantial growth in our population, and you begin to see why things are as they are. Again, official bed figures are inflated: some long-stay beds are included in the count of short-stay beds, for some reason. Since 2005, the Department has introduced a further refinement: beds are now counted during the month of August when the count is higher than average. But whatever the shortcomings of the bed counts, one indisputable fact emerges: we now have nearly half the quota of short-stay beds that we had twenty-five years ago. In 1981, our ratio was 5.13 per 1,000; in 2005, it was 2.96. While the trend today is to do as many operations as possible on a day-patient basis, there are limits to day-care surgery. A look at our European neigh- bours shows just how paltry our current stock of short-stay beds is. Austria and Germany both have more than twice our allocation, for example. Yet Brendan Drumm told a nurses' conference in October 2005 that the Republic was over-equipped with hospital beds by inter- national standards. Describing the demand for more beds as 'bizarre', he takes the view that 'by any measure this country is actually over- equipped with acute hospital beds'. Is this also the Government's view? Mary Harney has said that there is no question of extra beds 'for the sake of them', as they cost €1 million each. If there were 5,000 more beds, she believes, there would still be problems.

In 2002, the Programme for Government issued by Fianna Fáil and the Progressive Democrats promised 3,000 new acute beds. Three years later, only a fraction of these beds had been put in place. By July 2005, according to the Irish Hospital Consultants' Association (IHCA), only 419 new public beds had been installed. Department of Health figures, however, put this figure at 535. Whose sums were right, nobody knew: beds, like trolleys, seemed to be notoriously difficult to count. Today there are day beds as well as night beds. Such was the wizardry of the Department that the total number of new beds, including in-patient and day beds, now appeared to be 1,010. The number of day beds had increased by 475, or so it seemed, but this increase later turned out to be more apparent than real.

There was, for example, the question of when is a bed not a bed. In response to a Freedom of Information query, the Department revealed that a bed was a bed when the Department defined it as a bed. A bed, bureaucrats decided, could be a 'place', and either—or both—could be a 'device' or even 'an arrangement'. So, a couch could be a bed, or a recliner, or a trolley, *anywhere*, could be a bed, as long as there was an arrangement in place that permitted a patient to recline, lie down, or otherwise recover 'in the course of an elective day admission'. Not surprisingly, this kinetic definition of a day bed did much to boost the day-bed population. It later transpired that day procedures were actually being carried out *routinely* on trolleys, recliners and couches.

As for night beds, by 2005, A&E had become the fast track to nocturnal accommodation. A letter to the Minister underlined just how acute the bed crisis had become. Cork and Kerry's only medical oncologist (who provided services to 500,000 people) told Mary Harney that he was unable to get in-patient care for dying cancer patients due to lack of beds. Four months after Dr O'Reilly's letter was published in the *Irish Examiner*, however, the Minister for Health still felt able to question publicly the need for more beds.

NOT ENOUGH STAFF

Muiris FitzGerald, the Dean of Medicine at University College Dublin, memorably described consultants as 'a higher elite' that consisted of 'five-star generals'; below them, he said, is 'a steep drop to a very large pool of non-commissioned officers, who do not have a permanent contract'. The glittering prize that beckoned after fourteen years of serfdom in hospital medicine was given to relatively few. Those not appointed to the ranks of consultant were doomed to continue as senior registrars, fully qualified specialists on permanently temporary contracts. And this was the system: the exploitation of the many for the advancement of the few. Today, the non-commissioned officers are very well paid for their long working hours, but they still await permanent commissions.

More recently, consultants have been appointed in greater numbers, but, by international standards, Ireland is still hugely short of hospital specialists. Consultant physician John Barton points out that Ireland currently has a ratio of 22 doctors per 10,000 of population, far below the EU average of 33:10,000. 'If *consultant* numbers are increased to 3,600, as promised, we will then have a per head ratio of hospital specialists of 9:10,000—less than half that of Finland.'

Nor is hospital understaffing confined to medical specialists. Like the government cap on medical training places that lasted for a quarter of a century, cutbacks in nurse training also led to shortages. INO President Madeleine Speirs says: 'No one in management should seek to justify or defend the many examples of one nurse looking after up to forty elderly patients for up to sixteen hours per day.' Hospital understaffing leads to unnecessary deaths, Speirs underlines. International evidence shows that four patients per nurse is the optimal workload: increasing that workload to six means patients are 14 per cent more likely to die within thirty days of being admitted to hospital; while a patient–nurse ratio of 1:8 leaves patients 31 per cent more likely to die.

In December 2002, the Government froze public sector employment at existing levels. This freeze came after a 66 per cent increase in health management and administrative staff from 1997 to 2001, three times the rise in nursing, medical and dental staff. Services were restricted to 'existing' levels. Cutbacks followed. Hospital wards closed; staffing levels dropped. In a year when the population increased by 1.8 per cent, jobs in health and social services rose by only 0.6 per cent. Forbidden to recruit additional staff nurses, hospitals began to employ private agency staff, reportedly at double the cost. From 2001 to 2005, while the numbers working in health and social services rose, most additional staff were employed in the private sector.

FÁS disputes the nursing shortage. But according to the INO, 3,000 Irish-trained nurses left Ireland to work abroad in 2003, compared with 800 in 1998. According to the Department of Health, 'hospitals compete against each other for the limited supply of nurses available.' The workforce is becoming more culturally diverse: in 2001, for example, only a third of nurses registering for the first time with An Bord Altranais had trained in Ireland. There is an acute shortage of nurses in some areas, the Department of Health says. Demand has dropped for sick children's nursing, for example. The same holds true for midwifery. Since 1996, training places in both paediatric nursing and midwifery have been left unfilled.

Nevertheless, a 2005 FÁS report pretended that we did not need to increase our quota of nurses, on the rather questionable premises that, firstly, we could step up our poaching of nurses from developing countries, and, secondly, we could substitute care assistants for quali-fied nurses, given that nurses spend 25 per cent of their time on non-nursing duties. But official statistics are collected in ways that mask personnel shortages and hamper workforce planning. The FÁS report was premised on deficient data: while Ireland appears to have a higher than average ratio of nurses per head of population, many nurses work part-time, making international comparisons risky. In 2000, for example, only 58 per cent of nurses and midwives in the public service worked full-time, that is, thirty-nine hours per week. Secondly, there is a world-wide scarcity of nurses. Many countries are now experiencing severe shortages; high nursing turnover has become the norm. In Ireland, a study done by UCC Professor Geraldine McCarthy showed an annual turnover among nurses and midwives, nationally, of 12 per cent. Finally, the ethics of poaching nurses from developing countries are dubious. And, as the Department of Health warns, 'the future supply of nurses from abroad is unpredictable and is dependent on recruitment drives, the attractiveness of Ireland as a place of employment, language competency, the standard of nursing education and the presence of a surplus of registered nurses from other countries.' Moreover, FÁS's proposal to substitute care assistants for qualified nurses carries distinct dangers for patients. Even where training is mandatory and standards enforced, this kind of de-skilling can be hazardous for patients. However, in Ireland, no training is required, nor are any standards in force, for care assistants.

FÁS also proclaimed, on the basis of figures that were wildly unreliable, that we did not need more midwives. The Department of Health continues to confuse midwives with nurses. One result of this is that no accurate midwifery workforce figures exist. The shortage of midwives, particularly in the Dublin region, has been heralded for a number of years. INO figures show that midwifery is dying on its feet: only 16 per cent of those who pay annually to maintain their midwifery registration are in practice, and of these, an unknown number work part-time. For FÁS to contend that we do not need more midwives is absurd: it does little to inspire confidence in that body's predictions for the rest of the health sector.

So, we are short of beds, doctors, nurses, midwives. In a period of plenty, the Government has totally reneged on its Programme for Government commitment to provide 3,000 new beds. But there is no shortage of superbugs....

Chapter 3
The Killing Wards

Hospitals are not places you should be in unless you're really ill and have to go there.

Minister for Health Mary Harney on the risk of
contracting MRSA in Irish hospitals

HOSPITAL INFECTIONS

The so-called 'winter vomiting bug' has now become a familiar visitor to our hospitals. The virus, which causes stomach pain, nausea, vomiting and diarrhoea, lasts two–three days and poses a threat to the very young and the very old. It also interferes with hospital functioning. Every winter, visitors are asked to stay away, departments close and planned surgery is cancelled. Take, for example, one purported 'centre of excellence': Dublin's St Vincent's Hospital. On 14 March 2006, the picture was grim: 'despite the hospital taking all the necessary precautions to curtail the spread of this highly contagious virus, practically all ward areas are affected, including parts of the emergency department,' a hospital spokesperson said. By then, the winter vomiting bug had infected 173 patients, along with 105 staff; ten new cases had just been recorded. Other hospitals were also affected, but not as badly. Despite its name, the bug can now be found during the summer months, at least in Irish hospitals, with Tullamore Hospital recording an outbreak in July 2006.

According to Hilary Humphreys, a professor of microbiology, one hospital patient in every ten develops an infection: 'hospitals with a complex caseload, e.g. those with national or regional specialties, may have a higher infection rate than smaller hospitals.' Those most likely to pick up an infection are those who can least afford to: 'vulnerable, elderly ill patients'.

However, once the winter vomiting bug—or any other microbe—gets into a hospital, lack of isolation facilities makes the virus very difficult to control. Professor Martin Cormican, President of the Irish Association of Clinical Microbiologists, says that not enough infection control staff are employed in our hospitals. Some have no infection control doctors at all. 'There is all this talk about preparing for an influenza pandemic but if we can't stop the norovirus [winter vomiting bug] spreading, how do we think we can stop an influenza pandemic spreading?' he asked. He might have asked the same question about MRSA.

Hospital infection is a worldwide problem. Every year, 15 million hospital patients are infected with a viral, bacterial or fungal bug. Nearly 1.5 million die as a result. In the United States alone, two million patients get hit every year: up to 100,000 die.

As the Minister for Health has observed, hospitals are dangerous places and no one should go to them unless they are really ill. Ms Harney was referring to the considerable risk, for Irish patients, of contracting MRSA in public hospitals. This 'formidable hospital invader' can 'rot the lungs, poison the blood, or infect bones, skin and joints'. MRSA has killed thousands of hospital patients in Britain and the US. Infection rates in Canadian hospitals have climbed ten-fold since 1995.

MRSA is far from being the only nasty bug in circulation, however. Some experts believe that we are on the threshold of a 'post-antibiotic era' where common infections will be untreatable. Almost two-thirds of E coli infections in Ireland, for example, are resistant to ampicillin. HSE CEO Brendan Drumm told the Joint Oireachtas Health Committee that clostridium difficile—a hospital-acquired infection that, up to recently, had got little publicity—was a significant cause of illness and death in our hospitals.

Other hospital nasties, such as vancomycin-resistant enterococcus (VRE) and vancomycin-resistant staph aureus (VRSA) also pose significant threats. Writing in *The Irish Times*, a nurse told readers that, while the MRSA issue was serious, 'the VRE and VRSA issue is terrifying'. 'Wait until this mother of all super-bugs hits the public,' she added. This 'mother' has proliferated alarmingly here in recent years. Ireland is now the second worst infected country in Europe: official figures show that, in the case of VRE, the proportion of antibiotic-resistant bugs increased from 11.1 per cent in 2002 to 29.3 per cent in 2005.

ENCOURAGING THE BUGS

Antibiotic resistance is a problem that was created through the combined activities of the pharmaceutical industry and the medical profession. Penicillin used to be effective in treating certain bugs, but since the 1960s, the over-prescription of antibiotics has led to the growth of superbugs, new strains that show a resistance to penicillin and other antibiotics. What were once treatable bugs have, over the decades, become potentially lethal.

S. aureus is a bug commonly found on the skin or in the nose: one person in every three is a carrier. If the bug gets into broken skin and infects a wound, poisons the blood, or gets into the lungs, S. aureus can cause real problems. Many S. aureus strains became immune to antibiotics that were previously used to zap them, such as methicillin, hence the name: methicillin-resistant S. aureus, or MRSA. MRSA teaches us that too much medicine can be bad for your health. More and more bugs are becoming immune to penicillin: in 2004, for example, 42 per cent of all S. aureus bugs were methicillin-resistant. They are also becoming super-immune: S. aureus is now becoming resistant to a wider range of antibiotics, including vancomycin (VRSA). And so-called 'emperor' bugs capable of resisting glycopeptid antibiotics have appeared in France and the United States; they will almost certainly arrive in Ireland in the not-too-distant future.

Despite growing knowledge of their dangers, doctors continue to prescribe more and more antibiotics. General practitioners here prescribe antibiotics more frequently than family doctors in many other countries. Official figures show a steady increase in antibiotic use, particularly by medical-card holders, as well as an accompanying rise in 'broad spectrum' antibiotics. Yet, unbelievably, we have no comprehensive national data on either private prescriptions (issued by GPs) or on the prescription of antibiotics in hospitals.

Official figures reveal a fairly high use of antibiotics in Irish hospitals, higher than in many other European countries. Over 50 per cent of antibiotics in Irish hospitals may be inappropriately prescribed. Employing a chemist with a mission to correct deficiencies in prescribing can halve a hospital's antibiotic costs. In one hospital alone, in one year, the bill dropped from an estimated €650,000 to €370,000. Clearly, employing antibiotic pharmacists is cost-effective as well as being life-saving.

People with a history of taking broad spectrum antibiotics are

known to be at greater risk of developing MRSA. Yet doctors in Ireland
tend overwhelmingly to prescribe broad spectrum antibiotics in
preference to narrow spectrum ones. Their prescribing patterns
compare badly with those of doctors in other countries.

MRSA

MRSA is now endemic in Ireland. Recently, the actress Marsha Hunt, a
cancer survivor, told the world how she had travelled to Ireland for
breast surgery, and had contracted MRSA in St Vincent's Hospital.
Some months ago, also in the private wing of the same hospital, the
mother of a friend had surgery to remove part of her stomach; MRSA
was subsequently discovered in the wound. Another acquaintance had
major surgery in Beaumont hospital, another 'centre of excellence';
she, too, developed invasive MRSA.

In the 1970s, MRSA was found mainly in burns, surgical wounds and
traumatic skin lesions: blood, bone, or deep wound infections were
rarely seen. Today, these have become more common. For people
whose immune system is already compromised, contracting MRSA
may be catastrophic. Some suffer severely; others have limbs amputated. Many have to fight for their lives. While some manage to beat
the bug, others do not. There are no comprehensive statistics: we do
not know how many have died, or how many have suffered grievous
harm. What we do know is that people with MRSA in their blood are
twice as likely to die from their infection as patients whose staph
aureus responds to methicillin.

Death certificates in Britain show a huge upsurge in the number of
fatalities associated with MRSA. The figures are extremely worrying. In
England and Wales, for example, deaths jumped fifteen-fold from
1993 to 2002. In 2004, 168 deaths there were linked to MRSA. In many
cases, of course, people who die of MRSA are critically ill for a variety
of reasons, so MRSA may not be the main cause of death.

How many deaths in Ireland are linked to MRSA? The short answer
is that we have no idea: unbelievably, the HSE refuses to release the
information. In March 2006, Brendan Drumm declined to give
figures to the Oireachtas Health Committee for the number of people
who die from MRSA in Irish hospitals. If these figures were made
public, he said, they might frighten people. 'To give that figure to the
public would be almost unfair,' he opined, in the best paternalistic
medical tradition. But, leaving aside the democratic deficit, withholding

death rates for hospital patients who contract MRSA ensures that public pressure for hospital reform does not build.

People are already frightened. According to Dr Teresa Graham, from Tramore, Co. Waterford, a spokesperson for an MRSA group, 'people are delaying, or putting off, going into hospital because they are afraid of MRSA'. Fear of MRSA was 'quite common', she said. 'I would feel that way myself. I need to get my varicose veins done, but am postponing it. They are painful, but I'm going to wait until they are really, really bad.' Dr Graham witnessed her husband Dermot, a cancer sufferer, die in pain after he contracted MRSA.

PREVALENCE

In the 1970s, the role of MRSA in doctor-induced infections was 'poorly understood', according to an official report. Today, we are paying dearly for that ignorance. MRSA blood-poisoning levels in Ireland are now among the highest in Europe. In 2004, the HSE website recorded that 550 people were infected with MRSA in their bloodstream. The Executive did not draw attention to the fact that these bloodstream statistics under-represented the true figures for invasive MRSA disease: they did not include deep wound, bone or chest infections.

Ireland urgently needs figures for the number of patients infected with MRSA, broken down by hospital. However, institutions such as Beaumont Hospital have refused to release *any* information on their MRSA rates.

A North–South study found that nine out of ten MRSA sufferers were hospital in-patients: cases were found in almost all wards in all departments. The vast majority of sufferers had had surgery or an invasive procedure within the previous month. MRSA has been found in hospital equipment, in the switches on machines, in the buttons on ventilators, on the pumps that dispense intravenous drugs or food to patients. Worldwide, ventilators and catheters have been shown to be prime carriers. Catheters, for instance, 'simply act as a water-slide for germs'.

MRSA is a national calamity that could have been prevented, had the Government had the political will to do so. Finland, for example, showed that it was possible to eradicate MRSA. France reduced its levels in the mid-1990s from 5.9 to 0.8 per 1,000 patient bed nights. Contrast this with Ireland. In 1998, our MRSA count was 29.1 per 1,000 beds occupied in acute hospitals. One might have expected that these

figures would have acted as a wake-up call, but they did not. Health
authorities fiddled while Rome burned.

THE 'WAR' ON SUPERBUGS

> The use of single rooms by private patients seems to take precedence over
> providing isolation for the control of MRSA.
>
> Risk assessors commenting on priorities in the Lourdes Hospital,
> Drogheda, in 2001

MRSA has been allowed to proliferate in Ireland for the past thirty
years, virtually unchecked, until very recently. Until 1999, for instance,
no one kept a watching brief on antibiotic resistance, although by 1995
it had already surfaced as a health-care problem. We then produced
paper guidelines but today's infection levels suggest that these were
never implemented. Serious discrepancies in infection control were
found in hospitals on both sides of the border. Yet more guidelines
were produced in the south in 2004. Incredibly, these guidelines,
launched with panache by the Minister, took six *years* to produce.

Ireland is one of the few countries in Europe *without* a national
system of surveillance of what used to be called 'iatrogenic' or doctor-
induced infections. Such an information system has been a legal
requirement in the EU since 1998. We continue to breach this legislation.
Incredibly, MRSA has been a legally notifiable disease since only 2004.
Until then, hospitals were not obliged to notify the state of even serious
cases of infection. They were not obliged to report deaths, either.

On 22 August 2006, five years after SARI* launched its first report,
the HSE finally came out with its hands up, saying it needed €20
million a year to combat MRSA (not €5 million, as promised). This
money was needed to employ more consultant microbiologists, more
infection control nurses, more antibiotic pharmacists and more
surveillance staff.

Many of our public hospitals are dirty. Hospital dirt is believed to
be another factor contributing to the rise of MRSA. Dust acts as a
reservoir for MRSA (and other bugs). Bugs have been found on door
handles, light switches, curtains, bedding, mattresses, lockers, bed
rails, phones, keyboards and computer screens, even pens. The bug
can travel from bathtubs and toilet seats to cabinets and tables; it can
migrate from ties, coats, shoes and uniforms.

---

*   Strategy for the control of Antimicrobial Resistance in Ireland

The overall standard of hygiene in my unit was appalling. In the 24 hours I spent there, there was no toilet paper or soap or tissues, despite highlighting this to staff, both midwives and cleaners, on numerous occasions. The food was disgusting and overheated. The same bag of rubbish stayed under my bed from my arrival until I left to go to delivery [the labour ward].

A posting on Holles Street Hospital on irishhealth.com

Speaking on the *Late Late Show*, a relative of an MRSA patient described how a cloth, which had been used to clean a toilet, was subsequently used to wipe a tray carrying food to a hospital patient. Few public hospitals, if any, employ their own cleaning staff. If hospitals are dirty, it is partly because their cleaning has been contracted out to private cleaning firms. These cleaners are temporary, their contracts insecure, their benefits nil and their pay low. Under these circumstances, as one of them pointed out on RTÉ Radio 1's *Liveline*, workers are unlikely to give of their best. But outsourcing is a problem that goes unrecognised in official reports. These reports tend to focus on infection control solutions, ignoring the wider structural issues, such as outsourcing, the nursing shortage, bed congestion or trolley gridlock.

A STRUCTURAL DISEASE

It now looks as though MRSA has reached a stage where it cannot be eradicated. Infection control experts have little to be optimistic about. They say that many hospitals will find it difficult to implement MRSA guidelines because of the lack of resources. The Minister for Health has zoned in on the failure of hospital staff to wash their hands, but she has neglected to draw attention to other factors that lie within her own bailiwick, factors that require public expenditure. Hand washing is essential, she says. And so it is. Hand washing is at the centre of infection prevention, yet hands are washed only one-third to one-half as often as they should be in Irish hospitals.

What if there are no accessible sinks in the room? No alcohol rubs at the foot of the trolley? Not enough staff to care for patients? While MRSA is spread mainly through staff hands, research shows that more patients catch MRSA where locum or temporary staff are employed. Yet the numbers employed in the public sector have been capped since 2002. Poor patient–nurse ratios also contribute to the rise of hospital infections, such as MRSA.

And staff are less likely to wash their hands when they are run off their feet. 'I have witnessed one nurse looking after fourteen patients alone, most heavy and bed-ridden, almost all in need of dressing and feeding, six with MRSA, one with VRE,' nurse Florence Horsman-Hogan says. Providing safe and hygienic care in this situation, she said, was impossible.

LACK OF INFRASTRUCTURE

Steps, the Minister says, must be taken to prevent patient overcrowding. She does not spell out how these steps can be taken, given the demands placed on our public hospitals and their continuing inability to meet those demands.

Although some strains of MRSA are known to be highly infectious, there are no plans in this country to isolate MRSA patients. Isolation rooms are needed, according to infection control experts. Isolation works: in one study, MRSA rates were reduced sixteen-fold when those carrying the bug were isolated. The non-isolation of MRSA patients in our hospitals is directly related to the Government's refusal to provide more public hospital beds, however. Noël Browne had the right idea in the 1950s when he isolated TB patients, yet today, when many of our public hospitals are rampant with MRSA, the best the Minister can do is to recommend the isolation of *patients in intensive care*. In Canada, MRSA *carriers* are isolated. In Ireland, there are no plans to isolate even those who become infected with the disease, unless they require intensive care. Even in intensive care, clinicians say, patients with MRSA are frequently nursed alongside patients without MRSA, due to lack of isolation rooms. This is a shocking indictment of the Government's refusal to give hospitals the resources they need to ensure patient safety.

An overcrowded hospital should be seen as unsafe, just like an overcrowded sports stadium. Overcrowding is a major factor in contributing to the spread of infectious disease. 'Overcrowding in our hospitals with patients waiting for admission on trolleys in A&E departments or patients on trolleys transferred to already full wards is a serious impediment to making progress'. Increasing the number of beds in an area heightens the risk of cross-infection with MRSA, studies show. When a fifth bed is put into a four-bedded room, for example, the risk of being colonised by MRSA triples.

Mary Harney agreed with Marian Finucane that over-occupancy of beds could lead to infection. Yet Irish bed occupancy rates are among the highest in the developed world. Government under-funding ensures that bed occupancy rates exceed 100 per cent. Professor Martin Cormican says: 'Our hospitals are too full of too many people all the time. Hospitals should be run at 85 per cent capacity as their baseline, whereas, in most hospitals in Ireland, not only are all the beds full at any one time but there are people on trolleys in A&E waiting to get into beds that are not available'. Hospital studies show that when the distance between beds decreased from 2.5 to 1.9 metres, MRSA increased three-fold. How many centimetres separate the trolleys in our A&E units?

According to Hilary Humphreys, 'Many hospital wards contain too many patients in too small a space. Recent national guidelines on the control of MRSA recommend at least 2.9 metres between the centres of adjacent beds and a minimum of one isolation room for every six to seven general acute beds.' A recent survey of infection control in our acute hospitals showed an average of just one isolation room for every sixteen hospital beds. Only nine hospitals in the country had specially ventilated isolation rooms.

Dealing with hospital infections costs. Canada spends an estimated \$42–59 million annually isolating and treating patients who are MRSA carriers. Not dealing with hospital infections will cost more, if not today, then tomorrow.

And how are MRSA victims being treated? In September 2006, a horrific story appeared in the *Evening Herald* about a 72-year-old man who had contracted MRSA in the Lourdes and had been left for four days to die an agonising death in a chair in the hospital's A&E department. 'Doctors struggled to find an ambulance to bring him to Beaumont,' Eoin Reynolds reported. 'His leg was black and the smell was awful. It was like a piece of meat you'd left out for weeks,' his daughter commented. Eddie Crosby had contracted the virus after Lourdes Hospital staff treated a small cut in his foot. By May 2006, the infection had spread. Despite repeated promises, he had never succeeded in seeing a specialist. He died after four days in Beaumont, his body riddled with sores, having waited fifteen months for a specialist appointment.

Chapter 4
Principalities and Politburos

A CENTRE OF EXCELLENCE

I was very unwell, in a lot of pain, running a high temperature. My husband brought me to Vincent's [Hospital, Dublin]. When we arrived, I couldn't walk, he had to carry me. I was brought straight to a cubicle. It was 9.30 at night. The nurses were fantastic. I saw a doctor at around 2.30 a.m.

Next morning I went for a scan: they thought it was renal colic. By now I'd been moved from a corridor onto a trolley. The corridor was so full of trolleys that people couldn't get by with other trolleys. There was a nurse trying to do an ECG in the corridor, but she couldn't do it because another porter would come along with a trolley. Eventually, they snapped at each other. I felt sorry for both of them. They are great people, to continue to work under such huge adversity in a system like that.

Being examined on a trolley, it's terribly undignified. The doctor was trying to examine my tummy. He was quite sensitive, but he missed the clue as to where the pain was coming from.

I'd been put on a drip, but it tissued, so it wasn't working any more. But none of the nurses were qualified to put in a line [a drip], they told me. Most of them were Asian. So they had to get a doctor to do it. I'd been admitted by the surgical team and, because I was under their care, the casualty doctors wouldn't touch me. Why not? Because the system is hugely political. How do I mean? Consultants have this deal: a member of one team never, ever looks after the patient of another team.

But the surgical doctors were very, very busy. The doctor never came even though she said she would. So I spent fifteen hours without a line in my arm. I could have needed hydration [but they didn't know that]. I was supposed to fast but I couldn't.

A nurse walked with me to the bathroom. I expected her to wait outside the door, but I had to walk back on my own. I could have collapsed from the pain I was in. It was really very poor care. For example, they gave me a morphine drug, it didn't work; then they gave me another drug that did work. But the surgeon crossed out the one that had worked and put the other one, the one that hadn't worked, back in. He wasn't thinking. I really needed some pain relief.

There's this huge wastage of drugs. When surgeons took over my care, they gave me a drug that stops you getting a clot in your leg. It was so wasteful—you don't need it when you can move your leg. It's a litigation issue.

I was there until twelve at night. The trolley was directly under a button that you had to press to get through a door. It must have been pressed 200 times over my head! At twelve o'clock, I said, 'I'm going home—I'm too sick to be here.' I was put into a cubicle then. The following day, they did an abdominal upper ultrasound, but they didn't scan the pelvic area, even though I'd told them this was where the pain was coming from. Why didn't they listen to me? Because they were surgeons, and surgeons don't focus on gynae stuff. I had another full day on the trolley.

They moved me at 8 p.m. into a ward. The wards were cleaned by contract cleaners. They were not up to the standard we'd been used to. The locker hadn't even been cleaned after the last patient; her breathing apparatus was still there. I was scared. There was blood on the locker, someone else's blood. It was really revolting. The place stank, it was like a nursing home smell. The bathrooms were filthy. There was visible dirt. I wouldn't have used the bath. But casualty was very clean and nice. Except there was someone else's blood on the trolley I was on, and on the blood pressure machine. Common decency would say you shouldn't have to put up with that.

Finally, on Thursday morning, they did the pelvic ultrasound, but the cyst [in my ovaries] had burst by then. I'd had three tests in three days! If they'd been more efficient, and done the tests earlier, they'd definitely have taken me to theatre [to burst the cyst], so at least I was spared that! I got peritonitis. At four or five in the afternoon, the gynae reg [registrar] came to see me.

Everything seemed to take hours, it took twenty-four hours to organise a test, for instance. You'd see the young doctors, the interns, rush off with cards for their patients, organising tests instead of writing letters of discharge. The idea that they have to physically go to the ultrasound department.... Yes, they are competing for slots, for surgery and tests, for their patients.

No, I didn't eat at all while I was there. I wouldn't have been able to. The food smelled revolting. Corned beef or shepherd's pie. And ice cream and jelly for dessert; can you imagine, in this day and age! Not very nutritious. Getting fruit was impossible.

There were a lot of untrained care assistants. Lots of them were students, earning beer money or whatever. My six-bedded ward had one staff nurse, one student nurse, and maybe one care attendant. They had no training, none. At night-time, the staff there were agency nurses; it was maybe 50:50. The agency nurses knew the place very well: they were obviously used on a regular basis. The Asian nurses tended to be new. The Irish ones were saying the system is so frustrating, so difficult, working with care assistants who are not trained, with Asian nurses who might have language difficulties, maybe not understanding something that's said to them, but saying yes as though they do—it's that Asian thing of not wanting to lose face.... Trying to work effectively under these conditions is so hard. The Irish nurses are incredibly patient with them.

I observed three care assistants with a lady who had just come down from the high dependency [intensive care] unit, who had just had surgery. There was a fluffy mattress to be put under her. They did not know how to lift her. There was no nurse with them, no one to supervise. It wouldn't have been allowed in the old days. There were lines in her neck, lines in her arm; they got caught in the bed. She was in such pain I cried looking at her.

There is a lack of standards. No quality control, no sign of anyone, no one coming round to ask how're you doing, have you brushed your teeth today, that kind of thing. The chaplain was the only person to come around. Not that if you'd had a complaint that it would have made a difference.

Twenty years ago, I was a patient in Vincent's for three weeks, and it was that that inspired me to do nursing. Now, I couldn't run far enough away from the place. The nuns had the place running like clockwork. It was efficient twenty years ago; it was probably very cost-effective as well. I can't believe the state of it now. It was very inefficient. Crumlin [Hospital] is a palace compared to Vincent's, and that building hasn't changed.

Why is it not efficient? There's more pressure on the emergency services, but there are still the same number of beds, still the same number of in-patients that there were twenty years ago, so…. There *is* a huge amount more of paperwork to be done, though. When we were nursing, we had a nursing card index, that's all, now they have five or six A-4-sized pieces of paper to fill in any time they do something.

The corridors are full of the stuff, files, cabinets, there's an awful lot more red tape. They seemed to be physically bursting at the seams—it was such a mess. But everything is disposable now, so you need more space.

By the time you get to the Complaints Office, it's too late for quality control. There were three of them in it. They were bureaucrats, yes. They wouldn't have been able to investigate an issue of malpractice; they wouldn't be able to question the doctors.

There was no sign of the patients' charter. When I looked for it, I was told it was on a file in a drawer in the nurses' station! I said it should be up on the wall; they said we can't put it up for infection control reasons, we'd have to get it laminated. Well, right, get it laminated! Then there's a patient information booklet, that's at the entrance to the hospital, I was told. But I came in through A&E, so I didn't get one. What about giving a booklet to every patient? I asked. We're not in the business of running an information service, they said. In the Adelaide Hospital when I worked there, everyone got an information booklet: it tells you very basic things, things you need to know as a patient. I found it shocking that there was no reference at all anywhere to the patients' charter.

I have BUPA cover, but I'm not paying for anything, I didn't see a consultant. You can't be a private patient in Vincent's because all the rooms are taken up with MRSA patients. They're bursting at the seams, having to cancel all their elective surgery.

Vincent's is too big. They made a huge mistake. The bigger it gets, the more inefficient it is. Why? Well, for one thing, the time taken to walk from A to B is time wasted. It takes so long to get anywhere in a hospital like James's.

Has the change to university-based nurse training made a difference? Definitely. We were student nurses for three years. In your first year, you gave personal care, cleaned, washed, brushed teeth, did the things people need to maintain their dignity. In second year, you gave drugs and injections; in your third year, you'd nearly be running a ward. Today, they're missing out on a huge amount of skill. The fact that training has changed has been a huge spanner in the works; you can see the calibre of what's coming out. Their last year is all practical, and they do a bit in third year.

We did six weeks' study every year, it was the inverse of what they do now. You were accountable 100 per cent for your actions. That pressure made you do things properly. Here the students are not accountable; they have no responsibility.

That very basic care that used to be there is completely gone. You know the kind of thing: Are you comfortable? Will I fix your pillows? Nurses don't touch you any more. They use machines to take your blood pressure, they don't look at you while they're doing it, they're looking at the machine. There is a detachment there now. The Nightingale thing is gone. We wanted to care for people; that's why we went into nursing. Now it's a very uncaring and a very un-empathetic environment. There's no love in it. In the old days, you'd be looking at the patient while you were taking their pulse; now there's no connection: no one looks at you. There's this huge feeling of being a number, of not mattering very much. It's very sad. Nursing's changed on every level.

They will never change the training back. Careers are disposable; young people won't stay with something if they don't like it. It's very scary. One night a student went off after taking the obs [observations] and took them with her inadvertently. In our day, you'd have had to face the matron the following morning and you'd have been shaking.

There are too many layers of non-medical management now. Maybe there's more value for money, more cost-efficiency now, but the care was better long ago. There's a deep disrespect for plain average Joe Soap. The idea that they wouldn't provide you with decent basic care, a wash, help with changing your clothes, a mouthwash even. The system is disrespectful.

They have a brand new building, a new ICU, but patients still have to sleep in that cesspit. You walk in this bright new shiny door, into the old hospital that's smelly, dingy, manky, chaotic. This isn't going to pass. I don't see how it can get any better.

I looked for my records. They looked for photo ID: I was standing there, still wearing my hospital bracelet. It should have been enough but it wasn't. There were three people working in the complaints department. Why do you need three clerks if you're running a hospital properly?

Maria Maguire, a former intensive care nurse, spent three days in St Vincent's Hospital. Her interview highlights, once again, the overcrowding, with nurses trying unsuccessfully to do procedures, such as ECGs, in public: the indignity of being examined in public. Corridors jammed with trolleys now seem more dangerous: cross infection is the first thing that comes to mind. The nursing shortage is all too visible: the erosion of skills, the use of agency nurses and untrained care assistants, the arguably over-academic training, and the disappearance of 'the Nightingale thing'. Then there are the dysfunctional work practices: the demarcation lines between teams/specialties, for example; the bureaucracy that wastes nursing time; the inordinate delays in getting tests done; the medication error that has to be corrected; the defensive over-prescribing that wastes resources; the overall lack of standards—the dirt, the blood, the smell, the food. And at the bottom of the heap, the patient: neglected, uncared for, not talked to, not listened to. And all of this—despite the best efforts of staff—in a 'centre of excellence'.

(Ironically, Florence Nightingale applied to train as a nurse at St Vincent's during the 1850s. Her application was rejected: the nuns were not prepared to admit lay trainees.)

POWER GAMES

A rigid, hierarchical culture derived from a semi-militaristic and religious service background.

The Commission of Nursing on hospital culture in Ireland

Who controls our hospitals? Who polices them? Just how good or bad are their outcomes? How do they spend our money? These questions may look simple, but in Ireland, they are quite difficult to answer. Executive power over all public hospitals and private non-profit hospitals now lies with the National Hospital Office. But private non-profit hospitals—the 'public voluntary' hospitals, as they are misleadingly called—have traditionally been independent principalities, outside the net of state control. Long after the Irish Hospital Sweepstake was discontinued, long after they became dependent on state coffers, these hospitals continued to assert their independence from the state. Catholic bishops lost no opportunity to buttress the power of Catholic hospitals. Most of Ireland's private non-profit hospitals are concentrated in the capital: of the thirty private

not-for-profit institutions, twenty-four are in Dublin. They have
always been quite a force in Irish medicine.

The Commission on Nursing characterised Irish hospital
culture as 'a command and control model of management', underpinned by a tendency to retain information. Muiris Houston paints
an interesting picture of command and control in the Lourdes
Hospital, Drogheda, in the 1970s:

> The environment would have been one of leadership from the top, a
> leadership supplied by a handful of consultants and religious adminis-
> trators. In the health service of the time, entire hospital wards were often
> allocated to specific consultants and administered by a religious ward
> sister. Between them, the consultant and the sister had huge autonomy in
> the running of their particular part of the hospital.

All is changed, changed utterly. Consultant and undaunted election
candidate Bill Tormey describes how, when Dublin's James Connolly
Hospital in Blanchardstown was taken over by the Northern Area
Health Board, the first thing the new administration did was to send
a letter to staff telling them that 'Management Consultancy' would
inspect them. Consultants blame administrators today, and vice versa,
for the ills besetting the health services. 'Administrators often play
Mickey Mouse power games, frustrate doctors and try to turn them
into middle-grade civil servants. There are posts to watch posts, to
manage other line managers. If a brush were run through a whole
load of them, I don't believe the hospital's core service would be
affected in any way.' Tormey also complains about the numbers
employed in human resources. What role do they actually play? he
asks. He complains about 'the excessive layers of checks and balances,
with people "marking" others and often being very slow to come to a
decision'. He believes there are 'layers of redundant supervisory staff',
with medical secretaries, for example, reporting to 'clerical staff
supervisors'. He is not a fan of the new 'directorates': 'new layers of
managers have been placed as a buffer between the CEO and consultants
running departments or staff providing direct patient services. This
convolutes decision-making and retards the speed of change.…
Administrative sclerosis is becoming endemic,' he observes.

'The next army in hospitals is the general nursing staff,' Tormey
continues. And managing both armies, he might have added, are what

have been called 'the five-star generals'. (The use of war metaphors in medicine is extremely common.) The nursing hierarchy in Beaumont Hospital, as Tormey describes it, resembles a mini-corporation: at the top is the director of nursing; underneath, there are seven divisional nurse managers who manage about 170 nurses each in the different specialties, such as medicine, neurosurgery, A&E and so on.

You sense the ongoing, daily power struggle between three hierarchies, medical, nursing and administration. Doctors tend to believe that hospitals are run by health bureaucrats and nursing unions; nurses understand that hospitals are run by consultants and bureaucrats, while bureaucrats maintain that they cannot do their job because consultants and nursing unions are a law unto themselves.

Reading between the lines, one gets the feeling that a state of actual or incipient warfare is not uncommon between these potentially warring armies, with times of open conflict interspersed with periods of uneasy truce. Within those hierarchies, as well as between them, there may be interpersonal battles: those between consultants, as in Beaumont and Cavan Hospitals, may threaten the future of an entire service. Those between consultants and health boards may end in the High Court.

'BLIND DRUNK OR CARRYING A SHOTGUN'
In December 1999, the North-Eastern Health Board suspended consultant physician Colman Muldoon from his post at Our Lady of Lourdes Hospital, Drogheda, for keeping his patients too long in hospital, thereby, the Board said, depriving others of hospital treatment.

By then, the issue of beds had become fraught. The question of who controls them—doctors or managers—had long been a matter of dispute. The turnover of beds determines the productivity of a hospital. This was the time when bed-blocking was a consultant activity. Surgeons, particularly, were known to keep a patient 'warming' the bed until such time as the next surgical patient could be organised to take it over, possession being nine-tenths of the law. While this had the benefit of ensuring an uninterrupted flow of work in the theatre, it also led to waiting lists and wasted scarce resources.

Cormac Muldoon appealed to the courts for an injunction restraining the Board from putting him on administrative leave. By the time the case reached the High Court, the dispute had been running for six *years*. NEHB had barred him from entering the hospital;

the consultant told the judge he was no longer welcome at the hospital where he had worked for twenty-nine years.

Earlier in the year, the Board had set up an 'independent inquiry' into his practice, but the physician had declined to participate. (All health inquiries are presented as 'independent' when they are simply external. Like all bodies, training colleges and others have vested interests: they usually have a stake in the outcome of any inquiries they undertake.) Yet another independent inquiry, the court was told, was scheduled for January 2000, this one by his colleagues at the Royal College of Physicians. Muldoon initially appealed even this decision to the Minister for Health, but later agreed to be bound by the outcome.

The case pitted board against consultant in a critical area: the discharge of a patient. A medical commentator opined that the dispute was 'rooted in the tension between clinical independence and accountability in the health services'. Behind this lay an even more fundamental issue: what should be the limits of 'clinical independence' or consultant power? Cormac Muldoon considered the Board's action an attack on his autonomy: he maintained that the decision to discharge a patient could be made only by a consultant on clinical grounds, for patient-related reasons. The Board had said it intended to interfere with the clinical management of his patients, the Lourdes physician told the judge. 'I am not prepared to tolerate changes which diminish the care of patients and particularly impair delivery of patient care, for which I have the ultimate responsibility.'

Professional independence lay at the heart of the case. The court was told that the contractual clause under which the Board had enforced his leave of absence applied only where there was an immediate and serious risk to the safety, health or welfare of patients or staff. The Irish Hospital Consultants' Association (IHCA) was reportedly 'angered' by the Board's use of this particular clause to justify its action against the consultant. In an interesting interpretation of the contract, General Secretary Finbarr Fitzpatrick said that, when the clause had been negotiated three years previously, the intention had been to give boards the power to remove a consultant who arrived into a hospital 'blind drunk or carrying a shotgun'. Fitzpatrick claimed that the Board had turned the clause on its head: 'If this clause is to be used like this, the independent clinical judgement of the consultant is completely eroded and consultants can be made to discharge their patients as quickly as is necessary to meet the needs of management.' Fitzpatrick further claimed that using such a clause 'relieves the health board of the obligation to open more beds and brings more and more to the fore a budget-centred hospital service'.

Another medical doctor, Ambrose McLoughlin, the Board's assistant CEO, told the court that the hospital could treat 1,000–1,600 additional patients annually if Dr Muldoon were 'within the norms of his specialty'. (Hospital administrators submit service plans detailing how many procedures will be performed during the year: this forms the basis of funding requests.) 'Doctors' decisions,' Dr Muldoon told a journalist, 'must be solely based on medical grounds and not influenced by financial and other constraints.'

Cormac Muldoon claimed that, at the time of his suspension, sixty-one of the hospital's 360 beds were closed and that up to six patients frequently slept overnight on trolleys. He had complained to management six months previously, he said, when an elderly patient of his died waiting for an appointment. The physician said that he kept his patients in hospital for an average of 10.8 days, 2.1 days more than the hospital average. The average length of stay, nationally, *The Irish Times* reported, was 6.7 days, with the Lourdes averaging 5.8. The Department of Health, it transpired, had fined the hospital £1.2 million over the previous six years for keeping patients in too long. (The Department operates a 'case-mix system' that is used to penalise hospitals for over-lengthy stays.)

Mr Justice Ó Caoimh refused Muldoon the injunction he sought against the Board: in conflicts between doctors and managers, he said, the health and welfare of patients was paramount. A couple of days later, on 15 January 2000, 1,000 patients marched through the streets of Drogheda in support of Muldoon, while 10,000 signed a petition demanding his reinstatement. Hospital consultants were deeply divided on the issue, with some signing High Court affidavits against Muldoon and others petitioning or marching in his support. Of the hospital's twenty-two full-time consultants, nine, along with eight part-time consultants, swore statements backing the health board. The case was settled in October 2000, reportedly for around £600,000.

BULLYING

Bullying appears to be endemic in the health services, not only between nurses, but between doctors, and between doctors and nurses.

Bullying has been described as 'a major source of stress, breakdown and malfunction' in Irish hospitals.

What counts as bullying? 'Persistent offensive, abusive, intimidating, malicious or insulting behaviour, abuse of power or unfair penal sanctions, which make the recipient feel upset, threatened, humiliated or vulnerable, which undermines their self-confidence and which may cause them to suffer stress.' A recent study found that about 30 per cent of junior doctors had been subjected to one or more of these bullying behaviours; those from within the European Union reported significantly less bullying than those from outside it. 'It is not too difficult to postulate a connection between bullying, harassment and racism,' the study concluded.

Its author, Dr S. Cheema, is blunt: 'Many junior doctors in Ireland experience bullying during their training; there are cases of juniors being physically abused, pushed around, verbally abused, ignored and being given a dressing down in front of other staff and patients by their consultants and senior staff of the team.' Some forms of bullying, such as threats over medical references, are 'more insidious', he points out. (Trainees are totally dependent on the good graces of their consultants for the advancement of their careers in medicine.) Part of the problem, Dr Cheema thinks, is that progress in the profession 'still works on a system of patronage and word of mouth'.

According to the Medical Council, there are over 3,000 non-consultant hospital doctors working in Ireland; just under 50 per cent are non-nationals.

THROUGH ENGLISH EYES
In the wake of the Caesarean hysterectomy scandal at the Lourdes Hospital in Drogheda, the North-Eastern Health Board commissioned a London consultancy in 2001 to review its five hospitals.

The risk assessors found high MRSA levels; infection control was a non-priority and bathroom and toilet facilities for patients were inadequate. Junior staff were said to perform surgery at night on both children and orthopaedic patients. Rest periods between shifts for those in theatre were inadequate; surgical lists were very long. Critical care was inadequate, as was A&E; while staffing in the pharmacy was so inadequate that nurses were 'routinely' dispensing out of hours, often unsupervised by a pharmacist. There were reports of patients going unnoticed for extended periods, collapsing in toilets or bathrooms.

Audit was described as 'ad hoc'. The consultants found no policy on patient charts, or on managing patient records. Examples of unsigned reports in patient records were numerous, as were reports filed in the wrong place; test results were 'lost altogether' and 'had to be repeated'; while charts went missing 'at the rate of several per week'.

On the issue of management, the review was equally trenchant. 'There are no clear communication processes within and between management and clinical staff, within and between clinical departments, within and between clinical disciplines and between relevant hospital staff and external stakeholders.' Could this, with equal justice, not have been said of almost any hospital in the country?

SOVIET HEALTH INC.

Many believe that there are far too many bureaucrats in the health sector. The bureaucracy has been building for over a quarter of a century. From 1980 to 1993, for example, the number of administrators increased by 32 per cent, while the number of medical staff fell. One solicitor says: 'We need more doctors, more consultants, more nurses and fewer administrators. Over 40,000 administrators are employed in the health services. It staggers me.' A consultant working in James's Hospital says that 65 per cent of the spend goes on management. 'Absolutely chaotic, James's is.'

The management of the health services has recently been centralised. Until the creation of the HSE, there was a clear line of public accountability. Under the 1997 Public Service Management Act, the Secretary-General of the Department of Health was accountable to the Minister and the Oireachtas for delivering our health services. The 2004 Health Act abolished the regional health boards and created a new bureaucratic monster, the Health Service Executive, to control and manage the delivery of all health and personal social services. The new leviathan employs about 145,000 people. Consultant Maurice Neligan commented: 'It is a vast number of people to provide a palpably inadequate service.' The more services are centralised, the greater the number of bureaucrats needed to manage them. The media uncritically backed this concentration of power at the top, even as we witnessed the creation of a Soviet-style 'politburo'.

The wider health landscape now contains no fewer than eighty-three bodies, all of whom exercise some kind of regulatory power in health. Many, like Comhairle na n-Ospidéal, have disappeared into the maw of the HSE, but a number remain outside, buzzing about in the landscape.

Many clinicians feel sidelined. Commenting on hospital management, for example, the Nursing Commission reported that there was a need 'to foster an open system of management' where information is shared openly and frankly, and to show a willingness to listen and seek the view of nurses and midwives. More widely, the Irish Nurses' Organisation believes that 'protecting' and 'enhancing' management bureaucracies has taken precedence over acknowledging and dealing with fundamental problems. INO President Madeleine Speirs gives the example of nurse–patient ratios which, she says, have been determined in an ad hoc fashion, with nurses not being allowed to have any input into the process. No attempt, she says, has yet been made to include clinicians in the HSE's corporate management structures. 'In fact, every effort has been made to avoid doing so. This basic flaw and failing must be addressed if the needs of the patient are to be put first, rather than the needs of the bureaucrats'.

The HSE increasingly behaves like a corporation, with senior executives getting beefed-up bonuses on top of what many regard as highly inflated salaries. Commenting on the absence of any visible link between performance and pay, Green Party health spokesman John Gormley said: 'News of the 22,000 cancelled operations comes on the same day as reports that HSE executives awarded themselves generous bonuses of nearly €1.7 million over the last 18 months'.

In recent years, health authorities have shown themselves to be increasingly willing to resort to drastic measures to enforce medical treatment. Recently, parents from Co. Meath watched helplessly as the state removed their children from their home, having spent years unsuccessfully banging on the same state's door, desperately seeking suitable services for their four children who suffer from autism. Services for such children are extremely limited in Ireland, and for young adults with autism, they are non-existent. When parsimony is backed up by power, the results can be ugly.

A new willingness to coerce is evident—a belief that people can, and should, be compelled, if necessary, to accept medical treatment, however unwanted. This is particularly true of maternity care. Fetal rights have been enshrined in law in many countries. Ireland amended its Constitution in 1983 to give the fetus a right to life equal to that of its mother. The 1980s vogue in the United States for forcible

Caesarean section reached Ireland a decade later. There is now a perception on the part of some obstetricians and bureaucrats that legal proceedings to protect the fetus, authorising enforced medical treatment, may succeed before the courts. The Coombe Women's Hospital recently obtained an emergency order in the High Court forcing a fully conscious Jehovah's Witness mother to submit to an unwanted blood transfusion following the birth of her child.

Paul O'Beirne refused to sign the form for his son's detention in a psychiatric unit. His son, who suffers from anorexia, had been discharged from an acute hospital; the health board took the view that he required to be committed to a psychiatric unit. Parents do not seem to count, Mr O'Beirne said. The new mental health legislation, he believed, meant that involuntary committal was a thing of the past. Meanwhile, the South-Western Area Health Board waxed lyrical about 'best practice', 'clinical assessment' and 'continuous review'. Paul O'Beirne believed that a psychiatric unit could do nothing for his son; he eventually sourced what he believed was appropriate treatment for him in England at a specialist unit for eating disorders, having been contacted by another parent whose child also suffers from anorexia. She told Paul O'Beirne that the health board had eventually agreed to pay for treatment for her 23-year-old daughter at Huntercombe Centre, after months of lobbying. Her mother said that anorexia was misunderstood here—that it was a psychological disorder, not a psychiatric illness.

Underlying the issue of forcible medical treatment is a central issue: the right to self-determination. But personal autonomy and bodily integrity are not rights that are widely upheld in areas such as psychiatry or obstetrics. However, as hospitals and health authorities increasingly resort to the courts in an effort to secure compliance with their diktats, patients are themselves going the legal route in an attempt to discover the truth about their medical treatment.

Chapter 5
The Last Waltz

A mother of three was reported to be seriously ill with secondary lung and liver cancer. Tests showed cancerous cells in the bowel but the hospital took over a year to inform the woman of the results. Deirdre Conlon from Lucan, settled her action against Tallaght Hospital for around €200,000; the hospital also apologised.

We have no idea how many people are injured, or how many die, as a result of medical treatment in Ireland. Doctors do not know; the health authorities do not know; no one knows. But international research suggests that the numbers killed or injured in our hospitals may be quite staggering. Research done in two London hospitals, for example, showed that 12 per cent of patients had been injured; one-third of these injuries led to moderate or severe disability or death. A review of 30,000 patients at Harvard Medical School found that 4 per cent of patients had 'adverse outcomes'. Doctors estimated the annual cost of medical malpractice in the United States to patients, their families and the economy to be at least $60 billion. In 2006, RTÉ's *Prime Time* estimated that 14,000 people were injured or died as a result of medical treatment every year in Irish hospitals. This figure was later accepted by the Minister for Health and gave rise to considerable debate within the medical profession as to the meaning of 'medical error'—a term that covers negligence and malpractice as well as mistakes.

However, while medical consultants continue to protest about applying rates derived from international studies to Irish hospitals, they have been unable to tell us just how many patients *have* died or sustained damage as a result of negligence or malpractice. They cannot tell us because they do not know. Consultants may or may not compile statistics on their outcomes. Despite the advent of 'evidence-based medicine', the information deficit is huge. Ireland is 'surveillance poor'. While the Government boasts of Ireland's 'knowledge economy', medical records have yet to be computerised in many public hospitals, for want of funding. For an industry that costs taxpayers €14 billion a year, this is an extraordinarily dysfunctional state of affairs.

Nevertheless, one area of medicine where some statistics on outcomes are available, nationally, is obstetrics. We are constantly being told that Ireland is the safest country in the world in which to have a baby, but the reality is rather different. Our death rates in or around the time of birth are among the worst in the European Union. Only Britain, a country with a disintegrating health service, and some of the new member states show higher rates. In addition, for some years now, Ireland has had a worryingly high stillbirth rate, for reasons that have yet to be explained. Poor outcomes in birth are usually linked to poverty. But in one of the richest countries in the world, high infant death rates in maternity care demand an explanation.

LITIGATION

Medical litigation surged in the United States in the mid-1970s. The wave finally reached Ireland in 1988, when the tsunami of the Dunne Case hit one of the most self-regarding hospitals in Ireland, the National Maternity Hospital. After a healthy pregnancy (her second), Catherine Dunne gave birth to twins in Holles Street; the first baby was brain-damaged, the second stillborn. It took two years for her to get a copy of the post-mortem report from the hospital. Only after the Minister for Health turned down her request for a public inquiry did she resort to legal action. After a spectacular High Court retrial involving ten mothers who refuted the hospital's evidence on its monitoring of twins during labour, the National Maternity Hospital settled the action. Interestingly, Catherine Dunne was a private patient. She felt extremely unwell during labour, but by the time her consultant arrived at the hospital to attend to her, irreparable damage had been done.

In the wake of the Dunne Case, those working in the health services developed a new form of paranoia not yet recognised by psychiatrists as a disease: litigation paranoia. Irish obstetricians can expect to be sued twice every three years, according to the IHCA, while one lawsuit in every seven years is the norm for other specialists. Irish legal opinion says that these figures are misleading: they do not take into account the shortfall of consultants in Ireland, the higher level of medical activity and the larger volume of private practice compared with Britain. The medical view is that some claims may be without foundation.

> *Doctors frequently express concerns about frivolous claims, cases based on no rational argument, leading to compensation. This worry is the basis of the frequent calls for tort reform. It has been difficult to determine how commonly unnecessary cases are taken against doctors.*
>
> J.F.A. Murphy editor of IMO journal

Colm MacGeehin, a prominent civil liberties lawyer, says that it is medical injuries, not frivolous claims that lead to litigation. 'Solicitors will not waste time and money on cases that have no merit,' he points out. 'Also, it is extremely difficult to mount a case of medical negligence in Ireland. The medical profession has traditionally closed ranks, although this is beginning to change. In the past, medical witnesses had to be flown in from abroad, adding greatly to the difficulty of bringing an action.'

A 1998 report by an indemnity insurer, the Medical Defence Union (MDU), shows that claims against obstetrician/gynaecologists have been taken for entirely rational and understandable reasons. Just seven types of injury or complication, some of them fatal, accounted for 85 per cent of all claims. Brain damage and death in newborn babies, for example, accounted for 38 per cent of lawsuits. Women who suffered serious physical trauma as a result of a ruptured womb, a bladder injury or a damaged pelvic floor also sued, as did women who had sustained urinary tract damage, a wound infection, or a Caesarean hysterectomy. Like Caesarean section, hysterectomy accounted for a significant number of claims, as did laparoscopy, a common keyhole investigation. The cases taken in gynaecology were equally serious: bowel and bladder injury, perforated wombs, major blood vessel damage and burns. These were the 'errors' that led women to claim. 'Foreign bodies' had been left in patients, the report also revealed. Staff had forgotten to remove surgical instruments, catheters, drains, swabs, needles and stitches. Some of the surgical instruments left inside women's bodies were enormous, as Theresa Tobin, a mother of six from Clonakilty, Co. Cork, confirmed to the High Court. She discovered that her sterilisation had failed when she became pregnant with her sixth child. To add insult to injury, an instrument about the length and breadth of a shoe 'tree', a vaginal dilator, had been left inside her body following the procedure.

Insurers like to believe that Irish people are litigious. So do doctors. IHCA secretary Finbarr Fitzpatrick blames the 'compensation culture', which, he says, is 'fanned by ambulance-chasing' solicitors. But Ann O'Driscoll, a claims manager at St Paul's, then one of the main insurers here, maintained that there was no evidence of a 'compo' culture in Ireland, only signs of 'sub-standard care' and 'non-communication with doctors'. In ten years of assessing liabilities, she said, she had seen only two vexatious claims. Leading plaintiff solicitor Michael Boylan is adamant: 'We need to separate fact from fiction—the fiction that patients are very litigious. Many more have valid cases than pursue them. If they recover without long-term damage, they say: "I'm happy to get on with my life, to have my health back."' He believes that the number of medical negligence claims is tiny. 'Patients only sue if some serious injury with lifelong consequences has been inflicted.' Law Society director Ken Murphy confirms that only a very small proportion of justifiable claims are actually brought against doctors.

On the other hand, the IHCA claims that Ireland has the highest level of litigation in Europe, second only to the United States in the 'world league'. This myth was first propagated by the MDU in Ireland in 1991, just before a hike in the company's charges. In the United States, consumer watchdog Ralph Nader says that insurance companies are frightening doctors by invoking high levels of litigation that do not exist. Take the Harvard study previously mentioned: of those who suffered injuries or illness as a result of their medical treatment, only 10 per cent took action. In the US, eight times as many patients are injured by medical malpractice as have ever filed a claim; sixteen times as many suffer injuries as receive compensation.

So, just how high is the rate of medical litigation in Ireland? Looking at the figures, it is clear that only a small proportion of those entitled to take action do so. The total number of claims in the Republic was only 1,300 in 2000, up from 949 in 1990, hardly a dramatic increase. And, until July 2002, one case often involved several insurers, so these figures overestimate the actual claims. Michael Boylan estimates that the actual number of claims, annually, is around 1,000. But if 14,000 patients are damaged by medical treatment, even assuming that only one in ten claims, then we should be seeing 1,400 claims every year. The evidently low level of claims was borne out by *Prime Time*: in 2006, the programme established that while there had been 25,000 adverse incidents in Irish hospitals over the previous eighteen months, only 620 claims had been lodged—one claim for every fifty incidents, a rate of 2 per cent.

If people take legal action, it is partly because there is a cover-up culture in medicine, Ken Murphy points out. The law has always been seen as one of the main routes to truth. Patients frequently find their attempts to investigate their care frustrated. Complaints to hospitals often get nowhere. Inquests do not necessarily allow people to discover why certain things did or did not happen. Even in complaints that appear to involve gross negligence, the Medical Council may not agree that there is a case to be answered. Many of those who take action against hospitals and/or doctors do so solely in an attempt to discover the truth. Official records show that 70 per cent of claims notified to insurers do not go past the first step: the disclosure of medical records. If a claim proceeds, of course, and liability is admitted, there can be no further questions.

INDEMNITY INSURANCE

Professional insurance is a problem worldwide. Medical defence organisations have left the market or made their premiums prohibitively expensive. St Paul's, for example, pulled out of the Irish market because it was not profitable. Globally, companies have learned how to break down their risk pools, stratifying them into smaller groups, such as orthopaedics, in order to charge more. High-risk specialties, as a result, have become almost uninsurable. In Australia, for example, the government stepped in when insurers refused to insure obstetricians. Medical indemnifiers *could* follow the lead of car insurers, who charge more if you claim (this is known in the trade as 'experience loss rating'). But insurers are unwilling to charge doctors who incur claims higher premiums: companies make more money by charging those who have never incurred a claim the same rates as those whose negligence or malpractice has led to pay-outs.

In Ireland, medical insurers have been stoking up a 'crisis' in indemnity for nearly two decades, lobbying for tort 'reform'—a euphemism for cutting back on patients' rights—by claiming, among other things, that awards are higher here. Michael Boylan disputes this: pay-outs in Irish courts are higher for minor injuries, he says, but for serious injuries, damages in English courts are significantly higher. Taking an overview, the awards for damages may not differ hugely, though, as English courts are more likely to compensate for every aspect of loss, while Irish courts are more inclined to compensate for general pain and suffering.

Until recently in Ireland, hospitals, consultants, non-consultant hospital doctors and others had separate insurance cover, footed mainly by the public purse. Taxpayers picked up 80–90 per cent of consultants' insurance bills, depending on the size of their private practice. The cost of this insurance more than trebled over ten years. In 1991, medical indemnity cost us €2.32 million. By 2000, the total bill for medical insurance had jumped to €41 million.

In 1999, obstetric insurance rose by 88 per cent, more than *seven* times the percentage increase for other specialties. Two years later, MDU premiums for obstetricians rose from £68,600 to £393,000—ten times the salary of a qualified nurse. Fortunately for taxpayers who were footing the bulk of the bill, MDU members speedily transferred to rival insurers, the Medical Protection Society. (These medical indemnity bodies are not insurers in the traditional sense, however: they are not required to have the reserves normally demanded of insurance companies, nor do they have the same accountability requirements.)

The state then devised a new indemnity scheme for health service employees, 'enterprise liability'. Our Clinical Indemnity Scheme (CIS) resembles the British crown indemnity scheme: under this, the Government assumes liability for personal injury claims against hospital consultants and other staff involved in treating patients. The scheme would, it was hoped, save time, effort and, above all, money. (On this point, the crown indemnity scheme has proved disastrous: claims have rocketed since its introduction.) The scheme protects individual practitioners, replacing the concept of *individual* responsibility with *institutional* liability. Whereas before, three insurers (the consultant's, the hospital's, and the health board's), each with its own legal team, passed around the poisoned chalice of liability, the 'enterprise'—or hospital—is now the only entity that you can sue.

The new arrangement, covering in-house, but not off-site, private practice, finally trundled in on 1 July 2002. Consultants' unions, the IHCA and the IMO, refused to join the scheme. They had a number of issues with it, including cover for past claims. The Government was willing to cover new claims, hitherto unreported, for past negligence, but not 'historic liabilities' notified prior to July 2002. By September 2003, the MDU was preparing to pull the plug on its Irish members, refusing to cover their past claims. The problem of historic liabilities was 'more or less confined to obstetrics', *Medicine Weekly* revealed. The MDU claimed to have spent tens of millions in obstetric pay-outs; it was now facing an estimated bill for 'known and incurred liabilities' of €130 million. The MDU offered €60 million, payable over five years; the Government declined. It later declared itself willing to back doctors who decided to take the MDU to court in an attempt to force the insurer to pay up. The MDU contended that it could not afford to pay out in these cases, as it had already spent €62 million in obstetric damages since 1977, despite having taken in only €25 million in Irish subscriptions during the same period.

One of the doctors refused cover by the MDU was James Barry, a general practitioner from Cork. He tried, unsuccessfully, to force the insurer to cover him for damages sought by a number of his former female patients, who had filed civil claims against him for alleged sexual and indecent assault. Barry contended that he had bought indemnity from the London-based insurer for more than thirty years, and that he was entitled to cover; the MDU disputed this, claiming 'absolute discretion' to allow or refuse to pay his costs, in whole or in part. The GP lost his case in the Supreme Court on a technicality.

Before long, the bill for 'medical error' had jumped to €400 million. This should have heralded a public outcry about medical negligence and malpractice. Media coverage of the conflict, although extensive, was ill-informed. Journalists seemed unaware of the fact that insurers had assessed these claims—reported to involve some thirty-five obstetricians—and made a finding of medical negligence or malpractice. No one questioned the implications for patient safety of €400 million worth of claims relating to adverse outcomes in maternity care, *judged by the insurer to be avoidable.*

THE WALTZ OF OBSTETRICS WITH LITIGATION

Both the insurance and the medical lobbies have been pushing for many years for a 'no-fault compensation scheme' for brain-damaged babies. But there are major concerns about accountability. One legal source said: 'You're on the road to fascism and dictatorship when you have people who are not accountable before the law.' Parents have fears that they will be unable to find out what happened to their child. The committee examining the issue is still sitting. In 2003, IHCA estimated that up to 200 babies with cerebral palsy were born every year. A number of these infants are brain damaged as a result of medical treatment. Should we not monitor hospital activity much more closely to prevent medical malpractice and negligence?

Today, litigation paranoia permeates the Irish health service. Defensive medicine is 'widely practised by all doctors and must be costing the Exchequer and health insurance providers millions of euro annually,' according to the IHCA. 'For many medical practitioners,' the union maintains, 'every patient is a potential litigant, and as a result, certain tests and procedures are performed *with the intention of protecting the practitioner* as much as ensuring the correct diagnosis of the patient' [emphasis added].

From the patients' perspective, some of the major risks of malpractice and negligence appear to lie in the dual specialty of obstetrics and gynaecology. Within the spiral of intervention that is driving obstetrics, 'we are seeing a deadly dance, the waltz of obstetrics with litigation. The more obstetricians intervene in birth, the more birth injuries occur; the more obstetricians get sued, the more they intervene'. Defensive practice in obstetrics has become hugely problematic, yet no attempt has been made to curb it. Irish Caesarean section rates have spiked in the past couple of decades. One baby in every four in Ireland is born by Caesarean section; but this national average conceals upper as well as lower limits. In certain hospitals, Caesarean rates exceed 30 per cent. This is indefensible. Private care is a marker for Caesarean section, of course, and the level of private obstetrics in Ireland stands at around 50 per cent.

Ireland is not alone in showing such a rapid growth: high Caesarean section rates are a consequence of industrialising birth. But such elevated rates are inimical to the health and welfare of mothers and babies. Nor do they help balance the health budget. Common as it is, the operation carries significantly higher risks than normal birth for both mothers and babies. In Britain, fear of litigation—or self-protection—has been identified as the main factor in the growth of Caesarean section. At over 28 per cent, Ireland's Caesarean section rate is now more than double the safety limit recommended by the World Health Organisation.

WHY OBSTETRICIANS ARE SUED

The question as to why doctors are sued brings us back full circle to the common contract that allows doctors to work without supervision, and to delegate their work to junior doctors. The contract allows them to absent themselves from their place of employment in order to make money elsewhere. Consultant absenteeism has led on occasion to death and injury. The MDU report hints that junior medical staff may on occasion work without proper supervision, attending difficult births, such as breeches and twins, in the absence of senior staff. To have junior hospital doctors performing procedures for which they may not be adequately trained—in the absence of their consultant supervisors—is to court disaster.

Over-treatment is another factor fingered in the report for adverse outcomes. Again, the MDU report suggests that some gynaecological procedures that 'can have fatal consequences' are being performed unnecessarily. Hysterectomy is one of the most common operations, not only in Ireland, but in other countries. Like Caesarean, it is a leading cause of litigation and is frequently performed without good reason.

Ireland has a highly interventionist system of care, as we have seen: admission to neonatal intensive care units is correspondingly high. Take, for example, one hospital, Our Lady of Lourdes, Drogheda. In 1999, as many as 29 per cent of all newborn babies were admitted to intensive care there; almost all of them had been born in the unit. In that year, two out of every five women in the Lourdes had their babies by Caesarean section, forceps delivery or vacuum extraction. The hospital maintains its rates of neonatal admission to intensive care and its rates of intervention are in line with rates in other Irish hospitals, but is this reassuring?

One question that needs to be asked is: are scalpels, forceps and vacuum extractors making babies sick? And, if so, should doctors resort to them as often as they do? A five-year study of cerebral palsy in the Rotunda Hospital showed that thirteen babies died from lack of oxygen around birth, thirty-two infants suffered convulsions during the first forty-eight hours of life, and of those, one in five developed cerebral palsy. Oxytocin or Syntocinon, a synthetic hormone associated with brain damage and death, routinely employed to induce and accelerate labour, was used on 44 per cent of the babies who seized, and on 32 per cent of the infants who died. The authors did not discuss the possibility that the action of the drug might have reduced the babies' oxygen supply, thereby leading to their deaths and disabilities. Oxytocin is used routinely to induce and accelerate labour.

Other sources of litigation included new technologies. Patients pay the price of learning curves. Poor outcomes in keyhole surgery have been linked to doctors less than fully trained in new microsurgery technologies.

There were also instances of substandard care, where staff, for example, did not ensure that the afterbirth had been delivered whole, leaving the mother at significant risk of bleeding.

Finally, medical culture itself leads to litigation. Carrying out procedures in the absence of informed consent increasingly gives rise to litigation, yet sterilisation is the only procedure where the MDU recommended that doctors should use a 'separate, specific' consent form. ('Blanket' consent forms are the norm.)

FULL CIRCLE

'The whole malpractice insurance premium business amounts to about what this country spends on dog food and is one half of one percent of health care costs in this country,' Ralph Nader observes. 'Isn't it about time to focus on malpractice prevention first and foremost instead of pounding on the rights of hundreds of thousands of Americans who leave their doctors far worse than when they greeted them?'

The new clinical indemnity scheme in Ireland was backed up by 'risk management', which involves the systematic reporting of adverse events by hospital staff. Four years after the scheme was introduced, one of its major hazards was identified: 'the risk of individual liability'. As the editor of *Irish Medical Journal* observed, 'Doctors, understandably, are apprehensive of being legally exposed if errors are reported'.

Had the wheel come full circle? Was fear of litigation now going to stymie risk management?

Chapter 6
Heart of Darkness

It was decided to submit the operation of symphys-
iotomy to as severe a test as possible.
Dr Arthur Barry, Master of the National Maternity
Hospital, explaining that medical experimentation was
the reason why doctors initially withheld a Caesarean
section from a mother, allowing her baby to
die because they wished to test symphysiotomy as
a procedure for obstructed labour. The baby's head
was trapped in her mother's pelvis for
twenty-four hours.

A RELIGIOUS REVIVAL

Until recently, most of us had never heard of symphysiotomy. Few texts in obstetrics or midwifery mention this obscure operation. Symphysiotomy is a radical surgical procedure used mainly in cases of difficult labour in countries where Caesarean section is not an option. The operation is known to be hazardous, especially for the mother.

The term 'symphysiotomy' comes from the *symphysis pubis,* one of the joints in the pelvis. While this joint widens a little during the final months of pregnancy, symphysiotomy enables the pelvis to 'open like a hinge', leaving it permanently widened, cutting through the cartilage that binds the pubic bones together, widening the curved canal that the baby passes through on its journey to the outer world. Symphysiotomy was devised to treat obstructed labour, when the child's journey is impeded through the birth canal, if the shoulders become stuck in transit ('shoulder dystocia'), for example. But this rarely happens. In developing countries, symphysiotomy is also done for disproportion, a complication of labour associated with rickets, where the mother's pelvis is believed to be too narrow for her baby's head.

Looking at the medical literature, you find symphysiotomy cropping up in journals such as *Tropical Doctor*. In developing countries, where access to blood is often limited, and operating conditions dangerously inadequate, this relatively simple eighteenth-century operation still forms part of what is called the 'obstetric arsenal' (war metaphors, again). Two centuries ago, doctors were debating the merits of Caesarean section versus symphysiotomy. Today, one or two plead for symphysiotomy to be taught in developing countries. Symphysiotomy is no longer taught, not because it is complicated, but because its costs to Western patients are seen as too high. Margaret Myles, in her classic 1975 text for midwives, put it succinctly: 'This operation used to be performed prior to the Caesarean section era. It is not popular in Britain today but is employed in some African countries where the women are unlikely to return for a repeat Caesarean section.' The medical literature is thick with references to 'maternal morbidity', or sickness, following the operation. Significant post-operative pain and 'gait' problems feature heavily, explaining the operation's lack of popularity.

Back in the eighteenth century, the cost–benefit equation was the reverse. Symphysiotomy was devised as an alternative to Caesarean section in 1777. In the latter half of the eighteenth century, to perform a Caesarean was to risk the life of the mother; to do a symphysiotomy in the second half of the twentieth century was to gamble with her health. In countries rich enough to be able to afford Western medicine, Caesarean section has been the treatment of choice for dystocia and disproportion for many decades. According to Myles, again: 'Following symphysiotomy, some women suffer permanent backache; others may have disability in walking.' In fact, the hazards of symphysiotomy were so well known within the medical profession that the technique had been shunned by doctors in developed countries since the early part of the last century. Or so we thought.

In May 2002, I went to a press conference in Dublin's Shelbourne Hotel. The place was thronged with women of all ages but mostly of an age when they should have been free of care, serene, at peace, enjoying their lives and their families. The sun streamed through the high Georgian windows overlooking St Stephen's Green, ten minutes' walk from the hospital where the operation had been revived. The room fell silent as they described how the surgery had left them unable to walk, in pain, incontinent. Women in their middle years, and older, some on the verge of tears, spoke of damaged mother–child relationships and ruined marriages, of wasted years and decades of incomprehension. Doctors had dispensed with consent: many mothers were not told even retrospectively that their symphisis pubis had been filleted in this way. They made this discovery years later, slowly and painfully piecing it together. A PhD student, Jacqueline Morrissey published an article in *The Irish Times* about the revival of symphysiotomy. The word got out.

Hundreds of symphysiotomies were done in Irish maternity units and hospitals from the 1940s until the 1980s. The first one was reportedly performed in Dublin in 1944, the last in Drogheda in 1983. The operation was widely practised in 'centres of excellence', such as the National Maternity and the Lourdes hospitals.

Dublin doctors, led by the Master at Holles Street Hospital, Alex Spain, revived the operation. This resurrection met with considerable opposition. British doctors described symphysiotomy as a practice 'of darker times', but Spain was undeterred. In the very first year of his term as Master, he performed four of them; by 1948, he had performed forty-three. In a damaging admission in the hospital's annual report, Spain admitted that he would have done the operation more frequently were it not for the fact that it was 'an entirely new procedure ... that has to be faced against the weight of the entire English-speaking obstetrical world'. Arthur Barry succeeded Spain at the National Maternity Hospital as Master; he continued the learning curve.

THEOLOGY

In a hospital that claimed to be eminent, in a discipline that claimed to be scientific, in a state that claimed to be modern, symphysiotomy was the triumph of theology over reason. Traditional Catholic values were being reasserted in the face of external threats to family life from free-thinking, post-war Britain. The Holles Street obstetrician was a devout and deeply conservative Catholic. As well as being a member of a secretive Catholic society, the Order of the Knights of St Columbanus, Barry was also a member of the Guild of Saints Luke, Cosmos and Damian, which was dedicated to putting Catholic teaching into medical practice. The guild's spiritual adviser was Archbishop John Charles McQuaid.

At an international congress of Catholic doctors in Blackrock College in 1954, the Holles Street Master told his audience that it was 'unnecessary to stress to Catholic doctors that the practices of contraception, sterilisation and therapeutic abortion' were 'contrary to moral law'. He cautioned his listeners against Caesarean section. Every Catholic obstetrician, Barry said, should realise that this operation was probably the chief cause of the 'unethical procedure of sterilisation'. Furthermore, he pointed out, Caesarean was very frequently responsible for encouraging the laity 'in the improper prevention of pregnancy or in seeking termination'. Symphysiotomy, he opined, was a natural procedure that was in accordance with Catholic moral law and teaching. Dismissing 'all the bogeys and pitfalls' found in research on symphysiotomy as 'sheer flights of imagination', he argued for its safety, then bragged about his prowess, honed on the pubes of over a hundred women. 'If you must cut something, cut the symphysis,' he concluded. The only challenge came from Kieran O'Driscoll, who asked about the risk of permanent disability to mothers and death to babies. Barry replied that permanent disability among women was rare, but he did acknowledge that more babies died from symphysiotomy than from Caesarean section.

A MOTE IN THE EYE

By the time his seven-year term as Master had ended, Barry had performed 165 symphysiotomies on women diagnosed as suffering from a complication later found to be imaginary. Hospital reports detailed the injuries caused by the operation, but hospital doctors continued to perform it. In the last report he wrote before stepping down as Master in 1962, Barry noted that twelve babies had died as a direct result of the surgery.

Outside the hospital, he crusaded: the contagion spread to other hospitals in Dublin and elsewhere. Irish doctors were well aware of the repeated attacks levelled at symphysiotomy by their British colleagues, but only the Protestant Rotunda Hospital opposed the practice. Reviewing the Dublin symphysiotomies, Professor T.N. Jeffcote from the University of Liverpool found that one baby had died, while several others had been severely brain damaged. At a meeting of the Royal Academy of Medicine in Kildare Street in 1950, he declared that the risk to the baby was such that one was left 'horrified at the *courage* of the obstetrician [emphasis added]'. The following year, the Academy heard further trenchant criticism of symphysiotomy from another visiting academic, Professor Chassar Moir of Oxford University: three symphysiotomy babies had been injured the previous year, two of them fatally.

By then, controversy raged: Donal Browne of the Rotunda Hospital pleaded with his colleagues in Holles Street and the Coombe to temper with humanitarianism their enthusiasm for symphysiotomy. Caesarean section, he pointed out, would result in fewer infant deaths and less maternal injury. The obstetrician's duty, he reminded them, was to secure the best possible outcome for the birth in hand: 'The child is not ours and it may well be that the mother may never have another pregnancy.'

Kieran O'Driscoll took over as Master at the National Maternity Hospital in 1963, ending the Reign of Symphysiotomy (and introducing the Reign of Active Management). O'Driscoll later established that disproportion existed mainly in the obstetric imagination: an audit of over 1,500 mothers giving birth to their first child revealed just four such cases. At a meeting of the Royal Academy of Medicine, the Master called the complication that had served as a justification for so many symphysiotomies a 'mote in the eye of the obstetrician'.

Kevin Feeney, an obstetrician at the Coombe, later explained the Catholic craze for symphysiotomy by saying: 'The real harvest of symphysiotomy is reaped in subsequent deliveries.' To do a Caesarean was to limit future childbearing: the dangers of repeated surgery limited the number of Caesareans that could prudently be performed. Medically, vaginal birth following Caesarean section was viewed with suspicion: 'once a Caesarean, always a Caesarean' was the obstetric mantra. As Arthur Barry and others saw it, Caesarean mothers were at greater risk, morally, prey to the manifold temptations of contraception, or worse. It was common practice, for example, for doctors to offer women sterilisation after a third Caesarean. To fundamentalist Catholic doctors, symphysiotomy was a pre-emptive strike, making repeat Caesareans redundant and preserving the moral fibre of the nation.

More than one mother at the Lourdes Hospital actually had a symphsiotomy *after* giving birth. More than one was placed in double jeopardy—subjected to *both* a Caesarean *and* a symphsiotomy during the same birth. The mother who had had a symphysiotomy could give birth vaginally over and over again, forever, regardless of what complications might present themselves in future births.

Barry's lecture to Catholic medics was published in 1955; as well as the imprimatur of John Charles McQuaid, the conference proceedings carried a message of support from Pius xii, signed by a future pope, Archbishop Montini (later Paul vi). The then Papal Nuncio, Archbishop Gerald O'Hara, Cardinal John Dalton, and John Charles McQuaid all paid tribute to the 'brilliant minds' of Catholic doctors who worked for the Faith.

DEFENCE

Irish obstetricians defended the latter-day practice of symphysiotomy in 2004. Dr Seamus O'Friel's belief was that symphysiotomy was less barbaric than Caesarean section. Underlining the need for tight wiring of the symphysis, he wondered why his colleagues had failed to take such a precaution. Former National Maternity Hospital Master Peter Boylan also wrote in defence of symphysiotomy, citing an article by a Swedish doctor. Department of Health officials subsequently nominated a doctor at the Karolinska Institute to review the latter-day practice of symphysiotomy in Ireland. The 'independent' expert was none other than Dr Bjorklund—cited by Dr Boylan—who had argued for symphysiotomy to be reinstated in the obstetric arsenal. It is extraordinary, given his documented partiality for symphysiotomy, that he was deemed an appropriate person to review the revival of the practice.

The last reported symphysiotomy was performed at Our Lady of Lourdes Hospital, Drogheda, in 1983. Hospital records show that a staggering 347 symphysiotomies were carried out at the hospital when it was owned by the Medical Missionaries of Mary. Why so many were performed there is puzzling, until you remember that the Lourdes was, in fact, an international missionary training hospital. The Medical Missionaries of Mary owned at least one hospital in Africa during those decades. Were these women used as obstetric 'material', so that junior doctors intending to work in developing countries could be trained in the technique, first-hand? Did the need to train medical personnel in tropical obstetrics take precedence over the safety of women's bodies in childbirth?

An even larger question concerns how, for four decades, Irish obstetricians working in various hospitals across the state could have performed a discarded eighteenth-century operation for obstructed labour at a time when Caesarean section had long been the surgery of choice for difficult births.

Dr Bjorklund subsequently declined the Department's offer to review the revival of symphysiotomy in Ireland. Up to 500 women in hospitals across the state were mutilated in this way, but the final toll of these mutilating operations will never be known. These women are the victims of institutional abuse just as surely as those who were incarcerated in industrial and reform schools. But there has been no investigation, no inquiry, no compensation.

AN UNNATURAL HARVEST

Scene from a hospital: a bucket containing a fresh womb is dispatched to pathology, while the doctor who removed the woman's uterus chats casually to a junior about some TV programme shown the night before.

Each consultant in obstetrics at the hospital had his own approach. One had a preference for symphysiotomy over Caesarean for obstructed labour, for instance, while another preferred Caesarean over symphysiotomy. Clinical practice at the hospital was entirely a matter of personal preference. The medical tuition, as a result, was erratic. Trainee obstetricians learned to do vertical cuts for Caesarean section, for example, instead of horizontal incisions; they later reported that they had never seen these incisions done routinely anywhere else. This method of surgery left women with long, disfiguring scars down the middle of their stomachs.

Patient treatment could be queried only if a patient complained: this was the iron rule. Many patients were private, and this made their cases untouchable, or so staff believed. The rate of private patients at the unit was high: 50 per cent of all mothers booked a consultant obstetrician.

Management at the hospital was pyramid-shaped, with a small number of consultants at the top, and thousands of patients at the bottom. The hospital culture was one of unquestioning obedience. Neither junior doctors nor midwives questioned how patients were managed; respect was what was required, and subservience, not initiative, or responsibility. They were not expected to exercise any authority or to be accountable for their actions. They were to look at the task in hand and no further. Patients got little continuity of care.

Infant death rates at the hospital were reported to be high, higher than average. Many babies died within seven days of birth, while others were stillborn. Bad outcomes were ignored, discussion not encouraged. Forceps were frequently used; failed instrumental deliveries resulted in not a few obstetric disasters. Twenty women died in childbirth at the hospital between 1960 and 1973. Further maternal deaths took place there during the following decade, one in 1982, another in 1983, and a third in 1984. Another woman died there in 1997; no one could recall her death, however. Staff members were generally unable to recall patients who had died having being transferred from the maternity to the hospital's intensive care unit. Their deaths were recorded in the hospital's annual reports, however.

Many non-national doctors trained at the hospital, trailing after consultants on their ward rounds, if they were allowed. One doctor in training said that consultants behaved like 'third world despots'. These junior doctors dared not speak: they depended on consultants for their jobs; training was their priority. Meanwhile, midwives and nurses were reported as fearing for their jobs.

Birthing practices at the hospital were medieval. Women were required to give birth on their backs, like stranded beetles, in the 'lithotomy' position, obliged to push against gravity. Some male obstetricians at the unit required women to adopt this dysfunctional position. Consultants ruled. Women having their second, third or fourth child were subjected to unnecessary birth surgery, cut during the act of giving birth: episiotomies were standard at the unit. Complaints that doctors were carrying out medical procedures without women's consent were widespread. Many mothers had their labours medically induced, their waters ruptured with an obstetric hook, their contractions accelerated by a hormonal drip. One woman died having been left by midwives on an oxytocin drip for twenty-four hours: following an emergency Caesarean section, she developed an amniotic fluid embolism.

Giving birth in the unit was tantamount to having an operation. Caesarean section began to be the norm in the 1970s. From 1974 to 1998, the Caesarean rates rose rapidly, going from 4 to 27 per cent, a seven-fold increase. Some operations were planned, others 'emergency'. Hysterectomy rates also escalated. From 1974 to 1998, the unit did eight birth-related hysterectomies on average every year: one hysterectomy for every twenty Caesareans. During the 1990s, the hospital's Caesarean hysterectomy rate was twenty times the average for hospitals in Dublin. The double operation that left women infertile grew in popularity; two doctors had a particular fondness for it. Medical record-keeping was described as 'abysmal'. The religious order who owned the hospital were oblivious.

For twenty-five years, consultant obstetricians voiced no concern, nor did qualified senior registrars. Junior doctors in training voiced no concern. Anaesthetists present during the operations, and who later spoke to each patient in the recovery room and subsequently wrote up the theatre notes, voiced no concern. Surgical nurses who handed the hysterectomy clamps to obstetricians and counted the swabs voiced no concern. Midwives who cared for the damaged women in the postnatal ward voiced no concern. Pathologists who received healthy wombs, ovaries and tubes in the laboratory voiced no concern. General practitioners whose patients had had these double operations voiced no concern. Until 1984, the hospital published an annual report that included the number and type of operations being performed; these were circulated to medical bodies, who raised no queries. A patient complained in 1980; the matron also complained, as did a tutor, a nun; a pathologist complained in 1981. The state did nothing to ensure that the unit offered a safe birthing environment for women. There was no inspectorate, no licensing, no scrutiny.

From 1974 to 1998, of the women who had had Caesarean sections, 188 had their wombs removed just after the operation, or very shortly afterwards. One obstetrician performed 129 of these double operations; 40 per cent of these mothers were having their first or second child. Two women who lost both their babies and their wombs found themselves childless: they had been expecting a first baby. Doctors performed hysterectomies on women who had been admitted for miscarriage; and, in two cases, women who had been admitted for a minor procedure, a D&C (dilatation and curettage) also had their wombs removed. One woman woke up in the recovery room to find that doctors had also taken out her ovaries. In another case, a doctor was called to attend a mother who had just given birth, because the afterbirth was slow in coming. He took out her uterus as well as her placenta. Shock waves rippled through the unit, however, when it was discovered that a staff midwife who had given birth at the hospital had had a Caesarean hysterectomy.

Nearly all of these operations, it later transpired, were unnecessary. Many were performed for imaginary bleeding, or for what later turned out to be non-existent complications, such as an adherent placenta. During those years, the unit was repeatedly accredited for training in obstetrics, surgery and midwifery by several colleges and regulatory boards. Hospital management focused on funding and staffing difficulties. Few members of middle management knew who was in charge or how to raise an issue.

Senior midwives at the hospital did a survey in 1996, showing a 93 per cent 'patient satisfaction' rate with the region's 'centre of excellence'.

After the scandal came to light, theatre registers were stolen. Records were traced, identified and removed, deliberately, methodically and systematically, to conceal the nature of the operations that had been performed. In forty of forty-four cases, at least, birth registers were unlawfully removed in tandem with the matching patient charts, obliterating all traces of those who had assisted in theatre.

A private non-profit institution run by nuns, the hospital was bought by the state in May 1997. The hospital continued to pose a danger to women's health until October 1998, at least. The Government eventually held a limited private inquiry into 'peripartum hysterectomy' at the hospital. One consultant obstetrician and two senior gynaecological nurses declined to give evidence. Only one obstetrician, the man who had performed 129 Caesarean hysterectomies, was investigated. Complaints of unnecessary deaths of babies, removal of ovaries, the disfiguring of women's bodies with midline incisions for Caesarean sections were not investigated. No one was tried, no one was jailed. A police investigation, failing to trace the stolen records, ran into the sand. No charges of assault and battery were ever brought against the doctors who had participated in these operations. Actions for civil damages were thrown out by the courts, on the basis that they were 'statute barred' or out of time. (A three-year deadline applied to personal injuries claims.) The sole obstetrician whose practice was investigated was eventually struck off in 2003, having been found guilty of unnecessarily removing the wombs of nine of his patients.

At the time of writing, a government compensation package for the women, judged by many to be meagre, was under negotiation. Women excluded from the inquiry, whose babies died unnecessarily, whose body parts were removed needlessly, or who were disfigured by vertical Caesarean incisions, hope to be included in the compensation deal.

OMERTA

For a quarter of a century, *omerta* reigned in Our Lady of Lourdes Hospital, Drogheda, just as surely as it did in the Mafia town of Corleone in Sicily.

Caesarean hysterectomy is a life-saving last resort, performed to stem uncontrollable bleeding in Caesarean section. It is very, very rare. Theatre staff at the Lourdes could hardly have failed to see what was going on in front of their eyes. Surgery is not a solo run, done by a single doctor: it is a team effort. Some of the those working in theatre were of lower rank—nurses and midwives acting as scrub nurses, and doctors in training. They, it could be argued, were too junior in the hierarchy to speak. But there were others who failed in their duty to patients—hospital specialists and other senior staff, whose silence served to maintain the status quo at the Lourdes. Consultant anaesthetists, for example, carry significant responsibilities for maintaining patient health and well-being during surgery; they could hardly have failed to notice that hysterectomy was frequently— too frequently by far—carried out under questionable circumstances, on patients who were not bleeding to death, who had not needed blood products during surgery. The anaesthetists failed to intervene. They seemed to attach little importance to the fact that women were rarely in a critical condition at the time a decision was taken to perform a hysterectomy; that, despite allegedly having lost large amounts of blood, they had stable pulse and blood pressure readings.

These double operations were openly recorded in daybooks, annual reports and theatre registers. They were also written up in the pathology ledgers. One pathologist, during the nine months that he spent at the Lourdes, became 'curious, concerned and alarmed' at the number of wombs, ovaries and Fallopian tubes lying around the laboratory. Other consultants, however, did not remark on the phenomenal number of organs being sent down to the lab—reproductive organs that were later found, bizarrely, to be healthy.

Others in authority also failed in their responsibilities. Midwives, as autonomous practitioners and specialists in normal birth, carried a special responsibility for the mothers under their care. The fact that wombs, for instance, were being taken out at every turnabout was an open secret. Caesarean hysterectomies were recorded in the postnatal ward daybook: the information was there for consultants and registrars on ward rounds to read. Senior midwives, such as the matron, her assistant, the labour ward superintendent, and the ward sisters, knew exactly who had had their wombs or other reproductive organs removed within hours of their removal. On one particular day, there were *two* women in the postnatal ward who had had Caesarean hysterectomies. The odds against this happening by chance were enormous. Midwives who spoke to the inquiry blamed consultants' 'personalities' for their failure to realise that Caesarean hysterectomy was being performed too often. 'Unquestioning submission to authority' was how Judge Harding Clark described it in her report, belatedly commissioned by the Government.

No one said anything about these aberrant practices for a quarter of a century. Not until October 1998, when two midwives went to the health board solicitor about another issue, was the whistle blown, by a midwife who had trained in Belfast. The *Harding Clark Report* readily accepted the various excuses proffered: staff members were too busy, too overworked, too tired; the hospital was under-funded; the unit was small. One consultant obstetrician at the unit told the inquiry that the Caesarean hysterectomies were none of his business. Midwives testified that they did not know what the statistical rate of Caesarean hysterectomy *ought* to be, as though statistical knowledge were the only form of knowledge there is. Anyone who had worked or trained in another maternity environment must have known that 'hysterectomy *with* pregnancy', as it is called, is a very rare phenomenon. There was, and is, a school of midwifery at the hospital; senior midwives involved in education must have been familiar, to a degree, with the norms that existed elsewhere. Drogheda's Caesarean hysterectomy rate was *twenty times* higher than that of the Coombe or the National Maternity Hospital.

Other excuses and explanations that did not stand up were also given: consultants were not to be questioned; junior hospital doctors could not progress in their training without a reference from a consultant; midwives and nurses told the inquiry that they feared for their jobs. This might well have been the case in the 1970s and 1980s, but by 1995, Irish health care agencies were recruiting nurses from abroad. Moreover, if staff were afraid they might be victimised, were they not union members? Or had they no confidence that their unions would protect them? The questions are endless.

The hospital's Catholic ethos was blamed. However, the convenient suspicion that many of these hysterectomies were performed as a form of sterilisation hardly stood up to scrutiny. Tubal ligation had been widely available since 1985; what woman would opt for the rigours of a major operation—and a premature menopause—if she could choose instead to have a relatively minor procedure? Moreover, the tubal ligation argument ignored the fact that, in 99 per cent of cases, these irreversible operations were performed without women's knowledge or consent. Mothers were generally not told about their sterilisation 'until some time had elapsed'. And, to cap it all, most of these operations were performed by a Catholic doctor, Michael Neary, who, by his own testimony, risked his career prospects as a trainee in Manchester by insisting that a conscience clause—giving him an opt-out on tubal ligation—be inserted into his contract. So the argument on sterilisation was paper-thin—comforting perhaps, but insubstantial.

A damning indictment of the owners of the hospital and many of those working there, of Irish hospital culture and of the Irish state, whose manifest failure to monitor medical practice left nearly 200 women stripped of their reproductive organs.
Colm MacGeehin, solicitor for Patient Focus, on the Caesarean
hysterectomy scandal

PEER LUNCHES
Representatives of the Royal College of Obstetricians and Gynaecologists visited the hospital twice, lunching at Dr Neary's house, and accrediting the unit for training purposes. They did not concern themselves with clinical practice, nor did they spot check the theatre registers, patients' charts or labour ward records, nor did they comment on the lack of audit. Inspections made by the Nursing Board of the school of midwifery failed to uncover anything untoward, while visitations from the Medical Council were confined to the general hospital, which was in a separate building.

Irish obstetricians exonerated Michael Neary: *two* reviews cleared his Caesarean hysterectomy practice. The first review, in 1998, was conducted by three eminent obstetricians from the main Dublin maternity hospitals. One concluded: 'It would be wrong to put restrictions on [Neary's] practice and it is my view that the mothers of the North-Eastern Health Board are fortunate in having the services of such an experienced and caring obstetrician'. The others jointly wrote that they had found 'no evidence of questionable clinical judgement, poor operative ability or faulty decision-making. Quite the contrary.'

In November 2006, in an apparent show of professional support, the Royal College of Physicians elected as its president Dr John Murphy, consultant obstetrician at the National Maternity and one of the three reviewers who had exculpated Neary. The RCPI is responsible for setting and overseeing standards in a number of specialties, including those of its affiliate, the Institute of Obstetrics and Gynaecology.

At the time of writing, the Medical Council had just found Dr John Murphy and his fellow assessors, Professor Walter Prendiville and Dr Bernard Stuart, both of the Coombe Women's Hospital, guilty of professional misconduct. The Institute also conducted its own review of Neary's practice, assigning three leading obstetricians to the task: Dermot MacDonald (Dublin), Edgar Ritchie (Cork) and Graham Harley (Belfast). They found the Drogheda obstetrician's double operations acceptable in 41 per cent of cases, faulting only 46 per cent of them, and concluded that a brief period of retraining was all that was required. Moreover, they refused to criticise Neary's highly unusual practice of vertical incision-making, opining that 'in many cases, his patients have been of an age where that type of incision was irrelevant to them'. These reviews remain unpublished, and there are no plans, currently, to investigate the Institute's report.

Seven months after investigating Michael Neary's clinical practice, in June 1999, the Institute of Obstetricians and Gynaecologists (IOG) decided to withdraw recognition, for training purposes, from two other maternity units in the North-East, those in Monaghan and Dundalk. The Institute, however, continued to approve the Lourdes— a hospital described at a press conference as a 'swamp'—for the training of obstetrician/gynaecologists.

An editorial in the *Irish Medical Journal* had exonerated the consultants concerned:

> Financial restrictions must not be used as an excuse for allowing time to stand still. There was a systems failure. There was lack of clinical and administrative governance combined with infrastructure underfunding. Tensions surrounding the Catholic Church's stance on reproductive matters caused difficulties and confusion.

To take refuge in 'a systems failure' is to refuse to condemn, to fail to take responsibility, to deny the reality of what happened.

The *Harding Clark Report* also disappoints: there is no indignation, no outrage, only regret and mystification. As if motives mattered. More importantly, its recommendation that important medical records be Freedom of Information (FoI) exempt will, if implemented, serve only to intensify the heart of darkness that engulfed the Lourdes, a hospital where, if the symphysiotomy survivors are included, well over 500 women had their female organs filleted or stripped out, not in error, but by design.

Only a hermetically sealed, profoundly patriarchal and violently authoritarian system could have permitted these horrors to occur.

III Empire-Building

Chapter 7

High Kings Without Opposition

She requires something more urgently than medicine. Take this, Sister, and get her champagne.

Dr Michael Cox, giving money to a nurse to buy
champagne for a patient suffering from malnutrition
in St Vincent's Hospital around 1900

Medical power has now swollen to such enormous proportions in Ireland that it has become a threat to democracy. Remember Henry vi's charter to a guild of barbers in Dublin in 1446? That marked the beginning of organised medicine in these islands. The Republic has been playing catch-up since 1922. By then, there was a veritable web of interlocking vested interests, royal colleges, university medical faculties and, last but never least, voluntary hospitals—private not-for-profit institutions, many under the aegis of the powerful Catholic Church, but others with roots in the former ascendancy and still influential business classes of Dublin and other cities. Centuries before the state began to imagine a role for itself in health care, the medical profession had established itself as a highly prestigious, wealthy, powerful, private members' club. In a society where priests and teachers were among the few who were educated, doctors' influence grew apace.

Their power, magnified hugely in recent decades, is partly a legacy of history, partly a gift from legislators. The new state, influenced as it was by the Catholic Church, as well as by liberal nineteenth-century thinking, was slow to get into the business of providing public health services. The post-colonial state preserved the status quo, signing off on the free movement of doctors across these islands and the mutual recognition of each other's medical qualifications. It took twenty-five years for the *idea* of a national health service to develop here. The hospitals were funded by gambling through a lottery set up in 1930 by the McGrath family; it was known as the Hospitals' Sweepstake. Catholic social teaching was strongly opposed to the idea of state enterprise, seeing in it the annihilating spectre of communism. Voluntary activity, on the other hand, could be an expression of religious faith. The Catholic Church did much to prevent the development of socialised medicine, backing doctors and their organisations in their attempts to protect their lucrative private practice. The Church's overriding aim was to ensure that Ireland's medical services reflected Catholic teaching, an objective that, as we saw, was to lead to the second biggest health scandal in the history of the state.

EDUCATION

Doctors have always been preoccupied with teaching their successors. Since the middle of the eighteenth century, at least, when hospitals were founded partly with a view to supplying 'clinical material'—live bodies—for the education of medical students, medicine has seen education as central to its professional project. Doctors have always controlled medical education and training, although much of this has been publicly funded for many decades. The 1858 Medical Registration Act gave the royal colleges and the Apothecaries' Hall a monopoly over medical education: only their diplomas and degrees qualified for registration under the Act.

Towards the end of the nineteenth century, in surgery, 'the flamboyant jack-of-all-trades gave way to the specialist'. Specialties had already developed in other areas of medicine: Oscar Wilde's father, Sir William Wilde, for example, decided to become an ophthalmologist in 1839, and went to Vienna to pursue his studies. In Dublin, Robert Woods was the first surgeon to carve out a sub-specialty for himself: otorhinolaryngology or ENT, ear, nose and throat.

Medical education has given private trainers, such as the royal colleges, enormous influence over hospital services. Not only do they have *carte blanche* to draw up their own curricula ('decisions on the content and duration of training programmes are taken by the various professional training bodies') but they also decide, 'following local inspection', which hospitals they will recognise for training purposes. 'Their decisions fix the capacity of hospitals to produce trained consultants.' They also fix the capacity of hospitals to provide medical services for their communities.

Ireland has always run its hospitals on a shoestring, using medical trainees to man the services. (These trainees, until very recently, offered a source of cheap labour.) Vital hospital services depended on the supply of doctors in training. A college's refusal to recognise a hospital for training purposes amounted to a death warrant.

Yet another piece of legislation, the 1953 Health Act, testifies to the power of the royal colleges. In a section still in force, the Act empowers the Minister to declare any hospital a teaching institution, if a college requires its facilities for teaching or research purposes. This could oblige the HSE to provide whatever the college requires for clinical medicine and medical research: patients' bodies are the main requirement. When you consider that the RCSI is now empowered to enter into partnerships with pharmaceutical corporations, the dangers this section of the Act poses to patient health and welfare are obvious. Not everyone wishes to be an object lesson for medical students; fewer still want to be guinea pigs for drug companies.

The profession's control over education is multi-layered. The 1978 Medical Practitioners' Act consolidated doctors' power over education, copper-fastening their ability to regulate and supervise medical education and training; to create medical specialties and sub-specialties, mandating the qualifications for those fields through the registration powers of the Medical Council. In doing this, the Act also set in stone the power of publicly unelected and unaccountable bodies such as the Institute of Obstetricians and Gynaecologists, itself a scion of the Royal College of Physicians, by empowering the Council to recognise these bodies for training purposes. Yet another body, the Postgraduate Medical and Dental Board, is involved in promoting and coordinating postgraduate education. The Medical Council has the final say on, for example, clinical training and experience.

Medicine is taught almost exclusively by doctors in universities and colleges. As a result, the profession has constructed an almost uniquely closed, hermetically sealed and self-referencing system of knowledge. The knowledge base of medicine presents particular problems that are beyond our scope here. Medical publishing is a gigantic industry; much of what is published is of poor quality. Methodological flaws, for example, are common, as is pharmaceutical involvement.

These cast doubt not only on the findings of individual studies, but, cumulatively, on the 'scientific' nature of medical knowledge.

The number of professorships in medicine is quite high; 6 per cent of all consultant posts are full-time academic ones. Several chairs are funded by pharmaceutical companies, such as Ciba-Geigy. Medicine is particularly strong in University College Dublin at present. Its President, Hugh Brady, a former consultant at Dublin's Mater Hospital and professor of medicine and therapeutics, has attracted widespread attention, and no small amount of criticism, for allegedly poaching academics from other universities. He has also been accused of introducing a us-style business approach into third-level education. One aspect of his presidential reign which has been largely overlooked is medicine's growing influence over the College. Since his accession, three of the most senior positions in ucd have been filled by medics.

THE CHANGING OF SHEETS
Another way in which the profession has historically exercised power is by controlling adjacent professions. The 1858 Act standardised the service by unifying the profession, growing the market for medical services. Its passing also meant that only men could practise medicine: the Act had effectively created a male monopoly. While there were nineteen gateways to the medical register, women were barred from all of them. The royal colleges, the university medical faculties, the teaching hospitals—all excluded women from their ranks. By the end of the nineteenth century, medical diagnosis and treatment were the sole prerogative of medical men; women were restricted to caring for the sick (as nurses) and attending women in normal birth (as midwives).

Nearly thirty years after the 1858 Act was passed, doctors incorporated the practice of midwifery into medicine: the 1858 Act was amended, strategically, to require all doctors to be qualified in medicine, surgery and midwifery. Meanwhile, in the community, a new form of medical practitioner emerged, one that combined diagnosing and prescribing, the functions of the physician, with dispensing, the function of the apothecary; the new general practitioner also practised midwifery.

In 1902, male doctors turned midwifery legislation into a vehicle for medical control. Medical men dominated the midwives' board in London. The midwife also threatened the practice of the family doctor in Ireland. Then, as now, doctors saw the pregnant woman as the gateway to the entire family; she offered access to a much bigger, and potentially lifelong, group of patients. Alleging that 'handy-women' (traditional midwives) were responsible for the high death rates of women in childbirth, general practitioners approached their colleagues, the physicians, in Kildare Street, in a bid to get the British 1902 Midwives' Act extended to Ireland.

Doctors' attempts to pin the high death rates of women in childbirth on handywomen were wide of the mark, however. The evidence pointed in quite a different direction: better-off women, attended by doctors, were at far greater risk of dying in childbirth than poorer women looked after by midwives. In Glasgow in the 1920s and 1930s, for example, the death rate for middle-class women in childbirth was twice that of working-class mothers.

By 1918, the efforts of the Royal College of Physicians had borne fruit. As in London, medical men dominated the Dublin midwives' board. Doctors now had a mechanism for disciplining midwives, a stratagem for settling turf wars. Complaints were frequent; for a midwife to fail to call a doctor was the most serious of charges.

Irish midwives continued to work under direct rule from London until 1950. The 1950 Nurses' Act enabled medical men to govern not one, but *two*, female professions, nursing and midwifery, cementing relations of dominance honed in hospitals. Over fifty years later, medicine is still in the driving seat.

POLICING THE TURF

The medical profession has traditionally policed itself. Since Victorian days, doctors have patrolled the boundaries of their profession, determining issues of registration, fitness to practise, and education for themselves, by themselves. The first medical registration council established by the fledgling state in 1927 consisted solely of royal colleges and university medical faculties. One of the council's main functions was, and is, to control entry to the turf.

The profession is still, at the time of writing, regulated by the 1978 Medical Practitioners' Act. This is a re-run of the 1927 Act, itself a relic of the 1858 Act, which, in turn, was a faithful reflection of royal college priorities. Like the human hand of a hunter encompassing a bird in an aboriginal painting, the print of the RCSI could be seen all over the 1858 Act.

The same could be said of the 1978 Act: it also provided for a self-governing medical profession. The Minister for Health was entitled to appoint just four out of a twenty-five-person Medical Council; private medical bodies, such as the royal colleges and university medical faculties, controlled the other twenty-one seats. With general practitioners given only three seats on the Medical Council, the regulator was weighted heavily in the direction of specialties and academics—the forces that still drive the services today. (This dominance of health care by specialist interests is central to the dysfunction of our services today.) Just *one* member of a fitness-to-practice committee was to represent 'the public interest'.

MONOPOLISING MOTHER AND CHILD

Socialised maternity care finally came in the early 1950s, in the teeth of opposition from both the medical profession and the Catholic Church. Medical men feared for their revenues from private practice if free care were introduced; men of the cloth feared for their power over women's bodies. The Church saw state maternity care as the gateway to hell, threatening the future of Catholic hospitals and the morals of Irish mothers.

Today, the idea of making comprehensive care freely available to all women, without charge, before, during and after birth seems perfectly harmless. But back in 1947, Noël Browne's Mother and Child Scheme was incendiary. Doctors were totally opposed to free state medical care. The Irish Medical Association (IMA)—described by Browne as

one of 'the two most powerful pressure groups in our society'—
opposed the bill on the grounds that it represented the 'socialisation
of medicine'. The chief medical officer for Meath, a general practitioner,
said that general practitioners would be completely 'wiped out' by the
state scheme, since they made 70–80 per cent of their income looking
after young children. A former member of the IMA Executive, Tom
O'Higgins, drove the medical agenda in government, although he
held the portfolio for defence. The other leading actor in the conspiracy to subvert the Mother and Child Scheme was the Catholic
Archbishop of Dublin. Interestingly, John Charles McQuaid was himself the son of a doctor, just like Tom O'Higgins.

The Church was troubled by the spectre of sex education: advice
and information on contraception and abortion that might conflict
with Catholic doctrine; and gynaecological procedures such as sterilisation practised in other countries that were contrary to Church
teaching. All were evils that might be visited upon women attended by
doctors who, within a state system, could not be counted upon to
uphold the Catholic ethos. The alliance between Church and medicine proved lethal: the Government crumbled and Browne resigned.
In 1952, medical consultants rejected a watered-down version of the
scheme, the Church got the bill it wanted, and doctors finally conceded
defeat, their 'best troops' lost.

After a seven-year battle, the Act that was finally passed was
niggardly. It gave free care during pregnancy, labour and after birth—
for six weeks only—to mothers and babies. To this day, our postnatal
care allocation is one of the most meagre in Europe. The new scheme
was restricted to lower and middle-income groups, as the Church had
demanded. Such was, and is, the glacial pace of change here that free
care was not extended to upper-income women for nearly forty years.

Viewed through today's lens of competition law, the Mother and
Child Scheme was a framework for medical monopoly. Browne, himself a medical doctor, based his Mother and Child scheme on medicine,
not midwifery. The scheme introduced in Britain eleven years
previously could not have been more different. There, women were to
get free community midwifery services provided by local authority
midwives. Here, mothers were to have 'an entirely free family
doctor/medical consultant service', with free general practitioner and
hospital care. And, as an afterthought, 'free visits to the home by a
midwife'. The main maternity hospitals were slated to provide these

medical services in Dublin; outside the city, mothers were to be looked after by district medical officers.

The new scheme fragmented the maternity services by separating care during pregnancy from care during labour and after birth. General practitioners and consultants were to provide antenatal and postnatal care, while midwives were to be called in at short notice, like gods in a Greek play, to assist women with the life-and-death business of having a child. There was no debate in Ireland on who should provide the services, midwives, GPs or consultants. In England, that debate raged for nearly a decade. Here, the fact that midwives were better qualified than GPs to provide care during pregnancy and after birth was ignored. Doctors' education in this area was then limited to a hit-and-miss six-month hospital 'rotation' or posting. This training in pathology ill prepared them to care for healthy women. Midwives' training, on the other hand, lasted for two years; or, for those who were then qualified nurses, one year. Moreover, they specialised in normal birth, in caring for healthy women, up to 90 per cent of the population. Midwives were also trained to advise mothers on breast-feeding and caring for newborn babies, both subjects the average male GP must have known very little about in the 1950s.

More than fifty years later, Irish women still have no continuity of care, and community midwifery services are almost unknown. Mothers are still being looked after by multiple carers during pregnancy, labour and after birth, shuttled from the community to the hospital and back again in batches, condemned to wait in teeming antenatal clinics, turfed out of hospital a day or two after having a child, back into a community with no local midwifery services of any kind.

CONTROLLING HOSPITAL BEDS

In an arrangement that is without parallel in other countries, the state gifted public beds in public hospitals to medical consultants for their private practice. The 1953 Health Act had enabled hospitals funded by the state to segment their accommodation into public, private and semi-private. The 1970 Health Act copper-fastened this bizarre arrangement, allowing public hospitals to charge fees for private and semi-private services. The 1991 Health (Amendment) Act then consolidated this subsidy to consultants, enabling hospitals to introduce quotas for private for-profit beds. Shamefully, this legislation—

allegedly brought forward to protect *public* beds—was later used, as predicted in 1991 by opposition deputies, to defend *private* beds against the ravages of the bed cuts of the 1990s; public beds were decimated.

Private health insurers were to pick up the tab for private accommodation. But public hospitals did not charge the Voluntary Health Insurance the full cost of the beds. Taxpayers were, and are, forced to subsidise private medicine, shouldering over 40 per cent of the cost of the for-profit beds. This, the public–private mix, is the worm that is eating into the heart of the dysfunctional system we see today.

COMHAIRLE NA N-OSPIDÉAL

The 1970 Health Act brought regional health boards with their ballast of elected representatives. But if the 1970 Act gave power to politicians, it also gave doctors a pearl of great price: near-total control over hospital services. The Act created a new and all-powerful fiefdom, Comhairle na n-Ospidéal (the Hospitals' Council), a cabal of top consultants. Through Comhairle, hospital medicine was given the power to write the script for its successors, to forge that link between education and occupation, between knowledge—exclusive to itself—and power, in the form of a market monopoly. Comhairle was any profession's dream—the structural link between education and occupation. The training bodies (the royal colleges) and the university medical faculties now had a mechanism—the missing link—whereby jobs could be tailored to specification. The birth of Comhairle was one of the climaxes of the professional project, that long, slow process of translating one order of scarce resources—special knowledge and skills—into another: social and economic rewards. Under the bill as introduced to the Dáil, Comhairle was to *advise* the Minister on consultant staffing. However, a ministerial amendment—clearly under pressure from medical interests—substituted the word 'regulate' for 'advise', turning Comhairle into an all-powerful regulator. The legislation also gave Comhairle power over specialist postgraduate training: the Council controlled the posts to which senior registrars enrolled in approved training schemes could be appointed.

Medical dominance was once again written into law, just as surely it had been in the eighteenth century, when the mad King George III gave the Royal College of Physicians the power to imprison those they convicted of 'medical malpractice'. Hospital medical consultants had an inbuilt majority on Comhairle, thanks to our legislators. The 1970 Act gave unaccountable medical bodies the power to build as many career ladders as they wished, without let or hindrance, regardless of the service needs of communities. The consultant post created by Comhairle determined the nature of the hospital service to be provided—or not provided.

Comhairle ultimately decided how many consultant and other senior medical appointments should be made; in which specialty or sub-specialty; on or off-site private practice; and, most importantly, the hospital or group of hospitals to be served. Hospitals or health boards could apply, the Department could approve, but, like God, Comhairle disposed. Temporary or permanent, full-time or part-time—it was all a matter for Comhairle.

The method of appointing consultants left, and presumably still leaves, a lot to be desired. It takes one year on average to appoint a consultant in the private non-profit sector; the same appointment in the public service takes eighteen months. The majority of consultant posts are filled *outside* the Local Appointments Commission (LAC), notwithstanding the fact that these jobs are publicly funded. Joint appointments—shared across both sectors—account for one in every three posts. In yet another indication of their power, private non-profit hospitals tend to control the selection process, even where the post entails working mainly in the public sector.

Just as worrying is the private non-profit sector's lack of transparency and accountability. Its processes are not subject to the same scrutiny and accountability as LAC. While each hospital has its own recruitment and selection process, each one appoints all members of the interview board itself, paving the way for favouritism; whereas, in the LAC system, health authorities nominate only one member of the interview board. This begs the question: why are hospitals, such as the Mater, Vincent's and James's, allowed to control consultant appointments that cost the taxpayer at least €6 million over the lifetime of each incumbent?

When it comes to jobs with formal teaching duties attached, interview boards are required to have a medical faculty representative on the panel, usually a dean of medicine. In the case of professorial jobs, three faculty nominees are required, presumably to ensure control over the selection process. But even in the case of full-time academic posts, the state pays.

In creating these jobs, Comhairle was creating new markets for medical services, as well as guarding entry to existing ones. Every specialty, every sub-specialty, was a niche market, a public sector job *and* a growth opportunity for private practice. On the face of it, there appeared to be a strong economic incentive to maintain a closed shop.

Until 1993, the number of consultant appointments made was paltry. Numbers have increased significantly since then. Over the years, long before *Hanly*, Comhairle quietly implemented the *FitzGerald Report*—a 1968 plan for regionalisation—nurturing a two-speed hospital service by not appointing a second or a third consultant, for example, to a service. (Shunned for their antisocial hours, 'one-man posts' were a crown of thorns often bestowed in the past on non-Irish doctors.) Many of the country's smaller hospital services were left without a second or third consultant. Hospital specialists across Europe have long decided to work in threes, or not at all, so today, those services—and those hospitals—are on Death Row.

Large, private, urban and university teaching hospitals developed at the expense of smaller, public, non-urban and non-university facilities. Over time, this led to a regional imbalance. Posts are unevenly distributed: Dublin, with its three medical schools and its thirty private non-profit hospitals, has always got the lion's share. Of the 486 joint appointments in 2005, for example, 280 were based in just one private non-profit hospital. Today, with 36 per cent of the population, Dublin has 47 per cent of the permanent consultant posts.

In 2001, the Health Strategy recommended that Comhairle be disbanded. Four years later, Comhairle was finally laid to rest, while a new monster, the amoeba-like Health Service Executive, emerged into being. But while Comhairle itself is deceased, its tentacles live on. The 2004 Health Act obliges the HSE to 'consult' with the royal colleges and others on all issues formerly dealt with by Comhairle. Since these colleges are controlled exclusively by the profession, and since the HSE is headed by a former chair of Comhairle—a professor of paediatrics who represented a private non-profit hospital on the council during the 1990s—whose *politburo* includes Comhairle's former CEO, the power of medicine to carve out lucrative, prestigious careers for its high priests seems secure.

THE ROYAL COLLEGE OF SURGEONS

In 1805, the Royal College of Surgeons 'acquired' its first property adjoining St Stephen's Green, a cemetery at the junction of York Street. Not baulking at the idea that the bones of the dead should pro-vide a foundation for its corporate headquarters, RCSI built over the graveyard. The College has grown enormously since my father and his three brothers studied there. Today, it is a leading player, not only in the Irish health system, but in the business and property sectors. It runs the biggest undergraduate medical school in Ireland.

A 'charitable body' in law, the College has an annual turnover of €91 million. CEO Michael Horgan expects that, within the next eight years, the College's overseas revenue will match its Irish-generated income. In addition to its extensive holdings in Dublin, the College holds a growing property portfolio overseas: it owns a medical school in Penang and is building 'a university hospital and health oasis' in Bahrain. Horgan is bent on branding RCSI globally: 'The concept from Bahrain could be replicated anywhere,' he says. RCSI also runs medical training programmes in Malaysia, Dubai, Bahrain, Kuwait and Jordan.

The College's feudal-sounding 'Court of Patrons' is a modern mil-lionaire's club, a golden circle whose members' activities enrich each other for the common good. The court includes some of the biggest names in business and property in Ireland, including Bernard McNamara of McNamara Builders (currently reported to be building on no fewer than four hospital sites) and David Hanly of Parc Developments (and the *Hanly Report*). McNamara's firm built RCSI's 'flagship hospital', the €8.9 million Smurfit building at Beaumont Hospital. Auctioneer John Finnegan is also a College patron: his com-pany, Finnegan Menton, acts for the College in property transactions.

The College ranks as one of the city's wealthiest landlords. Its Dublin properties are among the most valuable in the city. In 2001, for example, it paid €6.35 million for 121–122 St Stephen's Green. It owns Mercer Hotel and the former Salvation Army hostel on York Street—now demolished—to name but two. Two years ago, the College's fixed assets were worth €66.5 million, while its total net assets were valued at €37.2 million. RCSI is probably the only charity in Ireland to have its own property development company: Keating Investments. The company is operated by two of the College's executives.

The RCSI was granted charitable status in 1965. It was the first time the legislature had ever considered the Charter bestowed on the

College by Queen Victoria. This makes the College's activities immune from state regulation. Company law does not apply, and there is 'no regulation' of charities, according to the Charitable Donations and Bequests Office.

This status makes it immune from corporation tax, capital acquisitions tax, capital gains tax, deposit interest retention tax (DIRT), and dividend withholding tax. The College is also exempt from stamp duty. Just one property transaction illustrates the amount of money lost to the state in this way: the Ardilaun Centre on Stephen's Green, bought by the College for €75 million, should have attracted €4.5 million in stamp duty: no such tax was legally payable. The tax waiver also works the other way: corporate and personal donations made to the RCSI are tax deductible. For millionaire patrons as well as for the College, this is a considerable benefit.

So, while just 6 per cent of its income is from government grants, the public subsidy is much larger than this. What taxpayers actually gain in return is far from clear. Despite a student population of 2,670, the College does little to alleviate Ireland's acute shortage of doctors. More than 75 per cent of RCSI graduates work overseas. Paying €36,000 annually per head in fees in 2006, non-nationals account for three-quarters of the College's intake, as they have done since the 1950s.

The RCSI pulled off quite a coup in recent years, when it brought a private members' bill before the Oireachtas. Through it, the College sought to copper-fasten the status granted to it by successive monarchs, allying the privileges of a medieval fiefdom with the powers of a modern corporation, updating the royal charters while at the same time retaining the charitable status gifted to it by the Government in 1965.

The bill required very close reading: the charters it sought to bundle were not even presented to the Oireachtas for scrutiny. The RCSI had engaged its own lawyers to draft the bill, which required a large number of amendments to the original charters, written in the same archaic language as that of the 1784 charter granted to the RCSI by 'his late Majesty' George III. TDs were caught napping.

The bill provided for the maintenance of a self-electing and self-perpetuating elite, unfettered by public controls, unburdened by obligations to pay taxes or to make financial returns. Protecting the College from public scrutiny was another aim. The public control the bill envisaged was skeletal: the College saw no role for the Minister for Health, for example, in its activities. The only nod in the direction of democracy was that the College's by-laws should be approved by the Minister for Education.

With the honourable exception of Monaghan TDs Caoimhghín Ó Caoláin (Sinn Féin) and Paudge Connolly (Independent), deputies failed to see the slightest significance in the bill; most appeared not to have read it. The health committee spent all of ninety minutes scrutin-ising a bill that the RCSI's solicitors had spent years drafting. It was passed almost without debate on 30 June 2002. It was time to go on a summer holiday.

The Government had just given the College a licence to print money. There was the power to engage in property speculation, the removal of the ban on selling drugs and medicines, the possibility of going into partnership with unspecified business, medical or 'other interests'. Irish law-makers failed to see any conflict of interest—recognised in the 1885 charter—between the doctor as drug peddler and the doctor as drug prescriber. The Act also legitimised the gift culture: the College was now able to accept gifts of money, land and other property without restraint, even in the form of an obligation to disclose its donors. The planned school of biomedical science, with its rich opportunities for public–private partnerships in genetic engineering, took on a new aspect: Big Pharma beckoned.

A SWEETHEART DEAL

Doctors were unionised even before the warring trades united to form a single profession. The first medical trade union was the Irish Medical Association, founded in 1839. The Irish Medical Union followed in 1957. (Both united to form the IMO in the early 1980s.) In 1981, the Medical Union did a sweetheart deal with Taoiseach and former Minister for Health, Charles Haughey, which resulted in a common contract for all medical consultants working in the public sector. Today, 90 per cent of consultants are employed under the 'common contract', the biggest gift ever made to the medical profession by a government anywhere. Drawn up by a committee that included the Irish Medical Association as well as the Irish Medical Union, the contract gave consultants unlimited powers and privileges without any enforceable duties or obligations.

To say that the contract is consultant-centred is an understatement: reading it, you glimpse the grotesque inversion of a world where the hospital exists to serve the doctor, not the other way around. The job is for life. This contrasts with Canada, for example, where a doctor is given 'privileges' to work in a particular hospital; these privileges are renewable every few years—consultants can actually be fired through non-renewal of contract.

Here, consultants may be employees, but the contract envisages them sitting, enthroned, above hospital management structures, their professional autonomy boundless. On this topic, the contract is sybil-like: 'Clinical independence, like any freedom, exists only insofar as the limits within which it is exercised are known. These include patient consent, the law and standards of professional conduct and ethics.'

The contract defines a consultant as 'a registered medical practitioner in a hospital *practice* ... who *is consulted* by other registered medical practitioners and undertakes full clinical responsibility for patients in his care ... *without supervision in professional matters by any other person* [emphasis added].' 'Professional matters' have been interpreted as widely as possible by some, allowing consultants to block clinical audit, and even to stymie questions about how they spend their contracted hours. They answer to no one and, as a body, they protect their independence fiercely. When Noël Browne, for instance, brought in an order restraining the use of streptomycin to treat TB—believing that over-use would lead to streptomycin-resistant strains of the bug—the Irish Medical Association, with the backing of the Medical Research Council, forced the Government to rescind the order, seeing it as an affront to their professional autonomy.

The other vital aspect of the contract is that it empowers a consultant to *delegate* any or all aspects of a patient's care to appropriate staff or to share care with other doctors. (For those who hold private health insurance, this raises an interesting question: do consultants bill insurers for procedures that they have delegated to other doctors to carry out? The answer to this question is yes, according to one medical source. US government insurance schemes prohibit billing for delegated work, but here the common contract has fostered a culture where this kind of sharp practice has come to be accepted as the norm.)

Until recently, consultants had the option of a public-only contract. As many as ninety specialists (just under 1 per cent) opted for this contract in 1996. Some consultants are opposed to private practice; others work in areas where fee opportunities are few. In 1997, the public-only contract was withdrawn, on the basis that it was incompatible with the 'new emphasis' on private beds as money-making entities in public hospitals. The state has since spent a lot of time trying to re-introduce the public-only contract—in the teeth of consultant opposition. The stand-off continues.

The contract is also a growth promoter of private medicine. In addition to a permanent and pensionable job, the deal gave doctors the legal right to a sky's-the-limit private practice. Today's contract comes in just two versions: 'category 1' gives in-house private practice rights; while 'category 2' offers off-site private practice. (This version comes with a small reduction in salary, some €15,000 or so.) Almost two-fifths enjoy off-site privileges; 51 per cent of these contract holders work in the Dublin hospitals. With the mushrooming of private for-profit hospitals, coupled with the Government's policy of co-location, this version of the contract is a veritable goldmine. (It remains to be seen, of course, whether the new co-located hospitals will be defined as on or off-site for private practice purposes.)

Why should public employees, who are paid up to €250,000 per annum, be offered state contracts that allow them to be paid twice for doing the same work, or alternatively, that enable them to walk off the job, literally, in order to make money elsewhere? Such breathtaking privileges by now have come to be taken for granted both by consultants and, more importantly, by the public. This is an Alice-in-Wonderland deal, where doctors are paid exorbitant public salaries in return for a *nominal* thirty-three-hour week, yet are under no formal obligation to devote even an hour a week to their public patients! This hole in the contract amounts to an incentive for doctors to grab even more private beds in public hospitals. The revised contract contains a new prayer, that on-site private practice should reflect the quota of beds designated by the hospital as private. This prayer, first uttered in 1997, has yet to be answered. Public and private bed quotas are frequently breached, in defiance of the 80 : 20 split laid down by government. In some hospitals, private practice accounts for around 50 per cent of all activity.

Imagine the public broadcasting service we could expect if senior RTÉ employees had a contract that allowed them to work outside line management structures, earn unlimited private fees during working hours, access the station's facilities free of charge and take over staff, studios and editing suites whenever their deadlines required it!

This contract is believed to be unique in the industrialised world.

MILLIONAIRE INCOMES

The *Brennan Report* pointed out that in 2002 consultants were paid an average of €152,000 for a thirty-three-hour week, plus another €127,000 on average in private practice. (Basic pay is also supplemented by on-call and other allowances—for continuing medical education, for example, or additional responsibilities in management—and expenses.) 'No other group comes anywhere near such remuneration on the basis of personal expertise,' Michael Clifford commented. (He was wrong about remuneration being an index of expertise. Patients have no way of knowing which doctors get better results: bad doctors may earn as much as, or more than, good ones.)

Their contracts, he continued, 'are riven with potential conflicts of interest'. 'The allocation of private beds in public hospitals, the treatment purchase fund that allows consultants to allow public patients into private beds at public cost, the whole two-tiered system, all benefit consultants. Their thirty-three-hour week is unmonitored. They can do private work on public time, delegating public duties to junior doctors. The consultant then gets paid twice and the serf taxpayer pays both senior and junior doctors for the same work'. 'I could not believe such a contract could exist,' Professor Niamh Brennan told *The Irish Times*.

One legal source believes that 80 per cent of some consultants' income comes from private practice. 'The private income is a multiple of their public salaries,' he says. One specialty where private fees can be calculated without too much difficulty is obstetrics. Private maternity fees yield, on average, around €500,000, every year, per head, in addition to the state salary, and since obstetrics and gynaecology are a twin specialty, consultants also earn an unspecified amount from private gynaecological work. As one mother observed, it's like winning the Lotto every year. Curiously, the winners are nearly all men: 80 per cent of consultant obstetricians are male. Midwifery, in contrast, is an almost exclusively female profession. As midwife Philomena Canning observed: 'Midwives get paid around 8 per cent of what consultant obstetricians earn for more than equal work in normal birth.'

The IHCA has been investigated for price fixing more than once. In 2005, the Competition Authority investigated both the IHCA and the IMO to see if their negotiations with private health insurers amounted to price fixing, which is illegal. The IHCA subsequently gave the Authority an undertaking to refrain from certain behaviour.

HARDBALL

Medicine is arguably the most highly organised profession in the world, and, in many countries, one of the most influential. In Ireland, modern unions, such as the IHCA and the IMO, back up the eighteenth-century trade guilds that evolved into today's lofty royal colleges, all augmented by an over-arching Medical Council.

Greed has now become institutionalised. Although not yet twenty years old, the Irish Hospital Consultants' Association (IHCA) is possibly the most powerful trade union in the country. The IHCA was founded in 1988 by John Fielding, professor of medicine at the Royal College of Surgeons; Fielding could be relied upon to put up a 'dogged defence' of consultants' powers and privileges, private practice in particular. Under the aggressive leadership of former Fine Gael General Secretary, Finbarr Fitzpatrick, the IHCA has been ruthless in pursuing the interests of its members, showing little interest in the wider politics of health. The ethics of privatising our health-care system, for example, is not a topic the IHCA has taken a position on. When it was founded, the IHCA promised to campaign to reduce public waiting lists, but this was a figleaf that covered the naked pursuit of members' economic interests. In 2002, 87 per cent of practising medical consultants were IHCA members.

The IHCA has been playing hardball for a number of years. In 1997, for example, the Association threatened industrial action over a pay offer based on the *Buckley Report*. Its major gripe? No payment for the first thirty out-of-hours call-outs, and a limit on rest days. The union has also resisted all attempts by the Health Service Employers' Agency to make its members more accountable for their work.

THE STRIKE OF KINGS

In 2004, the IHCA threatened to bring down the public hospital system if the state clinical indemnity scheme—then in place for eighteen months—was extended to members without their say-so. Negotiations on the new insurance scheme had dragged on for a couple of years and the Government had finally decided to extend it willy-nilly to consultants on 1 February 2004. The scene was now set for a protracted battle: High Kings of Ireland v. Republic of Ireland. On 2 January 2004, Finbarr Fitzpatrick warned that the new arrangements would cause an 'absolute rebellion' by consultants if implemented without their agreement. 'All hell will break loose,' he predicted confidently.

This was not the first time the IHCA had threatened strike action over this issue. The union had held its first council of war meeting thirteen months earlier, just after the scheme was signed into law. The new indemnity arrangements threatened consultants' jealously guarded autonomy. Being able to access independent legal advice (albeit paid for by taxpayers), to influence the way a case was handled: this was how it had always been. Consultants would now be unable to defend their medical decisions, Colm Quigley, then IHCA president, underlined. 'The state will now control how these claims are defended and so will rob consultants of their clinical independence.' At that February meeting in 2003, at least two IHCA delegates urged members to strike if the indemnity scheme were brought in without negotiation. Members voted unanimously in favour of non-cooperation with the proposed health 'reforms', particularly the soon-to-be-unveiled *Hanly Report*. The union also decided to take legal action preventing the Minister from imposing enterprise liability when the old insurance system ran out.

Economic interests lay at the heart of the dispute, however. The new scheme, in many ways, represented a good deal for consultants, but IHCA members were still not satisfied. Whereas previously they had to pay 10 or even 20 per cent of their insurance costs, the new scheme would make even this modest contribution redundant. Work done in private hospitals under contract to the public sector—NTPF work, for example—would also be covered. But the new scheme did not cover one area: off-site private practice. Private practice would become 'unaffordable', the union argued, if consultants had to pay the cost of their own insurance.

By then, consultant privileges had acquired the status of inalienable rights. In June 2003 came the warning that around 25 per cent of anaesthetists might have to jump ship and abandon their private practice. The Government capitulated, as usual, to union demands: it was agreed that taxpayers would foot the insurance bill for work done by publicly employed consultants in private hospitals and clinics— over which the state had no control—for a 'trial period' of seven years.

Only one question remained: who would pick up the insurance tab for consultants who worked *only* in the private sector? Even this front had been breached. Taxpayers were already paying insurance for obstetricians working *solely* in private hospitals, a bill that amounted to €50 million annually, it transpired. In February 2003, John Perry

TD, Chair of the Public Accounts Committee, queried 'why well-heeled consultants who were not giving the benefit of their services to public patients' were 'being looked after in this way'. Michael Kelly, then Secretary-General of the Department of Health, said that the state had paid the insurance for consultants in the private sector in 2002 because the bill was unaffordable. Obstetricians were now facing bills of €500,000, he explained. If they withdrew from practice, the public maternity services in Dublin and Cork could not cope with an additional 3,500 births annually.

In October 2003, news emerged of a deal reminiscent of the sky's-the-limit agreement made by Fianna Fáil Minister Michael Woods with religious orders on compensation for institutional abuse victims. In an unprecedented offer, the Government agreed to pick up the tab for all medical malpractice and negligence awards in excess of €1.5 million, made against obstetricians working solely in private practice, leaving them to take out a relatively small amount of cover. It was a bonanza for the twenty obstetricians—those who were IHCA members, at least—working in hospitals, such as the Bons Secours, Cork, and Mount Carmel, Dublin (now owned by Harlequin).

Three months later, despite the enormous concessions already made to them by a supine government, the IHCA was still belligerent. Finbarr Fitzpatrick boasted in January 2004 that 'the public hospital system would crash under the pressure if the private sector closed down'. Consultants' private practice was now so vast and the public system so under-resourced that private patients could be used as pawns in the ongoing battle between the union and the Government. No one knew how many private patients were being treated in the private sector, but, if you included the public–private mix, the number of private beds came to around 6,200 or more, over 40 per cent of the national stock. The two-tier system was now hoist with its own petard: consultants could continue to treat public patients—fulfilling their contractual obligations—and *still* bring the system to a halt.

Medicine Weekly explained the causes of consultants' continuing angst. Enterprise liability, the editorial warned, 'may seriously impact on the long-term outlook for private practice outside the State Claims Agency'. Cunningly, the IHCA focused on the one aspect of the dispute likely to gain public support—the lack of cover for claims reported to the MDU before July 2002. Who should foot the bill for medical negligence or malpractice awards in cases where doctors were known to be liable? But how to gain public sympathy for such a demand? An expensive, full-page advertisement appeared in the national press. Misleadingly, the ad claimed that retired obstetrician Conor Carr had 'delivered 27,000 babies and now faces ruin', and that any number of legal cases could be taken against him and his colleagues 'for incidents which may not be their fault'. This was tantamount to equating cases with pay-outs. Dr Carr, a very amiable man, gave us to understand that the claim made by the ad was entirely speculative: no awards were pending against him, nor were claims imminent. He did confirm, however, that he had delivered 27,000 babies: one was tempted to ask just how many of those infants he had delivered himself, how many he observed being delivered by midwives, and how many, if any, were delivered by mothers.

No one made the obvious point: that only claims that succeed in proving negligence or malpractice result in awards: doctors not negligent or found guilty of malpractice had nothing to fear.

Five days after the Government extended the enterprise liability scheme to consultants, the IHCA held a strike ballot. Its message? That, if IHCA demands were not met, the union was prepared to use the ultimate weapon in defence of its members. About 300 consultants attended the EGM. The ballot, passed by a reported 85 per cent, was held in Dublin's Berkeley Court Hotel, a venue not usually associated with striking workers. But then, a number of those voting for industrial action, including obstetricians, were millionaires.

Criticism in the media of the strike ballot was timid, with one or two exceptions. There were mutterings about 'ethical responsibility'. (The Medical Council's position on the issue was adroit: industrial action is permissible, as long as doctors guarantee emergency services.) Finbarr Fitzpatrick later denied it was a strike, describing it as a 'curtailment of services'. He also denied that the union had threatened to withdraw from all non-emergency services, claiming that 'time-sensitive' and continuing care would be provided, in addition to urgent treatment.

IHCA members withdrew from interview panels, adding to the chaos in public hospitals. On 16 February 2004, the IHCA pulled the plug on public patients due to be treated under the National Treatment Purchase Fund, who had been waiting a year or more for medical treatment. Consultants were now ready to walk away from all non-emergency patients nationwide, who were booked for surgery, tests or other treatment in public and private hospitals.

The strike was called off, at the Minister's request, pending the resolution of the past claims issue. In September 2004, the MDU wrote to eight obstetricians and two surgeons, informing them that it would not cover them for alleged past negligence. The threat of industrial action loomed again. By 7 October 2004, consultants were reportedly refusing to enter talks on a new contract until the indemnity issue had been resolved.

Consultants in *two* unions now decided to join forces. On 4 February 2005, IMO consultant members voted—by 89 per cent—for industrial action, cancelling all out-patients, day cases and elective procedures. Adroitly, the IHCA scheduled *its* strike ballot for 6 February. It, too, voted overwhelmingly in favour of strike action. All public outpatients clinics, scheduled procedures and non-urgent treatment would cease from 14 March, consultants decreed. Faced with this unthinkable vista, the Government moved swiftly, deciding that 'no person who has suffered a medical mishap in Ireland would be left without compensation and no consultant would be left without cover'. The IMO withdrew its strike notice. The IHCA called off its threatened industrial action, later announcing that it would join the Government in taking legal action against the MDU.

In December 2005, still dissatisfied with government pledges on the issue, still determined to ensure that taxpayers would foot the bill for colleagues' medical negligence and malpractice awards, consultants boycotted medical admissions units designed to ease the pressures in heaving A&E departments in three Dublin hospitals. The issue of past claims, allegedly the kernel of the protracted dispute with government, melted away, like snow in spring. The legal action evaporated. Serf taxpayers, albeit unknown to themselves, have been picking up the bill for medical negligence and malpractice awards—those 'historic liabilities'—ever since.

The private practice issue surfaced once more. By October 2005, the cap had been reduced significantly: consultant obstetricians in the private sector now had to buy insurance cover for just €1 million, secure in the knowledge that the state would pay for all awards in excess of this amount. As a precondition to entering talks on a new contract, the IHCA demanded that the cap be reduced and that the lower cap be extended to cover other union members wholly engaged in private practice. The cap was duly dropped to €500,000 and extended from obstetricians to neurosurgery and orthopaedic spinal surgery, sub-specialties carrying a risk of brain damage that attract heavy premiums, in excess of €500,000 per head annually.

After more than two-and-a-half years of holding the country to ransom, the strike of kings was over.

SEE-SAW

Few question whether the power of organised medicine is compatible with the health of the nation. The habit of giving doctors control over managing and delivering health services has become ingrained. Health *was*, and *is*, medicine in Ireland. Private medical bodies, such as the royal colleges and the private non-profit hospitals, controlled the National Health Council in the 1950s. At the insistence of the Catholic bishops, legislators amended the 1947 Act to give doctors a majority on the Council. Patriarchy ensured a continuing, unbroken line of male power. Laws were passed that put male doctors in charge of adjacent female professions, such as nursing and midwifery. But while the medical profession had the power to rule others, it was allowed to regulate itself, to determine its own fitness to practise, for instance. But self-policing, it later turned out, was no policing.

Fifty years ago, there was some effort made in the running of the health services to balance the different interest groups and to give adequate representation to the public interest. While today consultant bodies have managed to rout politicians from health, doctors in the 1950s vied with elected representatives for power on local health boards. Law-makers then, unlike today, recognised the need for a balance of power: local authority health committees were equally poised between public and medical representatives. Regional hospital boards were similarly finely tuned. Until 2004, the power of doctors and of politicians oscillated to and fro, like a pendulum. Thirty-six years ago, the new health legislation was a balancing act: elected public representatives were given a majority on the health boards; medics clawed back their power on hospital boards where they held half the seats. These boards helped private non-profit hospitals, university medical faculties and medical training bodies in Dublin, Cork and Galway, to consolidate their power. Later, new regulations emasculated the power of elected representatives on health boards. The Reign of the Medical Technocrats had begun.

The medical profession has now seen off all challenges to its power from politicians. The 2004 Health Act brought the democratic deficit to

new heights. Twelve praesidium members sit on the new Health Service
Executive, by ministerial invitation. Expert knowledge is the sole
criterion laid down for membership. Being elected by the people
through the democratic process is the only legal bar there is to
membership of this body. While such a prohibition is common on state
bodies, it is extremely questionable in a national health authority.
Contrast this with the 1947 Act, which defined local authorities as health
authorities empowered 'to provide and maintain health institutions'.

Today, the pendulum has swung away from democratic controls of
any kind over medicine. A new and dangerous rhetoric has grown up
in Ireland in recent years. The concept of 'local representatives'
in health is now excoriated in some media, as the cult of 'expert'
knowledge gains ground over the democratic process. The uncritical
parroting of the prejudicial views of powerful medics, such as HSE
CEO Brendan Drumm, heralds the triumph of organised medicine
over the public interest.

The Act stripping the system of all vestiges of regional or local
democracy was pushed through the Dáil just before the Christmas
recess of 2004. The new Executive is accountable to the Minister for
Health, who is accountable to the Government, and through the
Government, to the Oireachtas. This slender thread is now the only
democratic oversight there is of our health and personal social services.
The HSE CEO, as opposed to the Department's Secretary-General, is
now the 'accounting officer' for the HSE's €14-billion health vote. We
now have what amounts to a double democratic deficit: a transfer of
power from elected representatives to appointed bureaucrats, and a
shift from regional structures to centralised decision-making.

While the Act does provide for regional forums, these are designed
simply to give an illusion of democracy: their powers are nil. The only
other consultative machinery that the Act provides for are
'panels' to enable the HSE to consult with 'local communities' or other
groups; and an entity labelled a 'national health consultative forum'.
The new legislation drastically reduced the ability, at national level, of
members of the Oireachtas to get information about the health
services. Oireachtas members have now been reduced to 'customers'
in government: a statutory instrument signed off in December 2005
announced that the Health Service Executive will deal with
correspondence and queries from Oireachtas members 'as expeditiously
as may be in accordance with a proper level of *customer service*'.

The vast majority of parliamentary questions relate not to policy but to its implementation: these queries must now be put to the HSE, *not* the Minister. To date, the HSE has taken around two months to answer a question; previously, the same question would have been answered in a matter of days.

The Act also throws up a smokescreen of confidentiality: this expressly covers 'proposals of a commercial nature or tender', ensuring that the veil covering public–private partnerships in health cannot be lifted. If this veil is inadequate in some way—too transparent, for example—the Executive can always cover itself from top to toe in the *burqa* of a confidentiality clause. The law does not require the HSE to disclose *confidential* information; this is defined as 'information that is expressed *by the Executive* to be confidential'. To paraphrase Humpty Dumpty in *Through the Looking Glass*: 'Words mean just what I choose them to mean'.

However, confidentiality is not the only barrier to transparency and accountability in the Act. The legislation has been designed to block patients and others from using the normal channels to make complaints about their medical treatment. It protects health-care practitioners, hospitals and other 'service providers', including the HSE, to the hilt, by excluding from its 'grievance and review' procedures all 'matters' relating to 'clinical judgement'. Hospitals and health administrators now have no legal obligation to review complaints made by patients about decisions relating to their care. The new regional health forums are also barred from making representations about anything that can be traced back to a clinical judgement or a medical decision. Since every aspect of a patient's care involves a decision, all decisions involve 'clinical judgement'. Had the regional forums been in existence at the time of the Caesarean hysterectomy scandal, no one could have raised the issue, involving, as it did, clinical judgement in spades.

The consumer panels and the consultative forum are both muzzled in the same way as the regional forums. To date, neither of these 'options' has been exercised by the Minister, and if they were, it is doubtful if they would lessen the democratic deficit.

This Orwellian legislation removes from hospitals and HSE staff any obligation they may feel to deal with patients in the aftermath of their treatment. Instead, cunningly, the Act provides for the setting-up of new grievance machinery by hospitals and other health providers, designed to *prevent* patients from having their grievances dealt with by those self-same agencies. Since complaints involving clinical judgement cannot be dealt with by the Ombudsman, either, unhappy patients will have no option but to address themselves to the Medical Council, a body not known for its protection of patients' rights.

In the run-up to the *Harding Clark Report* on the Caesarean section scandal at Our Lady of Lourdes Hospital, Drogheda, the Medical Council announced a '360-degree audit' of doctors' performance. It also announced plans to set up a committee to review 'concerns'— complaints made to the Council that were never investigated. This particular committee looks set to be very busy. From 1999 to 2004, the Council got on average 235 complaints every year. Over 90 per cent of them were thrown out without a hearing. In 2002, of the forty cases considered by the Council—some of which related to former years— only fourteen were judged worthy of further attention. Patients made 117 complaints about communication and rudeness. Just one was investigated.

The Act actually squares the circle, closing the loop by ensuring that all complaints made by patients will be dealt with by the medical profession itself. When you consider the Council's abysmal track record in dealing with complaints, the new order laid down by the Act borders on the totalitarian. In a country with 1,000 adverse events in the health services every week, the Government's response is to say: clinical judgement rules.

Has the only lesson of the Caesarean hysterectomy scandal been: how to cover up more?

Chapter 8
The Industrial Revolution

TRAUMA

At the antenatal classes in a Dublin hospital, they talked about 'active management':

> Labour can be painful but active management ensures you won't be in labour for a long time. We'll break the waters [surrounding the baby in the womb] if they haven't already broken. If you haven't made progress within a reasonable space of time, we'll give you oxytocin [IV hormone].

I never thought they'd use oxytocin if you were actually in labour. I knew I didn't want the waters broken: the waters protected the baby's head by keeping it off the pubic bone; there was a higher risk of fetal distress; and it could make labour more painful.

I showed my birth plans to everyone: they were in my notes in hospital, and we brought in a copy with us on the night. The plan said that we wanted the labour to proceed at its own pace; that I wanted to be able to move around, to change position [for the pain]; that I didn't want electronic foetal monitoring [of the baby's heart] or the waters broken, or an episiotomy [enlarging the opening of the birth canal] or an epidural; the plan also said that Mark wanted to be able to cut the cord, if possible;

that the room where the baby was to be born was to be quiet; and that I wanted to breastfeed.

We arrived in at about 3.30 p.m.; I'd been in labour for about fourteen hours. The contractions were now five minutes apart and lasting one minute. I was one centimetre dilated—the midwives said I wasn't quite in labour. They said they'd come back in an hour to do another vaginal examination. They came back and said: 'We were on to Aileen and we would like to break the waters: Aileen said we were to do this. I was still one centimetre—they said they'd be back in an hour. There was a student with me; a more senior midwife did the internals. The internal examinations were so invasive .... They were in control—you could be having a contraction, and they would do an internal in the middle of it. One of the midwives actually said to me: 'If I take my finger out right now, it will hurt more.'

They threatened me with monitoring, with repeated vaginal examinations. Two more senior midwives came in, the one who did the internals and another one, who might have been a sister. They stood at the end of the bed and said: 'We'd really advise you to let us break the waters. If you don't let us, we'll have to monitor you all the time, and we'll have to do hourly vaginal examinations.'

I wanted to be up, and the midwives kept telling me to lie on the bed—I had to lie down. Then they said they'd monitor me for thirty minutes and let me walk around for thirty minutes.

The midwives kept on saying: 'We want to break the waters.'

The second internal was extremely painful—the midwife was trying to break the waters. Some water and blood came away at that point. Then they said: 'We need to see if the baby is okay.' It was really intimidating. When I was having a contraction, they'd stand there, saying nothing, and wait for the contraction to pass—and then start again. I lost track of time. The monitoring was supposed to be continuous—then I'd go for a shower. I found the shower great [for the pain]. If the monitor lost contact, then the midwives would have to start all over again—between monitoring sessions, I was only getting five–ten minutes [of walking]. Then the midwives said they were on the phone again to Aileen, saying that they wanted to break the waters.

Finally, I had to let them: I felt I had no choice. What else could I do? It was three hours after I'd gone in. As they broke the waters, I suddenly became two centimetres dilated: I found it extremely unpleasant and extremely painful.

The midwives said the waters were clear [baby bowel movements are suspect]. Then, all of a sudden, they said there was grade 1 meconium [the least worrying]. From there on, I wasn't dilating in line with their charts.

I'd been in the labour ward for five hours, and I was five centimetres. They were doing continuous fetal monitoring.

Then the midwives started talking about oxytocin: they said Aileen said I should have it. I didn't want it because I knew that oxytocin makes the contractions stronger and more painful, and also because I wanted the birth to be as natural as possible—oxytocin didn't fit the bill. I said I didn't want it, but I finally agreed to let them put up the drip—I felt bullied into taking it.

They said they'd give me pethidine [for pain relief]: I was on gas and air. There were times when I didn't know what was going on—it must have been the effect of pure oxygen.

'I want to walk around,' I said, but I couldn't get off the table. After the oxytocin kicked in, the contractions went out of control. They were hot and heavy—I couldn't get from the table to the shower. I got to ten centimetres. I had no urge to push. The midwife was shouting at me to push—I was pushing all right, but I knew myself nothing was happening. 'You're not pushing,' they said. I felt like a slab of meat. They lifted me up, they lifted me down, they pulled my legs this way, they pulled my legs that way. The baby's heartbeat dropped.

Then they said they'd have to do an episiotomy, that the baby was in distress. I was given a local anaesthetic—the doctor did a great job. Aileen Murphy came in then to do the episiotomy. I felt the episiotomy—I could feel her cutting me. I grabbed her; I was trying to push her away. 'Hold her down on the table while I do this,' she said. 'Get her hands off me,' I said. They held me down: their hands were on my shoulders. I remember leaning forward to grab the doctor's hands to get her to stop: my hands were held back down. There were quite a number of doctors and midwives in the room by then, including two from the special-care baby unit. Lorna's head was turned slightly in the wrong direction—they turned her head with a forceps. Then I got the urge to push, and in three pushes she was out. They laid her across me; I didn't know what was going on. She was lifeless. Once the cord was cut, they took her over to the table and resuscitated her. She woke up after a couple of minutes and opened her eyes.

I had a sense of it being all over: Lorna was still on the table. Aileen delivered the placenta and stitched me up. The nurse brought me tea and cleaned me up. How did I feel? Relief—that it was all over. I didn't know what was going on; I just knew I had no baby and I was very tired. When

I heard them saying something about the Special Care Baby Unit, I said: 'What's that?'

'Just have a quick look,' the doctor said, before they took her away. Afterwards, it felt very strange. I was, like, what was that all about? She was in the special-care baby unit for a couple of days—I wasn't worried. The next morning, the nurse said to me: 'Would you like to see her?' She was in an incubator. The special-care baby unit nurse said she was still on the critical list—it just didn't make sense to me.

My mother was extremely worried—I was in a state of shock.

The baby was stressed—she had an Apgar score of 2 at birth. She wasn't reacting. She was sleeping, not responding. They started tube-feeding her on the second day. She had a brain scan, but nothing showed up. Then she started to respond—at six weeks, she was fine.

The second morning after the birth, I woke up crying. The tea-lady saw me and came over and gave me a big hug. Every so often, I'd start crying. One nurse asked me how I was, and she said to put it down to the 'baby blues'. I was in hospital for five days. After I came home, the breastfeeding didn't work out—I expressed milk for a fortnight. Two weeks later, I was still in floods of tears; I was getting panic attacks; I was having flashbacks onto the labour. The public health nurse suggested I go to my GP.

If the episiotomy had healed, it wouldn't have been so bad. Twelve weeks later, the episiotomy still hadn't healed. I'd refused to go back for my six-week check-up. I waited until I was twelve weeks even though I was in a lot of pain: I couldn't sit down properly.

I couldn't even go back to my GP, whom I trusted implicitly, for a check-up.

When I went to him, I burst into tears; I told him everything that had gone on. He talked about postnatal depression. He said I was suffering from post-traumatic stress syndrome stemming from the actual labour, not from feelings that I couldn't cope with the baby. He gave me anti-depressants.

The plan is to stick with them for another couple of months, then come off them. I never felt I couldn't cope with the baby, but I was having nightmares, getting panic attacks and flashbacks. Gradually, the flashbacks started to decrease, and the panic attacks calmed down, and the nightmares. I started to sleep better. Now I can talk about it without having to rush out of the room [to cry].

Subcutaneous tissue had been left on the outside, and the GP said no way would it heal. Aileen said it was scar tissue from the episiotomy, but it wasn't—she'd stitched me inside out. She removed it with silver nitrate—

I nearly passed out on the table with the pain—I couldn't believe she hadn't given me a local anaesthetic beforehand.

No matter what you read by way of research, their attitude is: 'We have to do this for the sake of your child.' They completely ignored the birth plan. What concerns me most about it is all those other horror stories you hear from other women. But they feel they can't talk about it—they don't want to scare off women who've never had a baby.

So the Master can keep on coming out with lines like, 'We encourage patients to make an active choice.'

The psychological bullying was the worst. To me it was a physical assault: it was psychological intimidation. It was like rape.

I wrote to the Master. He wrote back and said: 'Talk to Aileen.' I just wanted answers, but they got totally defensive, clammed up and said: 'You need to talk to someone else.' Aileen Murphy was the only one who sat down and talked to me. She was very sympathetic, but patronising. We talked it through. When I mentioned postnatal depression, it was like the postnatal depression accounted for everything, for how I felt.

But the episiotomy was like female mutilation, genital mutilation. There are areas down there, areas of numbness, where I can't feel anything, areas that won't go back to the way they were before. No, it's not compatible with either emotional or sexual well-being. The area is all battered and scarred. I suppose it will heal, that it will improve ....

We waited six weeks before writing to the Master. The midwives wrote back to me: 'All the procedures were done in the best interests of baby and mother, and with the consent of your consultant.' They had written in the chart: 'Waters broken at patient's request.' But [in his letter] the Master said: 'I note that the midwife clearly documented that the waters were not broken at your request, but that it was done at the request of Aileen Murphy, presumably for some medical reason ... we are the hospital which attracts more birth plans than any other .... It is our belief that patients should have an active choice in their mode of delivery, and I would refute any claims to the contrary.'

The birth affected my whole life. Before that, I was a very confident person, with a very strong personality. I have a fairly senior position with a consultancy firm: I need to be confident. I find myself taking everything personally. If anything happens at work now, I very much doubt myself. It's harder to ... deal with hassle. I wouldn't want people at work to know.

Lorna is now six-and-a-half-months old. It has put me off having more kids—I would be afraid. I was 34 having her—I did wait for a long while to have a kid. The thought of having another child now would freak me out. I'd have to be hospitalised—I'd be a basket case.

This is Sinéad's* account of her birth under a system known as 'the active management of labour' in a centre of excellence. Active management is a system of managed birth: it assumes women's consent to medical intervention.

CENTRALISED MONOPOLY

In 1976, Comhairle na n-Ospidéal issued a 'discussion document' on maternity care, its only one ever. The British Royal College of Obstetricians and Gynaecologists had been trying to centralise the services for birth since 1954, at least. (Centralisation was a pressing necessity in obstetrics: because obstetrics was the specialty of abnormal birth and few women had abnormal births, as few as 10 per cent, obstetricians needed—and still need—very high volumes of births to maintain their skills.)

Comhairle's message was blindingly simple: all women in childbirth, regardless of their health status, should give birth in units that were under obstetric supervision. Comhairle was parroting the *Peel Report*, written by a former chair of the Royal College six years earlier. The industry ignored the fact that birth was not an illness, that healthy women having normal births—up to 90 per cent—did not need obstetric care and that, if resources were to be used appropriately and cost-effectively, specialist obstetric services should be reserved for those who needed them. But Comhairle's own members were specialists, not generalists; the days of the generalist in maternity care were numbered, as far as they were concerned. Had Comhairle's thirty-page pamphlet been issued by a trade union, it would have been criticised as a badly researched and fairly unsubtle pitch for business.

The stock in trade was safety, as always. Childbirth was safer in maternity units managed by consultant obstetricians and paediatricians, Comhairle asserted. Claiming that theirs was the safer service was a tactic that had worked well for British doctors. There, as here, this claim was an assumption, not a fact. There, as here, doctors produced no evidence to support their stance. (This would have been quite impossible, as there was none.) But Comhairle's document was political,

---

* All names in this account have been changed.

not academic; theology, not science. The medical consultant body had simply *pronounced* on childbirth, not unlike a congregation of bishops speaking *ex cathedra* on sex. And, in the Ireland of the mid-1970s, no one questioned either the bishops or the doctors.

By then, the numbers of women giving birth at home had declined hugely; obstetricians' main competitors were the midwives, nurses and GPs running maternity homes. These homes had had a long and distinguished history. Private nursing homes, like private hospitals, developed at the end of the nineteenth century. Dedicated maternity homes developed, ranging in size from small facilities with half a dozen beds to large establishments with Caesarean section facilities. Standards were high, medical historian John Fleetwood records. Maternity homes were well regulated. Unlike other nursing homes, they were subject to health authority inspection and licensing. (Today, over a hundred years later, general nursing homes—and hospitals—are still unlicensed.)

Women in the eastern region, for example, could give birth close to their homes: there were maternity homes in Athy, Baltinglass and Wicklow, as well as in Dún Laoghaire and Dublin. And the huge sprawling county of Cork was well served, with local birth services in Bantry, Bandon, Castletownbere, Clonakilty, Fermoy, Kanturk, Kinsale, Midleton and Millstreet, in addition to Cork City.

Comhairle rested its case for 100 per cent market monopoly on the 4 per cent of infants with 'special needs', small babies and infants with congenital problems. Comhairle's only other argument was rooted in the hazards of medical intervention: consultants argued that these very dangers made it necessary to confine all women in obstetric units—where they themselves could supervise such hazardous medical practices, presumably.

Supervision was key to Comhairle's plan. A key concept in hospital medicine, supervision wallpapers over the craters of a system where hospitals are open 24/7 but consultants are required to work only 33/5. Supervision allows others to be delegated to do the work, even in the absence of the consultant who is doing the supervising.

Supervision is particularly pertinent in obstetrics: few consultants hang around the labour ward. Midwives have always done the work of looking after women during the sometimes long and demanding hours of labour; obstetricians have invariably pocketed the fees, where fees were payable, however.

INDUSTRIALISING BIRTH

Comhairle's 'model' maternity unit was a template for the industrial-isation of birth, something that had been going on for many years. The model talked about 'volumes', for instance, as though obstetricians were factory-owners. The model unit was to have a minimum level of production, annually, of 2,000 babies, based on a labour-ward turnover of three women per bed per twenty-four hours. But babies are wildly unpredictable, surely. One might take twenty-four hours to arrive while another could come in an hour. How could such a high turnover be guaranteed?

By the mid-1970s, fast birth had arrived. In the 1960s, obstetrics began to manage baby production in much the same way as agribusiness managed food production. The new system was called the 'active management' of women in labour. While farmers discovered that they could produce more meat if hormones were added to the animals' feed, doctors discovered that they could increase turnover in the labour ward if hormones were added to the woman's bloodstream. Synthetic oxytocin had a miraculous effect on the womb, causing it to contract harder and faster. No one quite understood how. But, like putting your foot on the accelerator of a car, oxytocin worked. Women could now be given a finite length of time in which to have a baby. The new system facilitated staff planning and contained costs. On 1 January 1963, it was formally implemented at the National Maternity Hospital.

Babies were referred to as units of production under the new regime. Without active management to rationalise the production line, the policy of penning all women into large, industrial-style units for 'delivery' could never have been implemented. The system came at a cost. The bed occupancy rate was three times higher than the norm for hospital in-patients. Such a turnover raised, and raises, issues such as infection control. Also, there were, and are, important issues of civil liberties. What of the woman who didn't want the hooks and hormones, who wished to proceed at her own pace? Centralisation was built on regimentation and standardisation: it deprived women of their liberty, their freedom to give birth as they wished.

These were just two of the issues that were ignored, not only by Comhairle, who represented a vested interest, but also by the Department, whose brief included the public good. Comhairle's model maternity unit was duly adopted as national policy, without public discussion. By then, the medical project of centralisation was well advanced in Ireland. In 1966, one-third of all births took place in hospitals with 2,000 births or more. Ten years later, over half of all mothers gave birth in institutions with those volumes.

Comhairle was scarcely challenged, publicly, on the devastating consequences of its proposals for women in non-urban areas. If all mothers were required to give birth under obstetric management, local maternity homes would close, inevitably, and women would then be exposed to the hazards of roadside births and roadside deaths. But not unlike a corporation that ignores *externalities*, the hidden costs of decisions made by the company and borne by others, Comhairle ignored the costs of its decision to women.

One by one, small nursing homes, run by midwives, general practitioners and nurses closed, as did cottage hospitals. Susan Lawlor,* a woman I interviewed, described one of the benefits of her local cottage hospital: no routine birth incisions of the kind famously described by Sheila Kitzinger as 'female genital mutilation': 'There were a lot of older midwives there. No students. A lot of midwives were married with children. Their episiotomy rate was almost nil.'

Comhairle did not advert in its report to the sordid subject of competition: it merely listed the country's maternity homes, all 108 of them, in an appendix. But such was the symbiosis between the health bureaucrats and the medical profession that, by the time Comhairle issued its 1976 edict, the birth centres had already begun to close.

Comhairle's report expressed what doctors had been thinking since the 1960s: big is good, bigger better and biggest best of all. 'A taste for the gigantic,' Jean-Marie Clement, professor of medical and hospital law in Paris V University, calls it. All over the world, this taste for the gigantic could be seen. In Australia, New Zealand, Britain, France, Denmark, Spain, Finland, the units of human production grew bigger and bigger.

By 1978, just two years after Comhairle's pamphlet was published, obstetricians' monopoly over the country's maternity services was almost complete. In that year, 91 per cent of all births took place in consultant-controlled maternity units. The competition had been routed, or nearly. In 1973, there were 108 maternity 'units', as Comhairle termed them, around the country. Twenty-five years later, there were just twenty-four.

* Not her real name

As more and more women were shepherded into larger and larger maternity units, birth became increasingly mechanised. Today, nearly half of all births in Ireland take place in units that produce 4,000 babies and more. The taste for the gigantic has led to very high surgical and operative delivery rates: half of all mothers having their first child in Ireland now give birth by Caesarean, vacuum (a suction or hoover device) or forceps delivery.

As Sinéad's story shows, women are ill served by McBirth. Although deeply traumatised by her birth, she made no complaint to the Medical Council, or the Nursing Board, nor did she take an action against the hospital for civil damages. Wounded mothers, whose bodily integrity has been violated in this way, scarcely ever do.

Centralising care carries other costs, too, forcing women in towns and rural areas to travel longer distances during pregnancy, and even during the height of labour, to more distant locations to access the services for birth. Denied access to local care, women in non-urban areas are forced to run the risk of giving birth en route to hospital; their only alternative is 'social' induction, or 'elective' Caesarean. Research shows that these medical interventions carry significant risks for mother and baby.

Maternity care is a major public health issue: three out of four women in Ireland will have a child at some point in their lives. The costs to society of centralisation have been glossed over. The technocratic view does not recognise them: it supports an industrial model of productivity, endorsing efficiency and bureaucracy. Comhairle's 1976 document on maternity care was a classic of this kind. It was grounded in a view of medicine that reduces the body to a machine, a view that is mechanistic and control-oriented, that values homogenisation and objectivity, sees the environment as peripheral, and technology as central. But there was, and there is, another perspective: the social model. This is a view that sees the whole person, one that integrates the physical with the psychosocial and the spiritual, one that is holistic and respectful of autonomy, that values diversity and subjectivity, and that sees the environment as central and technology as subordinate.

However, by 1976, this view was no longer in the ascendancy. Centralising the services for birth was only the beginning.

Chapter 9
Serfs and Emperors

They [the medical training programmes] closely resemble those deemed appropriate in the United Kingdom, which is densely populated and has a hospital system capable of supporting a high degree of specialisation. In Ireland, however, outside the urban areas of Dublin, Cork and Galway, there are many relatively small general hospitals which cannot support the degree of specialisation produced by the present training programmes.

Comhairle na n-Ospidéal on the lack of fit between
smaller hospitals and specialist medical training, 1995

I—THE IMPERIAL VIEW
High-Tech Shrines

Specialisation was the foundation stone of medicine: its very origins lay in the warring trades of surgery, herbalism and pharmacy. It took almost 400 years for the general medical practitioner to develop. By then, hospital medicine was highly developed and hospitals themselves, particularly the private non-profit institutions, had become powerful institutions in their own right.

Special facilities are essential for success, as a Dublin general surgeon realised when he visited the Mayo Clinic in the United States just before the Second World War. Mr T.J.D. Lane returned with one ambition: to develop a sub-specialty in surgery of the urinary tract (urology). In those days, sub-specialties were uncommon. Lane decided to build his own unit at Dublin's Meath Hospital. Failing to get the hospital's agreement, he looked to the Oireachtas, getting a law passed that paved the way for his urological extension. Opened in 1955, the unit achieved international renown; achieving global recognition has always been a driving force in medicine.

If we step back and glance at Western medicine for a moment, we see that we have become enmeshed in a massive professional project, the huge edifice that is modern medicine, built on the twin towers of technology and pharmacology. The high priests of medicine today are technocrats who are consumed, as Lane was, by the development of specialist, high-tech shrines.

This kind of medicine has always been expensive: it requires special facilities, critical volumes, larger units: centralisation, in a word. Ever since the beginning of the public hospital system here in the 1930s, doctors have sought to centralise hospitals. Hospital consultants laid down minimum volumes of patients for themselves as far back as 1968: a general hospital, the *FitzGerald Report* said, should cater for 120,000 and contain 300 beds. *FitzGerald* advocated organising the country's hospitals around the three university medical faculties of Dublin, Cork and Galway, centralising all in-patient services into four regional and twelve general hospitals, and turning the majority of the country's smaller hospitals into 'community health centres'. He was echoing the views of his surgical colleagues who, some five years earlier, had told an Oireachtas health committee that Ireland 'could only have a regional hospital based in a university city'. Outcomes were better, the FitzGerald group argued, in larger units—citing a single article and a *Lancet* leader to support this claim. Medical training would be enhanced, and costs lower. Like the *Hanly Report*, however, *FitzGerald* did not cost its proposals for centralisation.

The Government accepted the report in principle, but it was not overtly implemented. As Sean Flanagan repeatedly told the Dáil, hospital services could be centralised only on a phased basis. But the state gave the profession a consolation prize—the 'consultants' establishment board' demanded by *FitzGerald*—Comhairle na n-Ospidéal.

Comhairle's role was pivotal: it saw itself as harmonising the market for professional services to suit the educational programmes of the royal colleges, dovetailing *public service* appointments to suit their specialists and sub-specialists. From the beginning, Comhairle saw itself as 'rationalising' hospital services, implementing *FitzGerald* by stealth. Over the years, implementing one of the report's main recommendations, Comhairle gave hospitals in Dublin, Cork and

Galway the lion's share of consultant appointments. All three cities had strong university medical faculties and regional hospital boards controlled by doctors. And, while Comhairle expressed concern about 'the concentration of available specialists' in Dublin, only larger hospitals offered the high volumes of patients that consultants needed to be able to utilise their specialist training.

Another way in which Comhairle implemented *FitzGerald* was through the making of joint appointments, where consultants were appointed to both the public and the private non-profit sectors simultaneously. 'These are the only way to ensure the viability of jobs and *modern standards of medical specialisation* [emphasis added].' Each job was a one-off creation, structured by, among other things, 'specialty and sub-specialty interests'. Comhairle endeavoured 'both to service adequately the needs of the hospital(s) concerned and *to satisfy the appointee from a professional viewpoint* [emphasis added]'. Since 1972, joint appointments have been a strong feature of the Irish hospital services.

Long-term strategic manoeuvring was the third approach used by Comhairle (and other actors, such as health boards) to centralise hospital services. Grouping hospitals was a favourite. Setting up regional manpower review groups was another; as was the creation of 'joint departments' through the drafting of 'framework documents'. Take one example: the case of surgery in south-east Dublin. In 1994, at the invitation of St Vincent's Hospital, Comhairle masterminded a tripartite agreement centralising 'major complex' surgery at St Vincent's, with surgeons and management in two smaller hospitals, St Columcille's and St Michael's Hospitals. The framework document agreed in July 1994 prefigured today's *Hanly* and *Teamwork* reports. In another testimony to Comhairle's strategic abilities, the plan was that 'the joint department would act as the initiator of new and replacement consultant posts'. A small working group, chaired by a leading consultant at St Vincent's, Muiris FitzGerald, was set up to implement the framework. One of the main reasons for centralising surgical services in south-east Dublin was 'to permit and facilitate further sub-specialisation, which is the desire of the majority of surgeons in the region'.

Over the years, formal specialist training programmes replaced the ad hoc training of the past. By 1995, there were 157 recognised training programmes in different medical specialties and sub-specialties. Eye surgery, for example, had split into two—surgery of the retina and neuro-ophthalmic surgery—while students of anaesthesia could specialise in intensive care, pain management or children's anaesthesia. In pathology, Comhairle had previously observed, the training 'was designed to produce only mono-specialist pathologists'.

Surgery was by far the biggest propagator of specialties and subspecialties. By then, the general surgical training programme did not include even orthopaedic surgery or urology. In 2005, there were 364 surgeons; of these, only 49 were categorised as *general* general surgeons. The other general surgeons specialised in stomach (32), veins (24), breast (21), colo-rectal (5), liver (4), urinary tract (1) and children's surgery (1). Learning disability psychiatry had now split into two *sub* sub-specialties, adult and child/adolescent.

In 1989, Comhairle reiterated its concern about the 'service problems' created by the 'well-established trend towards greater specialisation'. 'For some considerable time,' Comhairle said, this problem had been 'particularly evident'. Physicians and general surgeons were increasingly oriented towards 'areas of special interest'. This presented 'problems of consultant staffing and hospital organisation'. The problem was exacerbated by the fact that, as older doctors in general surgery retired, they were replaced by younger consultants whose training was more specialised.

Comhairle saw itself as 'strongly influenced by the training requirements laid down by the professional bodies involved in postgraduate medical education'; trying to 'keep up to date with the latest thinking on postgraduate training and to reflect this in its [job] specifications'. By now, these bodies' demands had made the staffing of smaller hospitals hugely problematic. Comhairle's view was that smaller hospitals were inadequate to meet the needs of hospital doctors who had graduated from the specialist training programmes developed by trainers, such as the Royal College of Surgeons. Comhairle's overriding concern was the 'distinct possibility that, on completion of training, a sizeable number of individuals will find themselves working as consultants in circumstances where they cannot exercise their highly specialised skills on a continuous basis and where, on the contrary, many will need a wider range of skills not incorporated in the training programmes.' Moreover, providing more space, support staff, equipment, and so on for these medical subspecialties carried significant cost implications. Comhairle's view was:

'these are important matters which are rooted in the training programmes for doctors'.

If some in Comhairle acknowledged a dilemma, it was decisively and brutally resolved for them by the Royal College of Surgeons. In January 2002, Arthur Tanner, RCSI's Dean of Surgery, warned that its new training 'standards' might close some A&E units. The College had decided no longer to recognise casualty services *not* run by A&E consultants as training sites for students of 'emergency medicine'. One of the newest specialties had come of age: smaller casualty units did not meet its requirements. The new field, created in the early 1990s, was open to physicians, surgeons and anaesthetists.

Former Comhairle member—and chair, among other things, of a Comhairle committee on medical manpower in the north-east— Muiris FitzGerald put the case for closing small hospitals at a conference in Dublin in 2002. Like Patrick FitzGerald before him, Muiris FitzGerald was, and is, a leading consultant in a Dublin voluntary hospital and a professor of medicine at UCD. He claims that smaller hospitals are not 'viable', dismissing the view that they provide local services and respond to local needs. These '*very* minor virtues,' FitzGerald says, are 'completely negated when you find that these hospitals are not just looking for a niche area of medical activity. They want to have acute 24-hour full services in most of the mainline disciplines of medicine and surgery.' He finds this 'absolutely unsustainable from the risk management point of view, from the sustainable development point of view, and from an economic perspective.' Staffing smaller hospitals spreads resources too thinly, in his view: the problem with having such a dispersed network, he says, is that 'you cannot develop specialisation'. 'You are forced, in this model, to configure a generalist consultant delivery system *that can do a lot of things with reasonable competence,* but where you cannot provide specialist capabilities, such as sub-specialist care and sophisticated "diagnostic services" [emphasis added].'

Speaking at a conference in UCD's Smurfit School of Business in October 2002, FitzGerald highlighted the economic angle: 'Because you reproduce this generalist model in multiple locations, you then reduce the amount of money available to spend on specialist services.' Maintaining several small hospitals in a region, he believes, 'wastes resources'. 'When hospitals are jam-packed in the large urban metropolitan centres, there are vacant beds in some small county hospitals.'

Professionals cover the service in case people require the service. You are not paying them for actual work done.'

Risk management for complex surgery is his third argument: It was just not possible, FitzGerald continued, for 'complex surgery' to be provided in smaller hospitals where surgeons do not have the volume of cases needed 'to hone and maintain skills on a lifetime basis'.

His fourth and final argument against retaining 'peripheral' hospitals is that they do not meet the training expectations of junior doctors, because they are not recognised for training purposes. In some areas, FitzGerald says, 90 per cent of junior doctors in smaller hospitals come from 'the India/Pakistan subcontinent'. 'You staff these hospitals at great cost to the country and at great cost to these doctors.'

Non-Commissioned Officers

During the 1980s and 1990s, particularly, hospital medicine was a closed shop: doctors emigrated en masse. We had been training doctors for decades, but, paradoxically, we were acutely short of them. By 1998, the effects of the brain drain were making themselves felt. Belatedly, the Government set out to rectify this problem, setting up a forum on medical manpower in 1998 charged with developing a training and career structure for hospital doctors.

In 2002 came the forum's successor, the Task Force on Medical Manpower. In its report—dubbed the *Hanly Report*—the Task Force proposed a new training and career infrastructure for doctors, purportedly to stem the brain drain. Doctors would now train in giant hypermarket hospitals, catering for up to 500,000 people, offering every conceivable specialty and sub-specialty.

The other main plank the *Hanly Report* relied upon was the European work-time directive. European law, adopted in 1993, laid down a maximum working week of forty-eight hours, plus minimum rest periods, for workers. In May 2000, the Parliament extended the directive to doctors in training, giving member states nine years to implement it. Now down to fifty-eight hours since August 2004, the working week is set to be reduced by the directive to forty-eight hours in 2009, in theory at least, limiting the work of non-consultant hospital doctors (NCHDS) to a maximum of thirteen hours in any given twenty-four-hour period; and restricting night work to eight hours.

The *Hanly Report* will be discussed later. But first, how did the people of Ireland, and their elected representatives, respond to the doctrine of centralisation promoted by surgeons such as Patrick FitzGerald in 1968 and in 2002 by David Hanly, a member of the RCSI Court of Patrons?

> *Regionalisation, to my mind, is a first cousin of centralisation ...*
> *Regionalisation is only another move towards centralising the*
> *services.*
>
> Deputy Philip Burton, speaking in the Dáil debate on the *FitzGerald*
> *Report*, 1 May 1969

II—THE SERFS' VIEW

Medical culture in Ireland today is predominantly Anglo-American. European medicine has always had a negligible influence here, leaving the social model of health underdeveloped. Language barriers over the past two centuries have ensured that health professionals have generally emigrated to either Britain or North America. Irish medicine has never aspired to shake off the colonial ties that bind— the colleges held fast to their royal roots.

Professions are not unlike corporations: self-interest rules. This is perfectly understandable. As long as the professional project does not threaten the public interest, there should be no cause for concern. But the professional project was now increasingly driven by medical technocracy, particularly in the United States and in Britain. The generalist model was ignored in favour of a specialist model that demanded centralising services in larger units of medical production. This policy was one that adversely affected the health and welfare of the populations served by these health systems. One of the consequences of the US model, for example, has been to leave 46 million people without access to medical care. In Britain, as in other countries, community health services were left underdeveloped: within the technocratic model of health, health promotion and prevention have always been the Cinderellas of the services.

By the late 1960s, in Ireland, medical technocrats were beginning to consolidate their grip over the services. Then, as now, consultant bodies—in particular, the surgeons, the university medical faculties, and the private non-profit hospitals—were the lobbies that stood to benefit most from a policy of centralisation.

Patrick FitzGerald

The democratic deficit was not as pronounced in the late 1960s as it is now, however. The contrast between the sustained 1969 Dáil debate on the *FitzGerald Report* and the truncated 2003 'debate' on the *Hanly Report* could not be more marked. Legislation was debated in far greater depth and at far greater length than it is today, when crucial legislation is frequently rushed through the Dáil. Debate was not then confined to party spokespersons; many deputies contributed to both the first and second stage readings of the bill.

The *FitzGerald Report* proved explosive. Deputies objected to the fact that medical men were driving hospital planning in their own interests, not that of the people. (Thirty years ago, politicians were more questioning of medical power than they are today.) Sir Anthony Esmonde, a non-hospital doctor from Wexford, dismissed the report as 'purely a consultants' scheme which is totally unacceptable to rural Ireland'. Brendan Corish believed *FitzGerald* was 'lop-sided', weighted in favour of specialists. (Exactly the same accusation has been levelled at the *Hanly Report* today.) Pat Joe Reynolds said that he did not think 'professional men' were 'in a position to advise on where hospitals should be built'. That, he said robustly, should be a matter for public representatives. (Such self-belief is rare among politicians today. Perhaps it has been eroded by the sustained propaganda in the last couple of years, faithfully carried in the media, on the need to take 'politics' out of health.) Deputies were not slow to point out in 1969 that the hospitals earmarked for development were those the consultants worked in themselves. Mark Clinton decried the non-involvement of GPs, nurses and administrators in the *FitzGerald Report*. Noël Browne, himself a hospital consultant, broadly supported it.

Deputies underlined the risks to patients of having to travel up to 40–60 miles over bad roads to regional centres, for something as minor as an appendix operation. 'Is it suggested', Brendan Corish asked, 'that a person in Co. Wexford would have to travel 40 miles to Waterford for treatment for an appendix?' Again, this observation continues to be extremely relevant today, although there is a growing tendency, in thrall as we are to technocracy, to ridicule such concerns.

Having to travel 40—or 80—miles to access care is *exactly* what the Government is planning for the future of our hospital services. When this policy, devised by consultant bodies, is implemented, Wexford people *will* have to travel to Waterford for an appendix operation. But with the massively increased volume of traffic on our roads today leading frequently to enormous delays, centralising services carries more risks than ever.

James Dillon maintained that 80–90 per cent of problems that patients presented to county hospitals were well within the competence of their surgeons. He asked a question still relevant today, a question reiterated by the *Nenagh Hospital Report* in 2006: why, for the sake of the 10 per cent of cases outside the capacity of smaller hospitals, the 'inestimable benefit' of access should be removed from the other 90 per cent. Joan Burke (Roscommon-Leitrim) talked about the likelihood of people dying, with inadequate ambulance services and patients being transported up to 100 miles on bad roads. These are the very arguments made today by the Health Services Action Group against current government plans to close smaller hospitals.

Interestingly, health care was seen in a more holistic way in 1969: the social model of health was stronger then. Deputies stressed the psychological benefits of local care: the personal, friendly atmosphere encountered in smaller hospitals, the frequent visits from family and friends—all shortened the road to recovery, they said. Sean Treacy, from South Tipperary, articulated the argument well: 'Everyone knows everyone else. The doctor knows all his patients personally. There is a wonderful spirit of cordiality and goodwill that is bound to be conducive to speedy recovery. Yet here we have a proposal that the people must, in future, go to Cork, Limerick or Waterford, at the very nearest, for hospital treatment, to become *digits in a large institution … patients in an alien atmosphere, faced with an impersonal approach* [emphasis added]'.

The impersonal care that characterises high-volume industrial-style hospitals *does* leave patients feeling isolated, alienated and out of control. This is a critical issue, one that we need to examine today, in the light of current government plans to centralise all in-patient services in huge industrial-style units. Sprawling, centralised hospitals have proved impossible to manage well. Frequently overcrowded and understaffed, they are a nightmare for patients and for staff. Patients complain about 'getting lost in the system', being part of a factory instead of a caring institution.

Oliver J. Flanagan related his visit to a huge hospital in New York, the kind now planned by the Government to replace smaller hospitals:

One of the saddest experiences I ever had was when I visited a constituent of mine in the Bellevue Hospital in New York. It is one of the biggest hospitals I ever saw. It embraces a few blocks of the city .... One could barely walk between the beds .... I remember the patient saying that it was bad enough to be ill in Ireland but it was a pleasure ... compared with being ill in the US. He said that when one is ill in Ireland, one has many friends to visit one, but when one is ill in the US, one is out of circulation and is wanted no longer.

Referring to the proposed closure of Portiuncula Hospital (still on the hit list today), Brigid Hogan-O'Higgins raised the issue of a particular group who would also suffer disproportionately if they were deprived of hospital visits: sick children. It was imperative, she said, that their parents be able to visit them every day. This is a point that has scarcely been raised in the debate on government plans to centralise all children's services into a single monster hospital which will be based in Dublin. The social view, unlike the technocratic view, is one that attaches importance to hospital visits: when you are a patient, hospital visits *do* matter; and when you have a family member or a friend who is hospitalised, being able to visit *does* make a difference.

Brendan Corish also referred to the problems that would face people on low incomes if they had to travel to visit relatives. Again, this is another very important point the technocratic view ignores. Centralising services *is* a policy that further disadvantages the less well off. Despite our wealth, a significant proportion of our population continues to live in poverty, many of them in rural areas. They have perennial transport problems; they will bear the brunt of the cuts being proposed today.

Health Services Action Group chair Peadar McMahon told a meeting of the Joint Oireachtas Committee on Health that those most disadvantaged by *Hanly* were 'the poor, the isolated, the single mothers, the elderly and children' who would 'suffer extra trauma, pain and hardship' as a result of this policy. Interestingly, the bill was amended to provide for a public inquiry before a hospital could be 'discontinued'. But it was unlikely, the Minister said, soothingly, that any hospital would close: their functions would simply change. It was a line that could have been penned for today's Minister for Health. Hugh Gibbons observed that *FitzGerald* had recommended, not that

Roscommon Hospital should close, but that it should lose its urgent or acute surgical services, and that this could be done without an inquiry. He was suitably mollified by the Minister with blandishments about 'consultation'.

Sean Flanagan expressed deep misgivings about specialisation: 'Now there is no such thing as a pathologist. There is a biochemist and a haematologist and a half a dozen others. In my time, there was also a general surgeon. Now there is no such graduate and there never will be again. These are the realities of the specialisation that has taken place in medicine in the past few years'. 'It is not necessarily a good thing,' he continued, 'that this narrow specialisation is taking place but unfortunately I do not control it, we do not control it, and that is what is happening.'

Sean Flanagan was right: the state did not control it. Nor was it necessarily a good thing.

> *The worst feature of specialisation is that it makes doctors feel they are doing wrong to deal with even the simplest of cases if it lies within the protected area of somebody else's specialty.*
> Dr Maurice Gueret, quoting a London physician, Richard Asher

Did specialisation always benefit the patient? Best-selling author Marilyn French was treated for cancer in New York's Sloan Kettering, the oldest as well as the largest institution in the world dedicated to cancer care. French pinpoints the perils of specialisation for the patient, the feelings of isolation and alienation that come from the experience of fragmentation, of being treated as though you were a collection of body parts. Nobody, she complains, saw the whole picture: 'No one was taking care of my whole self. I felt that if no one saw me whole, no one could help me. Each doctor cared only about his specialty: the oncologist cared only about cancer, the neuro-oncologist only about nerve damage caused by cancer'.

Centralisation had long been promulgated by the British royal colleges. They have always exercised considerable influence here, ever since Ireland lost its native medical schools. Medical registration and training bodies in these islands have always had close relationships, unaffected by political changes. The Institute of Obstetrics and Gynaecologists, for example, enjoys very close ties with its elder sibling in Britain, the Royal College of Obstetricians and Gynaecologists.

Mutual recognition of medical training within these islands did much to protect and promote medical careers. Many Irish doctors, nurses and midwives trained and worked in Britain from the 1940s onwards. Some, like my mother who trained and nursed in Brighton during the war, returned. Others, like her two sisters, re-emigrated: from England, they went to New York to nurse, and they stayed there. More recently, many Irish hospital doctors, who trained in Ireland and subsequently worked in North American hospitals, returned to take up coveted consultant posts, bringing with them aspects of American hospital culture.

Warping the System

Over more than a quarter of a century, under Comhairle's tutelage, teaching hospitals in Dublin, Cork and Galway were fattened to supermac proportions, while general and county hospitals were starved to the point of anorexia. This had obvious consequences for the capacity of those hospitals to support medical training programmes. Comhairle's own reports bear witness to the geographic inequalities it nurtured. A two-speed hospital service developed, one urban and teaching, the other non-urban and non-teaching—a two-speed Ireland that served the career needs of its consultants, but not the medical needs of its communities. Exactly the same warped, elitist and inequitable system developed in France, according to professor of medical law at Paris V University, Jean-Marie Clement.

People living in the north-east fared worst of all: they had less access to specialist services than anyone else. Those living in the Dublin area did best: they had more than double the north-east's ratio of hospital specialists on their doorstep.

Medical training bodies, understandably, had only one interest: education. As in Britain, medical education entailed growing numerous sub-specialties, creating mini-empires. New fields of medical training sprouted like green leaves in spring. All a royal college had to do was notify Comhairle that such-and-such a sub-specialty had been created and, hey presto, a new sub-specialty was born.

For over thirty years, Comhairle designed hospital services—paid for by the taxpayer—that provided career structures for a seemingly endless proliferation of sub-specialties. By 1995, micro-specialties beckoned in psychiatry: old age, rehabilitation, substance abuse, learning disability, forensic (court-related) and something that sounded as though it might involve juvenile offenders, 'liaison psychiatry'. Looked at from the point of view of the public interest, it was an absurd arrangement, particularly in a country such as Ireland.

When did we reach a point where we had exceeded our requirements as a small nation for specialisation? By then, the perils of excessive specialisation had become obvious. But can a small country such as Ireland afford mono-specialist pathologists? This question was not asked. It is one of the great debates in health we have never had: how to square the circle between developing careers for doctors *and* providing services to communities. Comhairle, publicly unrepresentative and largely unaccountable as it was, facilitated the training bodies' demands unquestioningly. The notion that specialist medical training might be structured to fit community health needs did not begin to enter the equation. Developing a 'wider range of skills' was not something the medical bodies took the slightest interest in: it ran counter to the entire thrust of imperial medicine, which centred on the creation of micro-specialties and the building of mini-empires.

Hospitals for Doctors, Not for Patients

We now had both kidney and heart transplant sub-specialties. Transplant surgery, in particular, has huge cost implications. (It is one of the growth areas in medicine that is now threatening to plunge the French health system into bankruptcy.) Despite this, no one called a halt. Specialisation was a growth promoter of the 'knowledge economy', after all. Micro-specialties represented business, income, employment, partnerships, growth. Corporatism grew in health, as in other sectors. If specialisation was making the staffing of smaller hospitals impossible, there were only two choices to be made: cull the hospitals or curb the specialties. But so corporatised had medical thinking become that service problems were no longer seen as a priority. A greater imperative ruled: the needs of the corporation/profession. We had now reached a point where the hospital existed not to provide medical treatment for patients, but to create an infrastructure for medical practice. The notion that the function of a hospital is to serve a community's health needs had become outmoded.

Muiris FitzGerald's belief is that the need for hospital doctors to develop specialties and sub-specialties *must* take precedence over the service needs of local communities. Super-specialist services, by definition, are required by a very small minority of people, but in this

self-serving medical view, what matters is not who needs such specialist treatment, but who benefits from providing it. If you take the
corporate view, of course, axing smaller hospitals in order to develop
medical micro-specialties must seem perfectly legitimate.

A more generalist approach would be required to sustain smaller
hospitals, but such an approach will not be considered because it does
not encourage the proliferation of sub-specialties. What matters for
the vast majority of patients, however, is not risk management for
complex surgery, pace Muiris FitzGerald, but risk management for
common conditions, where proximity to hospital is the most important factor in safety and survival.

By 1995, specialisation had become a difficulty even for the larger
teaching hospitals. And still the process continued. Just as small
farmers at the beginning of the nineteenth century divided and sub-
divided their fields, so surgeons, pathologists and others divided and
sub-divided theirs. In its 2001 report, Comhairle noted that two large
hospitals in Dublin and Limerick had been *granted* posts of *general*
physician with 'specific responsibility for medical admissions units'.
Had a new sub-specialty been born?

The Hanly Gospel

In 2002, Comhairle's two-speed hospital approach was taken to its
logical conclusion, with RCSI providing leadership. Ignoring the fact
that Ireland had twenty injury crashes *daily*, and that, in the past,
casualty units had been run, in the main, by general physicians and
surgeons, the College decided, in effect, that A&E departments,
nationwide, would henceforth be run by emergency consultants, or,
alternatively, the services would close. The difficulty with inventing a
specialty is that there are no branches at the top of the tree. Heavy
pruning is therefore needed around the base. Emergency medicine
was a sub-specialty that did not even exist in 1989 but by January 2001,
twenty-one permanent consultant posts had been created in the sub-
specialty. Arthur Tanner was totally unapologetic about the fact that
smaller casualty units were to be sacrificed on the altar of emergency
medicine. Externalities, as mentioned previously, are of no concern to
self-interested corporations.

Ireland's smaller hospitals were to be sacrificed to make way for the
new medical Wal-Marts. Following the *Hanly Report*, and using the
pretext of the European work-time directive, the Government duly

signed off on a policy reducing the country's general and county hospitals to day-care centres. These hospitals are to be stripped of their urgent-care services, including emergency and maternity care. Hospitals likely to lose their acute in-patient beds include Bantry, Ballinasloe, Cashel, Cavan, Clonmel, Dundalk, Ennis, Kilkenny, Loughlinstown, Mallow, Monaghan, Mullingar, Naas, Navan, Nenagh, Port Laoise, Roscommon, St John's (Limerick), St Michael's (Dún Laoghaire) and Wexford, with a query over Tralee, Castlebar and Letterkenny.

The taste for the gigantic had now reached Ireland with a vengeance. But the bigger the administration, the greater the likelihood of error. Being told you don't have bone cancer when you do, because your chart got mixed up with another patient's, or being left with just one bad kidney, because the wrong one was removed by mistake: these are just two real-life examples of what has happened in 'centres of excellence'.

We were now subjected to relentless rhetoric about 'centres of excellence' that ignored the reality that patient safety in the country's biggest and most prominent hospitals cannot be assumed. The inefficiencies and hazards known to be associated with factory hospitals—the patient records and medical files that go missing, the many failures of communication between large multiple teams and narrow specialties, the proliferation of bugs in congested wards and corridors: all of this was ignored. To judge from the media, these are the hospitals most often sued by former patients who believe they have been damaged or injured by their staff. Take the case of Alan O'Gorman, a young man who presented himself at St Vincent's in 2002 with a suspected acute appendix. Surgeons at the hospital removed his entire stomach by mistake, after laboratory staff blundered. He was awarded €450,000 by the High Court in November 2006.

The litany of 'adverse events' in centres of inexcellence is too lengthy to be recited.

Amazingly, the Hanly empire was never costed, by either the Government or anyone else. Yet the cost implications of closing 3,200 beds and replacing them elsewhere were, and are, staggering. It made no sense to adopt a plan that entailed unknown financial risks of incalculable magnitude. Yet there was no shortage of expertise within the Hanly task force; David Hanly himself was no stranger to hospital costs, while the RCSI, as one of Dublin's major property developers, could also lay claim to significant expertise in this area. College patron Bernard McNamara, whose company is responsible for new builds at St Vincent's, Beaumont and James Connolly, in addition to the new hospital at Tullamore, could also have advised.

With all acute services to be provided in just ten or twelve hypermarkets, Comhairle's two-speed hospital train had reached its destination. As health economist Dr Catherine McNamara, formerly of Trinity College Dublin, observed, *Hanly* was based on the 1960s doctrine of centralisation. It reflected 'royal college preoccupations with building the medical empires required for hyper-specialisation in medicine'.

A further draconian feature of the *Hanly Report* that got virtually no attention in the media was its proposal to close all stand-alone specialist hospitals. In the capital, these include the three main Dublin maternity hospitals; Cherry Orchard, Ballyfermot (infectious diseases); Clontarf (orthopaedic); Crumlin (children's); Peamount, Newcastle (TB); St Luke's, Rathgar (cancer); St Anne's (cancer); Baldoyle and Cappagh (orthopaedic); and Dún Laoghaire (rehabilitation). Outside Dublin, the doors are set to close in the regional orthopaedic hospital just outside the village of Croom, Co. Limerick, a hospital run by my father, an orthopaedic surgeon, until his death in 1959. Other orthopaedic facilities set to close are Kilcreene, Co. Kilkenny, and St Mary's, Cork. All are scheduled to 're-locate' to the new hypermarket hospitals.

Closing the Doors
The plan, which proposed to strip up to twenty-three hospitals (or more) of their emergency and maternity services, was presented as 'rationalising' hospital care. Health economist Jim Bradley described the new policy as 'a direct attack on people's ability to access appropriate care'. No other country in the world had set out to destroy its tier of second-level hospitals in this way, the Health Services Action Group (HSAG) pointed out. If the plan is implemented—and it remains government policy—smaller casualty services will be replaced by daytime 'minor injuries' units offering 'lumps and bumps' surgery, outpatient clinics and diagnostic services—not much use if you are having a heart attack or a baby. Emergency and maternity services are set to be provided 'only in a handful of already overstretched and understaffed hospitals in urban areas'.

Hanly proposed to make an already under-resourced health service worse, by cutting 250 beds in each region. This would leave our hospital system short of more than 3,000 beds nationally—*in addition* to the deficit of 3,000 we are already carrying. Nor did this shortage include maternity: implementing *Hanly* would cut the number of maternity wards by up to half, reducing the number of accessible maternity beds in the regions by around a quarter. The Health Services Action Group (HSAG) pointed out that conditions in A&E units would worsen. Dr John Barton said that the key safety issue was lack of capacity. 'By removing in-patient care from the vast majority of our hospitals, *Hanly* will exacerbate our inability to care safely for the sick. At a time when the major problem facing Irish acute hospitals is the shortage of in-patient beds, *Hanly* proposes to close down in-patient care in the majority of our hospitals around the country.'

Ireland has one of the lowest levels of hospital allocation per head of population in the European Union. Hospital beds were slashed by 29 per cent during Rory O'Hanlon's reign as health minister. John Barton points out that 'Belgium is downsizing its hospitals at present. Yet, when this downsizing is finished, Belgium will still have twenty-eight hospitals per million citizens, four times Ireland's current ratio, pre-*Hanly*, of nine per million. Ireland has thirty-nine A&E units at present: post-*Hanly*, on present plans, this number will be cut to twelve or even ten.'

The new plan—disenfranchising hundreds of thousands of people living in non-urban areas—was peddled as 'regional self-sufficiency'. (This was a good example of the 'newspeak' that is now the norm in health, where what you hear is usually the polar opposite of what is happening.) Health bureaucrats, like consultant bodies, had completely lost sight of the patient.

The *Hanly Report* proposed a catchment area of 350,000–500,000 people for a 'viable' A&E service. Four of the former health board regions did not have sufficient population numbers to qualify for such a service, a Trinity College public health lecturer, Conor Teljeur, observed. Moreover, Ireland is sparsely populated: if 400,000 patients, to take a round figure, are needed to service a third-level, specialist hospital, its catchment area will span over 2,400 square miles. As a product of British royal college thinking, *Hanly* was derived from British population densities 'totally unsuited to Irish demographics', as Catherine McNamara points out. Ireland's population is only 6 per cent of Britain's and it is nearly five times more dispersed. How could anyone have thought that this was a model for Ireland?

Some people would have to travel for hours to access vital hospital services. But how many, and how far? Conor Teljeur mapped *Hanly*, showing how the *Hanly* model related to where people live. Implementing it would significantly reduce people's access to A&E within what is called 'the golden hour', he showed. If you are involved in a car crash, for example, the golden hour is that first hour after the accident when you need access to appropriate care, urgently, to ensure that you will not die or become permanently disabled. Research shows that 30 per cent of all major trauma victims die unnecessarily due to lack of proper care—the kind of care that any A&E unit around the country can provide. The golden hour has become the accepted standard in trauma care, as emergency consultant Conor Egleston underlines. Hospital records at Ennis General show that withdrawing 24/7 casualty services will lead to significant loss of life: at least twenty deaths every year in its catchment area can be expected. Yet the Government still plans to close *two-thirds* of our casualty units.

As things stand, our services are already extremely deficient by international standards. Conor Teljeur says that only 82 per cent of road traffic accident victims, nationally, can expect to access a casualty unit within an hour; fully implementing *Hanly* will cut this figure to 72 per cent. Contrast this with British Columbia: the standard there is that 98 per cent of the population should live within one hour of an A&E unit. Or New Zealand, where the benchmark is 90 per cent. And, depending on where you live, your chances of making it to an A&E on time may be even worse. Teljeur's averages conceal regional variations. Take the north-west, for example: the full-blown *Hanly* virus will mean that only 44 per cent of those involved in road traffic accidents will be able to access a casualty unit within sixty minutes. Is this really government policy for the north-west?

Closing casualty units leads to deaths, international experience shows. One London hospital has paid the price of centralisation in maternal deaths. From 2002 to 2005, ten women died in childbirth at the city's Northwick Park Hospital. Nine of these deaths were avoidable: an official inquiry established that the prior closure of obstetric services at the Central Middlesex Hospital had contributed to the deaths. Other research done in Britain shows that patients who live further from hospital casualty units die more often: traffic victims and those suffering from asthma and diabetes are particularly at risk, as are babies. Quebec research has shown significantly higher death rates among children under five, from conditions such as meningitis, in areas where hospitals are remote; Montreal statistics show that, in the absence of a local casualty unit, 30 per cent of medical trauma patients die during that first golden hour, unnecessarily.

What if there was a Disaster?

The bodies are placed tightly, side by side, on planks, on top of each other. A young man, who is working there under infernal conditions, breaks down one morning when he sees the body of his grandmother arriving. The smell is intolerable. A pestilential odour emanates from the refrigerators where the bodies are kept, their doors continually opened and reopened. Finally, we are obliged to hire refrigerated trucks, normally used to transport food, to make up for the lack of storage facilities. Families and visitors are kept away from these trucks.

This scene of devastation is not from a war zone in some far-flung part of the world; this is peace time in one of the great cities of Europe. This is Paris, in August 2003, during a heat wave that killed thousands. Mainly senior citizens, they died, Professor Jean-Marie Clement told me, because the city's smaller hospitals had been shut. In Dublin, a similar culling took place: hospital beds were slashed by 29 per cent during Rory O'Hanlon's reign as health minister. It would be a mistake to think that the issue of second-level care—local hospitals—is simply a rural one.

Health Services Action Group Chair Peadar McMahon told members of the Joint Oireachtas Committee that since Monaghan General had been taken off call, 'medical, surgical and trauma emergencies were taken by ambulance to other hospitals in Dundalk, Cavan and Drogheda, and, on occasion, to hospitals within the Six Counties. Since July 2002, there have been at least twelve cases where the patient did not reach hospital alive, or died shortly after arrival. These people could possibly have survived had Monaghan Hospital been on call for emergencies. During the same period, numerous patients, who presented at Monaghan General in private transport, were admitted, treated and survived—patients who know that they would never have reached another hospital alive.' There would be more needless deaths, he forecast.

The *Hanly* effect on health will further deepen existing urban/rural inequalities and lead to rural depopulation, Dr Tom Nolan, a general practitioner from Clare, told members of the Joint Oireachtas committee. All general practitioners in Clare were opposed to *Hanly*, on safety and other grounds. The Trinity College study, he said, showed that only in the Dublin area would international golden-hour standards be met post-*Hanly*. While 97 per cent of the urban population in the Dublin area would live within sixty minutes of an A&E department, only 60 per cent would do so in rural areas. Under *Hanly*, he predicted, the golden hour coverage of the population of rural Ireland would fall from its current 81–82 per cent to 61–65 per cent. 'If the vote of a constituent living in a remote rural area is equal to the vote of a constituent living beside a major hospital, why should his life be worth less under *Hanly*?' Tom Nolan asked.

Mortality statistics are all too real in Monaghan: seventeen deaths, judged avoidable, were logged from July 2002 to January 2005, when the hospital was completely off call. In August 2002, a 35-year-old Clontibret woman, Christina Knox, died en route to Dundalk: the health board had instructed ambulance personnel to bypass Monaghan General for all major emergencies and trauma victims. On 29 May 2004, Phillip Courtenay (48) from Castleblaney suffered a heart attack in Monaghan town. An ambulance arrived within six minutes. Instead of being taken to Monaghan General, he was brought to Dundalk, arriving there fifty-eight minutes after the emergency call-out. He never regained consciousness, and died on 4 June. Intubation, a procedure that could readily have been carried out at Monaghan's coronary care unit, would have secured the airway, the inquest into his death heard.

Bennie McCullagh also suffered a heart attack at his home, a few hundred yards from Monaghan General; the ambulance brought him to Cavan, thirty-seven miles away, again in line with health board protocols. He died en route to Cavan on 26 October. A consultant who specialised in caring for heart attack victims, who had worked at the hospital for twenty years, was on duty at the time of his death.

Paramedics

So, if hundreds of thousands of people were to lose their access to local A&E and maternity care services, was there a plan B? *Hanly* hinges on something that has been marketed as 'pre-hospital emergency care', provided, it is claimed, by 'advanced' paramedics.

This is a mirage. Despite its plans to make paramedics the lynchpin of the emergency services, Ireland's ambulance services, by international standards, are grossly under-resourced. Take Clare, for example. Only two-thirds of stations had 100 per cent defibrillator coverage in 2002. There was no budget for emergency medical technician (EMT) training or recruitment in 2003. Things are unlikely to improve in the near future. The new European-standard ambulances have one stretcher space, not two: this will double the ambulance stock requirements in the coming years.

The pitfalls of relying on ambulance services are legion. A national study found Irish ambulance responses to critical incidents 'inappropriately delayed'. No national standards exist. Coverage is poor, geographically. In a sparsely populated region, there is the difficulty of locating the person; expecting an ambulance to get to a patient within a reasonable timeframe may be unrealistic. Gaps in cover will inevitably arise as the Pre-Hospital Emergency Care Council has underlined. In Clare, for instance, once an ambulance has left the area to take a patient to Limerick Regional, the vehicle may be in transit for up to half a day, leaving the community without a service.

Rhetoric about 'advanced paramedics' is hollow. Ireland has only just begun to develop paramedic training: the first ever EMT course was held in 2002. The first ever EMT-A course finished in May 2005, with sixteen qualifying. While a small number of paramedics may have trained abroad, less than 3 per cent of EMTs have been able to train further in Ireland. No advanced paramedic course has yet come on stream in the Republic; the only course in place for all ambulance staff is at the level of emergency medical technician. Nor are there any plans to develop a fully fledged paramedic service; the HSE plans *eventually* to train some 30 per cent of EMTs to this level.

However, international research shows that paramedics, advanced or otherwise, cannot be relied upon to save lives. Nor can emergency medical technicians, with perhaps a week's training in childbirth, be seriously expected to substitute safely for midwives whose university training now takes up to six years.

Over 6,000 people are believed to die every year in Britain unnecessarily as paramedics fail to save lives. In 2003, London's ambulance service failed to restart the hearts of 95 per cent of heart-attack victims, while in Staffordshire—ranked the country's best service— paramedics revived only 16 per cent of all cardiac-arrest patients.

It may be that some patients will die in transit who might other-
wise have lived, though I believe this group will be small.
Economist Peter West, a proponent of the *Hanly Report,*
confirming the existence of *an acceptable level of mortality* in
relation to plans to centralise urgent care hospital services.

To rely on even well-developed ambulance services as a substitute for
hospital A&E is to gamble with people's lives. Trauma victims attended by paramedics, for example, are far more likely to die than those
transported by traditional ambulance services, research shows. Dr
Tom Nolan told the Joint Oireachtas Committee that 'advanced life
support' was to be the 'bedrock' of the emergency services post-*Hanly:*
'It is touted that the availability of advanced life support at the scene
of major trauma will compensate for the extra distance the unfortunate patient will now have to travel to the nearest A&E.'

The available evidence, however, shows that patients receiving
advanced life support were two and a half times more likely to die
than those receiving basic life support in severe trauma cases.
Dr Tom Nolan on the greater risks faced by major trauma
victims attended by EMT-AS as compared with traditional
ambulance personnel providing basic life support only.

For acute coronaries, he said, time was 'no less critical' in that 'each
hour saved in initiating treatment can lead to a decrease of 1.6 deaths
per 1,000'. He concluded that providing bedrock emergency services
via advanced EMTs 'cannot compensate for the more distant siting of
A&E services'. 'Not enough cognisance is taken of Ireland's essentially
rural nature, both in terms of topography and demography. The
requirements of the royal colleges … have to be balanced with the
moral issue of inequity of patient access to services.'

Peadar McMahon underlined the price to be paid by non-urban
communities under *Hanly:*

There are economic losses—inward investment will evaporate from an area,
which does not have reasonable health services; manufacturing industries and
agricultural activity need A&E services within close range; insurance companies

will load premia or refuse to cover workers' liability, and community activities, such as festivals and developments; visitors will not want to stay for any length of time in an area where these health services are missing; it will not be an attractive place for young families to set up home or for the elderly to spend their declining years.

Community spirit is being eroded, he said. 'Close knit communities, where there is an abundance of family and neighbour support, are being forced to adopt a "survival of the fittest" attitude to life. The sacredness of life is being demeaned.' 'Our health service is losing its humanity,' he concluded. 'It is becoming a faceless corporation, where people have become numbers and statistics. "Bottom lines" are more important than human beings.'

Nevertheless, the ambulance services remain central to government plans for centralisation.

Discriminating against Women

Hanly carried a hidden gender dimension. All the evidence shows that the costs paid by women will be particularly high. Dr John Gallagher, then Chair of the Institute of Obstetricians and Gynaecologists, said that cutting maternity beds would put thousands of women's lives at risk, unless midwife-led services were put in their place.

Babies' lives will also be placed in jeopardy: the numbers of women giving birth en route to hospital will rise. Giving birth without professional help at the side of the road, in a car, a taxi, or an ambulance is not just a nightmare: it is a risk. Unplanned out-of-hospital births carry very high infant mortality rates, eight times higher than hospital birth.

Birth in those hospitals that remain will become even more industrialised: the hooks-and-hormones approach to labour will become even more common. As numbers rise in larger, more centralised units, more women will have their labours accelerated as midwives are forced to rush women through increasingly overcrowded labour wards to avoid bottlenecks. More women will have their labours induced, as doctors bring women into hospital for induction to avoid a roadside birth.

But oxytocin, used to induce and accelerate labour, can be a high-risk hormone: it has led to infant brain damage and fetal death; maternal deaths have also been reported in connection with its use, as well as multi-million euro awards for cerebral palsy babies.

Inductions carry their own particular hazards, prematurity being the main one. Premature babies are at greater risk than full-term infants of dying. Moreover, if you are having your first child, having an induction trebles your chances of having a Caesarean.

Mothers are nearly four times more likely to die following 'birth from above' than birth from below. In 1999, for example, two young mothers died following Caesarean section in Dublin maternity hospitals. Caesarean mothers are more likely to be ill after birth, suffering from chest, breast, wound, womb and urine infections. Babies are also in jeopardy: those born by Caesarean for no medical reason are twice as likely to die as those born vaginally. They are also more likely to be admitted to intensive care. Having a Caesarean section doubles the risk, in a subsequent pregnancy, of having a still-born baby, for no identifiable reason, in a full-term pregnancy. Caesarean surgery has also been shown to impact negatively on women's fertility levels. At St George's Hospital, London, the Caesarean hysterectomy rate has risen seven-fold in ten years, as doctors battle to stem life-threatening bleeding in mothers having their second, or subsequent, Caesarean.

Safety in Numbers?
Medical ambition now blocked a major artery in health: patient safety. But in the world of newspeak, things were turned inside out, as usual. The numbers game played by the royal colleges was dressed up as a safety issue. The main thrust of the *Hanly Report* was to make services less safe, yet it dined out on risk, relying on what it termed 'volumes–outcomes' research.

The report alleged that treatment outcomes were related to patient numbers, that bigger numbers were synonymous with better outcomes. If true, this would have been a good reason for shutting smaller hospitals. While—unlike *FitzGerald*—the report cited several pieces of volumes–outcomes research, it misapplied or misunderstood the studies it quoted, Dr Catherine McNamara found. In one case, the authors did not appear to have read the study they were quoting. In fact, there was *no* scientific evidence to support the notion that, as a general rule, bigger hospitals get better results. The research quoted by *Hanly* established no basis for the view that larger hospitals generally provided more effective care. Patient survival normally bore no relationship to the numbers treated.

Only five procedures showed a link between volumes and outcomes: surgery for cancer of the throat and pancreas; child heart surgery; surgery for an unruptured aneurism (haemorrhage) of a major blood vessel (the aorta) in the abdomen; and the treatment of AIDS. These procedures are not done on an emergency basis; nor are they usually carried out in smaller hospitals. Using them to make the case for closing A&E units is wrong.

What about volumes–outcomes in this country? Ireland's bigger hospitals could not and cannot prove that their results are better than those obtained in smaller hospitals. While individual researchers may do one-off studies, few statistics, if any, are kept routinely on the outcomes of hospital procedures. (The only exceptions to this rule are the Dublin maternity hospitals; and this is a legacy of history.)

Even Muiris FitzGerald admits that a generalist consultant 'delivery system' can 'competently' provide a lot of hospital services. As consultant physician Dr John Barton points out, a good clinician will get good results wherever he or she practises. Volume, of itself, cannot produce results, good or bad. The vast bulk of the work done in smaller hospitals like his own—Portiuncula in Ballinasloe, Co. Galway—is routine: pneumonia, heart failure, gall bladder disease, acute appendix, and so on. 'These common conditions account for 97 per cent of the top fifty medical and surgical conditions,' he says. 'There is no reason to suppose that other smaller hospitals are any different. The evidence that smaller hospitals actually get better results than larger units is growing.'

Later, upon reading that surgeons at the Mater Hospital had done a double lung transplant, it occurred to me that even this argument was being used selectively. No one had suggested, for instance, that such a complex operation as a double lung transplant—the first in Ireland—may have been unsafe, due to insufficient patients 'to hone and maintain skills on a lifetime basis'.

And who was looking for complex surgery to be done inappropriately in smaller hospitals? Although medical commentators, such as Simon Mills, caricaturised the demands of local communities in this way, no one was looking for brain surgery in Goleen. What hospital groups, such as Monaghan's Community Alliance, were demanding was continued access to basic hospital services: A&E and maternity care.

Economics

There was a final argument: economics. Muiris FitzGerald argued that beds lie vacant in smaller hospitals, that we are paying for cover not for care. But his vacant beds theory does not stand up. Take three of the hospitals he identified as being unviable: Mallow, Bantry and Nenagh. Department of Health figures for 2002 show that bed occupancy rates in these hospitals ranged from an overall 118 per cent in Bantry to 92 per cent in Mallow, while Nenagh had a whopping bed occupancy of 106 per cent. His 'economic and efficiency argument' does not stand up, either. Smaller hospitals are less costly to run. And, if you prioritise the principle of access, you reorganise the services accordingly. There is no reason why surgery and medicine cannot be organised in smaller hospitals to support 24/7 A&E. Then you are paying for care, not cover.

Competition is at the heart of the technocratic vision. FitzGerald sees the patient as the starting point for a brave new world in which hospitals would *compete* for patients: 'First comes the analysis of patient needs and then a projection of what is required to meet those needs.' But patient needs cannot be contained in a mathematical model. To reproduce the generalist model in multiple locations, he says, is to duplicate services. But duplication arises only if you treat the same person twice for the same condition. Smaller hospitals are not operating twice on the same leg. The nub of the matter, as Muiris FitzGerald has admitted, is that smaller hospitals 'waste' money that would otherwise be available for specialisation.

It really *is* all a question of priorities. As Chris Lyons, network chief of the HSE North Dublin, observed, 'It takes a population of 200,000 to properly sustain a small hospital'—as though a hospital were a medical fattening station, to be fed by the people living in its hinterland. In this topsy-turvy world, the patient exists to serve the hospital; and communities exist to provide the essential nutrients that medicine requires for its empires—the disorders and conditions that permit its specialties and sub-specialties to thrive.

A Builders' Bonanza?

Is hospital centralisation a builders' bonanza? Cutting accessible urgent care services ran completely counter to government plans to decentralise the public service, a plan, according to Fintan O'Toole, that made 'perfect sense … if you remember the Government's deep and abiding affection for the property industry …. The scope for private enrichment is massive.' O'Toole warned that a new form of local patronage had emerged, one that 'appeals vaguely to a broad swathe of the population and sharply to an insider elite'.

Decentralising the public services, he said, was a 'classic Fianna Fáil scheme': it was a 'huge bonanza for the real establishment, including the little inner circle of property developers that has a place next to the Government's heart'.

Could the same be true of government plans to centralise hospital health care? With vast new extensions needed to double or treble the capacity of those hospitals that remain post-Hanly, closing the country's specialist and second-level hospitals would certainly trigger a building boom. Moreover, a sea of hospitals coming onto the market at knock-down prices could be a developers' dream. Closing Dublin's single-specialty hospitals, for example, would release a tidal wave of extremely substantial properties in prime locations, in Hume Street and Temple Street, for example. The National Maternity Hospital overlooks Merrion Square, one of the prime sites in the city, while the Rotunda Hospital, one of Europe's oldest maternities, would make a perfect city-centre five-star hotel, rivalling the Victorian red-and-gold bricked splendour of the Eye and Ear Hospital in Adelaide Road.

The Government's plan to centralise our hospital services raises issues over the kind of society we are creating, and have created: the dominance of technocracy, the loss of social solidarity, the rise of a small, powerful, urban, academic elite that has driven a particular agenda in medicine for forty years, or 400, resulting in a massive loss of equity for town and country alike. We now have a health system that actively discriminates against local communities, their hospitals and their staff. Consultants there (and elsewhere) practise a less prestigious, less careerist and more community-oriented form of medicine. There *are* different strands in medicine, different views; only one is in the ascendancy. Today, the untrammelled rise of the biomedical or technocratic model of health has all but snuffed out the flickering social model. With primary and community health systematically starved in recent decades, local communities are doubly in jeopardy.

Chapter 10

War

The medical imperatives must take precedence over community and political interests.

Dr Finbarr Lennon, consultant surgeon at the Lourdes Hospital, and medical adviser to the health board, on the need to close two of the region's maternity units, in a letter to Dr Jim Kiely, Chief Medical Officer at the Department of Health

IMPERIAL STRATEGIES

Centralisation has been at the core of the professional project in medicine for many decades. Since the 1930s, at least, the profession has tried to enlist the state in this endeavour. The state has always had its own interest in centralisation: it is a project that meets both bureaucratic and professional needs in roughly equal measure. In fact, so successful has the partnership been in recent years between organised medicine and the state that it is easier to treat them as an entity; while they have had their disagreements, they are now, at least temporarily, united on a single issue.

Manufacturing Consent

Expert groups

Central to strategic management in a 'modern democracy' is the manufacturing of consent. Consumer surveys, for instance, are a valuable latter-day tool, as we saw earlier, when, in true Alice-in-Wonderland style, mothers were interviewed about hospital maternity services that, unknown to them, were about to be pulled.

One of the first strategies to be employed by government in the manufacture of consent was the setting up of 'expert groups'. Organising 'independent' experts to devise recommendations in line with decisions already taken has become almost obligatory. These groups may be paid, as in the case of Teamwork, or unpaid, as in the case of *Hanly*. (Both of these groups, incidentally, made the same core recommendation; so both, clearly, worked off the same hymn-sheet.) The externality of these groups vis-à-vis government and the state is presented—and reported in the media—as 'independence': they give a veneer of objectivity to proposals that might otherwise be unpalatable, a gloss of expertise to decisions that might otherwise be challenged. Paid or unpaid, these groups offer unlimited potential for spin.

No firm hired by government is independent, by definition. Management consultants are never given a brief to devise whatever policies they please. How could they? If you are hired to write a policy document, the bones of that policy will generally be agreed in advance and you will deliver the product to that specification. Modern democracies work increasingly through manipulating voters. Employing external management consultants such as Teamwork has become the norm, particularly in health where the bill for such 'advice' runs into the hundreds of millions. In addition to a semblance of impartiality, these firms provide a convenient scapegoat, so that, when the backlash comes, governments can beat a hasty retreat, avoid taking responsibility for their actions and blame the 'independent' consultants.

One of the first expert groups of any consequence in health in this country was the 'consultative council' that produced the *FitzGerald Report*. Appointed by Health Minister Sean Flanagan, the council consisted solely of medical men; all were hospital consultants, and most were from Dublin, the power base of the voluntary hospitals. As a leading surgeon in a Dublin voluntary hospital and a professor of surgery at UCD, Patrick FitzGerald represented the main drivers of centralisation: the colleges, and in particular, the RCSI, the university medical faculties, and, last but never least, the private non-profit hospitals.

Official reports prefigured each other uncannily. A 1990s Comhairle report actually foreshadows the Government's 2006 decision to centralise services for children into one giant facility. In 1994, the Faculty of Paediatrics had proposed that there should be only one national children's hospital for the entire country. As you might expect, Comhairle endorsed the College's opinion. Tellingly, in an open acknowledgement of the strategic side of its job-creation programme, the 1994 report on paediatric services urged Comhairle to bear in mind the goal of a single hospital when devising future consultant appointments.

The year before, yet another expert report, the 1993 *Tierney Report* on medical manpower, also reiterated the FitzGerald gospel. Tierney was a joint production between Comhairle na n-Ospidéal, the Medical and Dental Board and the Department of Health. One year later, the Department produced a health strategy that was warmly welcomed by Comhairle. The strategy was peppered with buzzwords, such as 'self-sufficiency', 'coordinated network', 'complementary grouping', 'larger regional hospitals', 'specialised tertiary or supra-regional units' and 'catchment areas'. The document prefigured *Hanly* most presciently.

By now, medical manpower had become one of the defining pre-occupations. The next leading actor to appear on the stage was the Forum on Medical Manpower. An all-male quango, it was set up by Minister Micheál Martin in May 1998, ignoring government guidelines on gender mainstreaming (requiring 40 per cent of seats on government bodies to be allocated to the other half of mankind). While the term 'forum' suggested openness, transparency, civic society, even democracy, this particular forum was little more than a vehicle for consultant power. Nine of its fourteen members were doctors; the remaining five were bureaucrats. Behind the serried ranks of Comhairle na n-Ospidéal (represented by HSE CEO Brendan Drumm), the Medical Council, the Irish Hospital Consultants' Association, the Royal College of Surgeons and the Royal College of Physicians stood the voluntary hospitals.

The task force on medical manpower that followed the forum was chaired by David Hanly, then managing director of Parc, which had staffed a private hospital in Baghdad at the time of the first war involving Iraq. One of the top 1,000 Irish companies, Parc recruits for a wide range of industries, including construction, engineering and pharmaceuticals. A much bigger body than the forum, the task force consisted of fifty-two individuals, the majority of whom were doctors: the rest were mostly bureaucrats. With nineteen out of the fifty-two seats—around 40 per cent of the vote—consultants, as usual, got the lion's share. Health-service users, citizens and patients, were excluded, as usual. The sole 'representative of the public interest' was Senator Geraldine Feeney, a member of Fianna Fáil's Committee of 15. While David Hanly was invariably presented as an 'independent chairperson', his independence must, to some degree, have been open to question. He had chaired Comhairle na n-Ospidéal from 1989 to 1992, for example. (One of his colleagues there was none other than Muiris FitzGerald.) Moreover, as an 'inducted' member of the Royal College of Surgeons court of patrons since 1997, Hanly belonged to a select group of individuals that included Bernard McNamara of Michael McNamara (Builders), auctioneer John Finnegan and Michael Smurfit. He also served on the College's development committee for some years, so it seems reasonable to assume that he was both familiar with, and supportive of, the College's agenda. Sitting beside David Hanly on the task force was Arthur Tanner, Dean of Post-graduate Studies at the College of Surgeons.

MULTIPLE HAT-WEARING

While individual consultants may feel powerless to influence national health policy, as a body, they have considerable clout, through their membership of bodies, such as the Royal College of Surgeons; the former hospital regulator that was Comhairle; unions, such as the Irish Hospital Consultants' Association; and, last but not least, the Medical Council. Add to these myriad local and national advisory and executive groups, boards, committees, medical advisers (Department of Health), and medical executives (HSE), and you get the kinds of interlocking spirals of consultant power that come from overlapping membership and multiple hat-wearing.

Like the maternity unit in Dundalk Hospital, the Monaghan service was 'suspended' on 28 February 2001. The focus was on Monaghan. The closure of the unit made an interesting study in power politics, offering a rare glimpse of the balance of power between representative regional boards and national consultant bodies, between local communities and medical professionals. Hospital insurers were scapegoated for the closures, a fiction carried in the media as 'fact'. Nothing could have been further from the truth.

A blizzard of letters on file in the health board revealed just how the maternity units were closed:

16 March 2000: The goalposts are set for 'viability'. In a letter to Comhairle CEO Tommie Martin (now a member of Brendan Drumm's 'politburo'), Professor John Bonnar, then Chair of the Institute of Obstetricians and Gynaecologists (IOG), sets out the Institute's plan: it divides hospitals into a hierarchy of specialisation, not unlike a lift in a low-rise building. The ground floor (level 1) is a midwife-led unit, while the top floor (level 3) is a specialist obstetric unit. The bar is now set at three obstetricians or none: each unit is required to have 1,000 births annually for obstetricians to maintain their skills and train their successors, with each obstetrician supervising 300–500 women. Bonnar rejects the notion of 'geographic linkage'—small units forming larger units to meet the numbers requirement: each obstetrician, paediatrician and anaesthetist should be available within thirty minutes and this would not be possible in units that are distant from one another.

20 March 2000: Four days later, Dr Alphonsus Kennedy, consultant obstetrician at Monaghan Hospital, proposes that, in future, no 'patient' in her first pregnancy should be offered 'confinement facilities' unless permanent on-site neonatal paediatric services are made available. The letter, addressed to Dr Ambrose McLoughlin (who combines the role of NEHB deputy CEO with that of hospital programme manager), is referred to Dermot Condon, a former Secretary-General at the Department of Heath, now chairing a maternity services review commissioned by the health board in 1998, following the adoption of a five-year plan that provided for new maternity units in Monaghan and Dundalk.

27 April 2000: The axe falls on Monaghan's maternity unit. John Bonnar indicates to Dr Kennedy that 'a unit with a low number of births such as 335 per annum is below the level of a viable unit ... I would hope therefore that the hospital would agree to a Midwifery Led Unit for women who fulfil the agreed criteria.'

25 May 2000: Monaghan hospital anaesthetists insist on having a third trainee obstetrician present in theatre, lest a Caesarean baby need resuscitation. Alphonsus Kennedy applies to Tommy Coyle, the hospital's administrator, for a fourth non-consultant hospital doctor.

20 July 2000: For the second time, three paediatricians from the Lourdes Hospital complain to health board CEO Paul Robinson about the 'continuing NEHB practice of allowing infants to be born in Dundalk and Monaghan Hospitals where there is no on-site paediatric cover'. The doctors complain that three babies on ventilators at the hospital three days previously had been born without paediatricians being present. (The unit's own figures, however, showed that paediatric cover does not reduce admission to intensive care: in 1999, of the 647 babies admitted to ICU in the Lourdes, 605 were born at the hospital.)

4 August 2000: Dermot Condon informs Paul Robinson that the review group has contracted Lansdowne to do a survey of maternity service users.

23 August 2000: The IOG Chair advises the NEHB CEO, in effect, to terminate two of the region's maternity services. Bonnar's letter, a re-run of one sent to Comhairle five months earlier, ends with an extraordinarily confident statement: 'I am assured that these recommendations have the full support of the Department of Health and Children and I trust you will implement them without delay.'

29 August 2000: Paul Robinson assures John Bonnar that 'concern for safe maternity systems is high on our priorities'. The IOG Chair had underlined the need for consultants to adhere to a 'safe work roster'.

24 November 2000: Finbarr Lennon, a consultant surgeon at the Lourdes Hospital, welcomes the newly published *Condon Report*: it recommends closing the two maternity units immediately, and suggests a pilot midwifery unit for Dundalk but, inexplicably, none for Monaghan. Lennon, who acts as a medical adviser to the health board, tells the CEO that 'significant components' of the maternity services in Monaghan and Dundalk are 'inherently unsafe'. 'The protective protocols and procedures now operating in both units are unable to cope and are unreliable'. He evokes the long shadow of litigation: doctors and nurses, already vulnerable, are 'further exposed' by knowing that the 'full weight' of the professional advice is that 'units such as those in Monaghan and Dundalk are no longer able to maintain a safe quality service'. The health board does not apparently investigate the very serious allegations made by Mr Lennon.

27 November 2000: The Board decides not to accept the Condon recommendations in full and sets up a further review of maternity services in the north-east (the Kinder Review).

6 December 2000: Finbarr Lennon vents his 'very serious concerns' about the continuing delivery of maternity services in Monaghan and Dundalk to Dr Jim Kiely, chief medical officer at the Department of Health. He repeats his earlier allegations, but does not explain how the units became so suddenly 'unsafe' nor how management could have allowed such alleged breaches of safety to occur. He concludes: 'Both units are now unsafe. I have advised the relevant medical insurance companies including my own …. *The medical imperatives must take precedence over community and political interests* [emphasis added].' The Department does not apparently investigate these very serious allegations, either.

14 December 2000: Dr Kennedy puts Robinson on notice that he will hold the Board liable in full 'for anything untoward devolving on any patient' arising from the Board's failure to implement the Condon recommendations. Finbarr Lennon forwards the Monaghan obstetrician's letter to the hospitals' insurers (Irish Public Bodies) and to a solicitors' firm (Hanby).

22 December 2000: Who would be liable for an adverse event now becomes an issue. Dr Kennedy repeats his warning that the Board must 'accept responsibility for adverse events', if they continue with 'deliveries' at Monaghan Hospital. In the light of Condon, he feels unable to provide a 'safe level' of service. No deliveries should take place there, he says, until a paediatric neonatal service is in place. Dr McLoughlin replies that it is not acceptable for Dr Kennedy to treat patients and 'seek to have the Board held liable'. 'If you believe that for any reason you cannot treat patients you should not do so, but as long as you do so you must carry full responsibility.' (A copy of this letter is sent to Irish Public Bodies).

In a letter to Dr McLoughlin, Irish Public Bodies liability manager Pat O'Loughlin observes that the Condon recommendations are 'influenced greatly by the current complement of medical personnel and the birth rate in each area', not by the 'clinical effectiveness' of the four facilities in the past.

28 December 2000: The Board's legal powers now seem set to be over-ridden: the Department of Health's Dr Jim Kiely advises Paul Robinson that 'certain, appropriate, interim measures' may need to be taken *in advance* of the Board meeting to discuss the suspension of the maternity units. Only health boards had the legal power to discontinue, suspend or transfer a health service.

3 January 2001: The operating theatre at Monaghan Hospital closes 'on a temporary basis'. Ambrose McLoughlin reminds Dr Kennedy that he was party to the decisions to restrict surgical and gynaecological services at Monaghan. Dr Kennedy subsequently writes to all GPs, telling them he can see no future for the unit, unless the paediatric 'situation' can be rectified.

5 January 2001: Paul Robinson reminds the Department of Health's chief medical adviser that the Board has a 'statutory function in relation to the transfer or cessation of services'.

17 January 2001: For the third time, Dr Kennedy reiterates his view that the Board must accept 'full responsibility' for 'anything untoward' that happens as a result of continuing maternity services at Monaghan. Medical views on this are 'wholly uniform,' he observes.

Dr Kennedy and a consultant obstetrician from Dundalk, Dr Fallon, accompanied by the IHCA 's Donal Duffy, meet Finbarr Lennon. Both write to CEO Paul Robinson. Lennon requires that 'immediate interim arrangements' be put in place; Duffy demands 'immediate contingency plans' 'for prospective patients'. 'Maintenance of the status quo is not an option,' the IHCA deputy secretary declares. 'The two units in question are unique in the British Isles [sic] in that they are the only units dependent on the services of a single obstetrician/gynaecologist. They are also deficient in that they do not have 24-hour paediatric cover.'

18 January 2001: Mr Kennedy asks Ambrose McLoughlin to confirm that he, McLoughlin, 'would prefer that the Maternity Units of Monaghan and Dundalk be closed in synergy'; Dr McLoughlin denies this.

19 January 2001: Acting on the reservations and concerns expressed by both obstetricians, the Board's medical adviser and the IHCA, the

insurer gives NEHB until the end of February to implement 'appropriate interim measures' at both maternity units. Without these, Pat
O'Loughlin tells Paul Robinson, Irish Public Bodies will be unable to
continue to provide cover.

22 January 2001: The Board refuses to agree to the CEO 's proposal to
suspend obstetric services immediately at Monaghan and Dundalk
Hospitals.

23 January 2001: The consultants' union attempts to force the
immediate suspension of both maternity services: Donal Duffy
demands that all first-time antenatal 'attendees', all mothers due
within two weeks, and all high-risk mothers be referred 'onward' from
Dundalk and Monaghan. All 'other lower risk return attendees'
[women who are already mothers] should expect 'contingency plans'
for their 'confinement', which 'will take place in Drogheda or Cavan'.
Mr Duffy concludes: 'Regrettably, delaying until after the Board
meeting on Monday is not acceptable, as many patients will be seen
before then.' Robinson reminds him that suspending services is a
reserved function of the Board.

5 February 2001: The Minister intervenes, following the Board's
decision to seek approval for the appointment of five temporary consultant obstetricians and paediatricians to Monaghan and Dundalk.
Minister Micheál Martin warns the Chair, Dr Hugh Dolan, that, in
order to 'utilise' the NDP funding [£160 million] 'notified' to the Board
for capital developments, the Board should 'finalise a clear view' on
the services to be provided at each hospital.

6 February 2001: Donal Duffy fulminates at the 'total dereliction of duty'
by Board members, who 'for the fourth time totally failed to make any
contingency arrangements for expectant mothers at both units'. Without
Comhairle's approval, Duffy asserts, it would be illegal to proceed with
a consultant appointment. If the new posts are approved, this will
mean cuts in existing services: Board members will be responsible for
any ensuing deaths or injuries. He informs Paul Robinson that, if the
insurers withdraw cover, service at both sites should be wound down.
    Having discussed the matter with Dr John Bonnar, Dr Finbarr
Lennon advises Doctors Kennedy and Fallon to suspend delivery of

obstetric services immediately. He notes that the 'cumulative and consistent advice' he has got from all medical professionals, including themselves, is that there is 'a significant safety risk to mothers and infants'. (The letter is copied to Irish Public Bodies.)

7 February 2001: The insurer finally announces that it will withdraw cover from both maternity units as and from 1 March. 'The situation as presented here leaves us no room for manoeuvre,' Pat O'Loughlin underlines. 'In the light of the information available it would be clearly imprudent for us to continue to provide cover.'

8 February 2001: Cavan's obstetricians, paediatricians, anaesthetists and pathologists maintain that the Board's decision to maintain consultant-led services in Monaghan and Dundalk raises a 'raft of safety issues', notably the question of a 'critical mass' of deliveries. Their concern is that there is the capacity 'for only one viable unit in the area, irrespective of where that unit is located. The development of maternity services in Monaghan will have the effect of reducing deliveries in Cavan by probably 100 to 200 per annum'. (The letter addressed to Robinson, and signed by eight consultants, is copied to all the leading actors.)

John Bonnar also writes to Finbarr Lennon: 'The Institute of Obstetricians and Gynaecologists fully supports the decision to suspend consultant obstetric services in Monaghan and Dundalk and this decision is based upon the protection and safety of both mothers and infants.'

12 February 2001: The Faculty of Paediatrics, which, like its brother corporation, the Institute of Obstetricians and Gynaecologists, is a subsidiary of the Royal College of Physicians in Kildare Street, now raises the bar to 1,500 births annually: 'all other obstetric units should close.' Professor Tom Clarke, Dean of the Faculty, warns Paul Robinson that 'paediatricians should not be appointed in an attempt to keep open non-viable consultant-led maternity units, where the number of births will remain too few'.

13 February 2001: The Department of Health says it 'will not object' to Paul Robinson's submission to Comhairle na n-Ospidéal requesting the appointment of temporary consultants to both Monaghan and Dundalk Hospitals.

21 February 2001: *Half the mothers living in County Monaghan have their baby outside the county due to lack of paediatric services. If the services were in place, most of these mothers would have their baby in the local hospital.... In the past four months there has been frost practically every night sometimes with freezing fog and occasional snow.... Consultants and senior administrative staff consider it too dangerous to make the journey from Cavan to Monaghan. Therefore it is unreasonable to expect mothers in labour or haemorrhaging to be driven not just from Monaghan Town to Cavan but sometimes ten to fifteen miles beyond Monaghan.*

Extract from minutes of a meeting sent by Dr Rory O'Hanlon, a former Minister for Health (now Ceann Comhairle) to Paul Robinson

3 April 2001: The Faculty of Paediatrics, a sister faculty of the Institute of Obstetrics and Gynaecology which closed the maternity units in Monaghan and Dundalk, welcomes the termination of obstetric services in both hospitals.

OUTSIDE THE LOOP

Barry Desmond had tried unsuccessfully to close the maternity unit in 1984 on Comhairle's advice. 'They were totally opposed to single-handed units like Monaghan,' he recalled, forgetting, perhaps, that the single-handedness of these departments was down to Comhairle itself. Fourteen years later, the drive to close the unit was unabated. In 1998, the Board drew up a five-year plan including new maternity units for Monaghan and Dundalk. Management had other ideas. It commissioned a review. In addition to its chair, former secretary of the Department of Health, the review group consisted of just two consultant obstetricians and one nurse consultant; not a midwife or a mother in sight. Its report faithfully reflected the views of the Institute of Obstetricians and Gynaecologists. The group actually commissioned a 'consumer survey' from Lansdowne in response to pressure from the NEHB for local consultation. Exercises in consultation have become part of modern management. Condon group secretary Antoinette Doocey later admitted that those interviewed had not been told that two of the region's maternity units were scheduled to close.

Condon recommended the immediate 'suspension' of the maternity units at Monaghan and Dundalk. Warmly welcomed by management, the proposal was rejected by Board members. Yet another review was commissioned, headed by health administrator Patrick Kinder, with John Bonnar representing the Institute of Obstetricians and Gynaecologists. In October 2001, *Kinder* proposed the 'phased opening' of midwife-led maternity units in Monaghan and Dundalk. But, as Jimmy Livingstone, Bronagh's grandfather, later pointed out, it would be 2011, at least, by the time these midwife-led units had been piloted. These units had to be shown to be successful *before* similar services could be granted to Monaghan and Dundalk. The need for piloting was questionable; however, by then, there was a mountain of research on the safety of midwife-led units, as a letter from Montreal University later testified:

Montréal, 17 March 2003

To whom it may concern.

I would like to voice my opposition to the planned closure of over 50 per cent of Ireland's maternity units. Here in Quebec (Canada), seven free-standing birth centers—not attached to hospitals—were opened in the 1990s. Up to 250 births a year have taken place in these birth centers since 1994, under the supervision of midwives. Researchers from 3 universities evaluated these projects, and following this review, the Quebec Government decided in 1999 to legalize the profession of midwifery, and to authorize these birth centers to continue welcoming childbearing women.

There are also many small maternity units in Quebec that the Government is committed to maintaining. Some have as [few] as 500 births a year, and others 1,000. Maternity services have to be accessible to women close to their homes. Large maternity units run the risk of becoming 'baby factories' where women are treated as if they were on a production line, in a factory, as several social science studies have shown (Corea, 1985; Davis-Floyd, 1992; Martin, 1992). Bigger does not necessarily mean better. It means that things in such units tend to be organized for efficiency purposes, and not necessarily for the welfare of mothers and babies. One cannot treat health as though it were a commodity. The birth of a baby and of a family, the way it happens, the environment in which it happens, may have incalculable consequences for the welfare and health of all family members.

Women need to be able to choose the place of birth. If they choose to
have a baby in a maternity hospital or unit, then the hospital or unit has
to be located in or not far from the community where they live.

Hélène Vadeboncoeur
Ph.D. Applied Social Sciences, Université de Montréal

The death of baby Bronagh Livingstone on 11 December 2002 caused
a national outcry. Three days later, Micheál Martin, then Minister for
Health, commissioned former top civil servant Kevin Bonner to draw
up proposals to resolve the service and management issues at
Monaghan General Hospital. Bonner subsequently endorsed the
Kinder recommendation.

Crushing the Competition

The real reason for the recommended piloting now came clearly into
view. Comhairle now declared its opposition to these services, claiming that the nursing and midwifery council was 'not in favour' of
stand-alone midwifery units—a claim the council later rejected.
Comhairle seemed quite clearly oblivious to the fact that obstetric
supervision had failed spectacularly to prevent two of the biggest
medical scandals in the history of the state, the Lourdes Caesarean
hysterectomies and the religious revival of symphysiotomy.

Meanwhile, the long, slow process of closing units went on apace.
Strategic management was the order of the day. The drill involved in
closing an obstetric service goes like this: first, select your unit; then
carry out an inspection to assess the training it provides; and, finally,
write a damning report, shaking public confidence in the unit by
stressing the risk to public safety, particularly to unborn babies.

In 2003, the Institute of Obstetricians and Gynaecologists (IOG)
claimed that premature babies were 'at risk' in the only surviving
maternity unit in the former Midland Health Board Region, in
Mullingar Hospital; a question mark now hung over the unit's future.
The Institute's report castigated what it called an 'absence of cohesion'
between the hospital and Dublin maternity hospitals. (Defined as 'the
act or condition of sticking together' or, alternatively, 'a tendency to
cohere', cohesion is a gloriously imprecise word.) Alleging that there
was a 'huge problem' in relation to the transfer of babies from
Mullingar to the Dublin maternity hospitals, the report claimed that

there was 'no integrated scheme for neonatal and *in utero* transfers between Level II and Level III hospitals'. (While an *in utero* transfer might sound like an express delivery of a brown paper parcel containing a neonate, this was actually a reference to the transfer of the neonate's mother, the baby carrier containing the neonate.) Furthermore, the report went on, ominously, there was 'no formal structure or protocol' governing the delivery of maternity services in either of the Board's two maternity units. Both were operating as Level II units, and there was no formal structure or protocol governing 'this type of service'. The report then claimed that there was 'no cohesion' between Level II and Level III units, and concluded that this posed 'considerable risk for patients and particularly premature neonates'. Broadening the single issue of patient transfer into the much more complex area of hospital management, the report then launched an all-out offensive on the entire organisation of acute hospital services in the region, damning them because they were all second-level hospitals. Centralisation swam into view. And not only for maternity services.

A Final Solution
This required an entirely new approach, nationally, to the running of our health services. In October 2001, UCD's dean of medicine, Muiris Fitzgerald, urged that politics should be 'removed' from decisions on hospital location. Local communities—and all communities are local—and their elected representatives should no longer be involved in decision-making on hospital health care. Health policies, he said, needed to be 'politics-proofed' against parochialism. The assumption here, of course, and it is one that peppers pronouncements from medicine's high priests, is that medical politics is not politics at all. (Perhaps it is theology, the theology of professionalisation.)

Was the proposal to axe the health boards a Final Solution to the problem of troublesome elected representatives on health boards such as NEHB? A pre-emptive strike to pave the way for the axing of urgent care services in smaller hospitals across the country? Some medical consultants publicly welcomed the proposal to abolish health boards. They could no longer be allowed to stand in the way of consultant bodies' plans for giant hospitals. Consultants had been looking for a cut in the number of health boards for years; health boards offered the only countervailing force there was to the might of the medical empire. Now, with the setting up of the Health Service Executive, they were to be abolished forever. The NEHB saga was a learning curve the medical profession was determined not to repeat.

A PACK OF CARDS

Once again, Monaghan illustrates a strategic approach that can be applied to other areas: stripping out maternity services is key to downgrading an entire hospital, a maternity services forum heard on 21 June 2001. Without a maternity unit, there is no work for paediatricians, therefore paediatric services go. Without the epidurals and general anaesthetics needed for obstetrics and gynaecology, there is less work for anaesthetists. With fewer anaesthetists to staff operating theatres, casualty services and general surgery need to be scaled down.

Sooner or later, one of the colleges will decide that numbers are insufficient to allow them to continue to accredit the hospital for training. It was the College of Anaesthetists that first withdrew recognition from Monaghan General Hospital, for example. Or there may be a call for urgent surgery to be restored at the hospital, as there was in Monaghan. On 29 September 2005, five surgeons at Cavan General called for Monaghan General to be put back on call for surgical emergencies. HSE and hospital management immediately rejected this idea; the Royal College of Surgeons declared that it would be 'bad practice'.

Then the inexorable winding down of services begins again until you are left with the prospect of a treatment room staffed by a nurse practitioner or two—if any can be found to take on such a thankless role. Thus it is with Monaghan Hospital, which was finally put back on call, for medical emergencies, on 6 January 2005, after seventeen people had died needlessly, in the view of many.

'Selective elective' surgery—lumps and bumps—was also to be provided by a surgeon who would travel out and back from Cavan to Monaghan from Monday to Friday. (As it transpired, the surgical day was a short one: it began at nine, or shortly thereafter, and finished at three, just to make absolutely sure that no patient was still sitting around at five in the evening after his ingrown toenail had been removed.) This was the plan for the new state-of-the-art theatre at Monaghan General.

But A&E requires emergency surgery as well as emergency medicine. Dr John Barton gives the example of a patient admitted to hospital with an acute appendix on the point of rupturing: 'That patient needs immediate surgery to save his life. Any condition where the patient is threatened with massive septicaemia is potentially life-threatening,' he explains. 'These patients need to be operated on as soon as possible, not transferred to another hospital an hour's drive away or more. Emergency medical technicians cannot prevent systemic blood poisoning that may be lethal.'

Grist to the Mill

Whether acute medicine could safely be provided in Monaghan General in the absence of acute surgery was a moot point. It was a model of care to be found nowhere else in the Republic, the HSE admitted. Downpatrick Hospital—another casualty of the centralisation agenda—provides emergency medical services but not acute surgical services. But staff there do not recommend it as a model: they dread the day they urgently need to transfer a patient and the Royal Hospital, Belfast, is unable to accept the transfer because it has no bed.

The appalling vista—a needless death in a hospital that provided emergency medicine but not emergency surgery—materialised.

Pat Joe Walsh (75) died in Monaghan General on 14 October 2005, after hospital staff had failed in their efforts to transfer him for emergency surgery to stem a bleeding duodenal ulcer. During the night, three hospitals refused to accept the patient, the Lourdes (from which he had been discharged hours earlier, having had surgery for a hip replacement), Cavan (which was barred from doing the type of operation he needed) and Beaumont. Health board protocols prohibited emergency surgery at Monaghan General.

This tragedy then became grist to the mill of centralisation.

The 'independent' report into his death—the *Carey Report*—was drawn up by two surgeons, one a consultant in a large city teaching hospital, the other a professor of surgery. Its lead author was a nominee of the Royal College of Surgeons, a body with a mission to remove in-patient surgery from smaller hospitals such as Monaghan's. Clinicians were blamed for the consequences of decisions taken by managers. Bureaucracy was protected. The authors castigated surgical colleagues, particularly the consultant on duty in Monaghan General at the time, ignoring the fact that hospital staffing—and HSE protocols—had made it impossible to carry out even life-saving surgery in an emergency. The report ignored the fundamental fact that, if emergency surgery had not been withdrawn from Monaghan General, this was a life that might well have been saved. Pat Jo Walsh was a victim of the decision—impelled in part by the RCSI itself—to end emergency surgery at the hospital.

There seemed to be only two solutions, on the face of it, to the problem. One—the restoration of emergency surgery—the RCSI was not prepared to countenance. The other—the one promulgated by the report—was to end emergency medicine. The authors duly declared that providing urgent care medicine in the absence of emergency surgery was 'unsafe and unsustainable'. Their message? That in order to save lives, the hospital must be terminated, in effect. Research showed, however, that if lives were to be saved, the community needed its casualty unit. The solution lay not in removing the hospital's acute medical services, but in restoring its urgent care surgery.

The authors—noticeably exceeding their brief—recommended terminating *all* acute in-patient services not just in Monaghan, but also in Cavan, Navan and Dundalk, as soon as possible. *Carey* seemed unable to recognise that local hospitals provide an essential public service for their communities. The surgeons' concern was that highly skilled consultant staff in specialties that are scarce nationally, such as radiology, surgery and anaesthetics, were being wasted in hospitals such as Monaghan General, a view very similar to that of Muiris FitzGerald. In the technocratic scale of things, the monaghans, as they have been called, simply do not matter.

In a proposal that would give a publicly unelected and wholly unaccountable body an executive role in the management of public hospital services in the region, the report also recommended that the College's Dean of Surgical Affairs, Arthur Tanner, should take over from the lead surgeon in Cavan General.

Publication was delayed until 18 May 2006, the day Mary Harney stepped down as leader of the Progressive Democrats. Cunningly, the HSE published the *Carey Report* an hour before the Tánaiste made her bombshell announcement. This served to distract attention from the more damaging features of the review of Mr Walsh's death—described by one newspaper as an 'atrocity'. Family members, profoundly distressed at the circumstances of his death, found the doublespeak incomprehensible.

Teamwork

And, just to ensure that no stone was left unturned in the drive towards centralisation, the HSE had previously engaged a consultancy firm—later revealed to be Teamwork—to 'advise' on the 'configuration' of hospital services in the North East. (The Teamwork report is one of thirty-three 'independent' reports commissioned for the North East from 2002 to 2006.)

The firm has masterminded a number of public–private partnerships in Britain. Teamwork's 'clinical redesign projects' typically involve 'clinician to clinician interviews', as well as those most manipulative of all modern management tools, 'group work' and 'facilitated workshops'. In the North East, however, the company departed from these stratagems, claiming that, because it was not based on consultation with 'stakeholders', the report was therefore 'independent'.

The cover shows a sunflower waving about under photos of landscapes, of healthy families cycling together happily, of redbrick town houses. Chill, the message is: life is good. Inside is a dense forest of newspeak, where jargon and repetition intertwine so sinuously that only the most dedicated and patient reader could penetrate the thicket of language. 'Best practice' is repeatedly invoked. We now have best practice cycles (no, not the Tour de France). Best practice is 'about people', 'not about bricks and mortar'; it is a process, a catalyst: it is dynamic. In one of the very few readily intelligible sentences in the entire report, *Teamwork* spells out the new dynamic: 'no provision of acute critical care of any nature at the local level'. In a remarkable meeting of minds—had they worked off the same hymn-sheet? you wonder—*Teamwork* now proposed exactly what *FitzGerald, Hanly* and, latterly, *Carey* had recommended: terminating all urgent care in-patient services in the region's smaller hospitals. *Teamwork*, additionally, advocated building a brand-new hypermarket hospital somewhere in the southern part of the North-Eastern region.

Teamwork was *Hanly* plus privatisation. Its blueprint, unveiled on 14 June 2006, went significantly further than any of its predecessors, however. The expertise of Teamwork lay in bed-cutting, apparently, particularly in the public sector; the firm consists mainly of accountants, and, according to itself, has played a leading role in reshaping the NHS. Teamwork proposed an entirely new way of looking at hospital health care, dividing the services into 'clinical networks' that corresponded to markets long identified by for-profit corporations as profitable (or unprofitable). These are: (high-profit) planned care, radiology, pathology and chronic disease management, and (high-cost) A&E and intensive care. In segmenting the services in this way, Teamwork was preparing to turn health care into a market, unbundling and separating hospital services, like track from train. Few noticed.

The HSE duly accepted the Teamwork template and said that it would form a blueprint for the rest of the country. Blueprint or not, the British master strategists have recently been engaged to undertake yet another 'review' of services, this time in the Mid-West. Their report is due at the end of 2007. Meanwhile, in the North East, yet another steering group—this time headed by a Dublin surgeon, Eilis McGovern—was set up to implement Teamwork's recommendations.

II THE SERFS' REVOLT
Mobilising the Troops

Local resistance to the maternity closures in Monaghan and Dundalk was extremely high. There were protests, petitions, meetings and marches. Over 75,000 people signed a petition in both counties demanding that their maternity units be retained. Communities in those areas where hospitals were, and are, slated to close began to mobilise. One of the most vocal and powerful of these groups was the Monaghan Community Alliance, formed in May 2002; its sustained and imaginative campaign of public pressure has inspired many who face the same appalling prospect of needless suffering and avoidable deaths in their own communities. The issue, and it is one of equity, is a national one. In Clare, for example, in November 2003, over 25,000 people—representing every social, industrial, economic, sports, cultural, farming, union and political group in the county—turned out to demonstrate in the square in Ennis against government plans to shut the hospital's casualty unit. Urban communities are also threatened by these plans. In Loughlinstown in South Dublin, for example, Labour Party Councillor Bernie O'Halloran collected over 100,000 signatures from people living in the catchment area of Loughlinstown Hospital, which, like many others, is slated to lose its A&E services.

National health advocacy groups joined the battle. In Dublin, the National Birth Alliance—made up of parents and professionals—took to the streets in April 2003, to protest against plans to close maternity units. Up to 600 mothers, babies and buggies turned out for the protest. Bronagh Livingstone's mother, Denise, whose plight had shocked the nation, MEP Kathy Sinnott, Monaghan TDs Paudge Connolly and Caoimhghín Ó Caoláin, Wicklow Councillor Deirdre de Búrca and INO representative Deirdre Daly were among those who addressed the Merrion Square rally. If the government cuts went through as planned, the rally heard, up to half the country's maternity facilities would close.

In 2004, another national movement emerged, the Health Services Action Group (HSAG), to campaign against government plans centralising all in-patient services in just ten or twelve hypermarket hospitals. Twelve hospital action groups attended a mass meeting in Port Laoise in May: Monaghan Community Alliance leader Peadar McMahon was elected chair of the new coalition. HSAG and its affiliates have succeeded in raising public awareness around these issues, campaigning tirelessly on the issues of centralisation and privatisation, both now intertwined as a matter of strategy as well as policy. One message HSAG sought to get across was that, despite any appearances to the contrary—despite the chimera conjured by PR firms hired to manipulate the media—implementing the Hanly/Teamwork template remained, and remains, the unrelenting focus of both the Government and the medical establishment.

Successful HSAG projects have included a seminar for Dáil deputies and senators on centralisation; a presentation to the Joint Oireachtas Committee on Health, also underlining the dangers of centralisation; national conferences highlighting the risks posed by privatisation; letters to the press—one signed by up to eighteen affiliates nationwide; talks and lectures to various groups; and a constant stream of media statements and interviews.

These initiatives have been backed up by further huge protests and meetings attended by thousands of people in Monaghan, on 26 August 2004; 16 November 2005—following the death of Pat Joe Walsh; 13 September 2006—following the release of the Carey and Teamwork reports; and again on 25 November 2006. Over 2,500 people attended the monster meeting on 13 September 2006 in Monaghan Town: it was the culmination of a series of rallies and meetings in every town in the county. Over 10,000 irate citizens joined the Alliance protest almost two weeks later at the opening of the new Monaghan by-pass by Minister of State Pat the Cope Gallagher. As public anger boiled over, incited by provocative posing for local paparazzi, local Deputy and Dáil Ceann Comhairle Rory O'Hanlon, having unexpectedly driven through the crowd as he arrived, left the scene in a less regal manner, escorted by gardaí, to the accompaniment of boos from the crowd. Dr O'Hanlon, a general practitioner, is a former Minister for Health.

Judges Differ

Communities have also resorted to legal strategies. In 2003, for example, Monaghan Hospital Retention Committee decided to take legal action for a second time. Its first case, taken in 1983 against Barry Desmond, then Minister for Health, had succeeded. Tom O'Higgins, a former Minister for Health, and his fellow judges in the Supreme Court were unanimous: although he could close an entire hospital as long as he first held a public inquiry, the Minister had no power under the 1970 Health Act to discontinue hospital services. While the Minister could make 'arrangements for providing services', the Supreme Court ruled, these arrangements did not include their termination.

Mr Justice Aindrias Ó Caoimh took quite the opposite view in the High Court in 2004. Four Monaghan women had asserted that the health board had exceeded its powers under the 1970 Act in suspending the maternity service; the board claimed that its decision was necessary for reasons of insurance and safety. A few days after the case had opened in the High Court, a highly strategic leak occurred. A 2001 risk management report on Monaghan General Hospital—one of five commissioned by the North-Eastern Health Board in the wake of the Neary scandal—was leaked to *The Irish Times*. The headline? 'Report warned of risk at Monaghan Hospital in 2001'. The danger, it transpired, stemmed from 'lack of clarity and consensus' on the hospital's future, which the risk assessors claimed was endangering both staff and patients. The report also revealed a reported Caesarean rate of 29 per cent, an antiquated theatre, and a lack of services, such as paediatrics and neonatal intensive care. Monaghan was also castigated for not having a community midwifery service, a facility then almost unknown in Ireland.

Mr Justice Ó Caoimh decided that the North-Eastern Health Board's decision to suspend the maternity service did not breach the 1970 Health Act. It was clear from the evidence that the Board's decision to suspend the service had been taken in light of the prevailing circumstances, particularly the insurer's decision to withdraw cover. Boards must be enabled to choose where a service might be provided, as long as the decision was not such as to preclude the provision of the service to women residing in any part of their catchment areas. A midwife-led maternity service was to be introduced in Monaghan in 2005, he added.

One of the four women who had taken the case, Sinn Féin councillor Brenda McAnespie, said that, if the judgment stood, the Board could close any service it wished and move it to another part of the region. Deputy Paudge Connolly described the decision as tantamount to 'the recognition of CEOS as judges, juries and executioners, in relation to which services may be provided in the country's smaller general hospitals'. Monaghan Hospital Retention Committee subsequently decided to appeal the decision to the Supreme Court, where, at the time of writing, it rests.

Electoral Strategies
In a number of areas affected by the Hanly/Teamwork template, such as Clare, for example, elected representatives of all parties and none have worked together tirelessly to ensure accessible and safe services for their constituents. The same joint effort can be seen in Monaghan. Several meetings of the county council have been devoted to the hospital issue: the council also generously sponsored the Border Counties' Maternity Forum. These county council meetings have been paralleled in the town councils, while elected representatives have had numerous—and fruitless—meetings with the Taoiseach, the Minister for Health, other government ministers, and HSE management, sometimes accompanied by Monaghan Community Alliance leaders, to whom elected representatives have given unfailing support.

Electoral strategies are central to communities' efforts to maintain their hospitals. James Breen, a Fianna Fáil dissident and a farmer, was elected on a hospital ticket in Clare, for example. The issue also played a part in the election of a general practitioner in Wexford, Liam Twomey, who ran as an independent, later joining Fine Gael and currently that party's Health Spokesperson. In Monaghan, Independent Deputy Paudge Connolly, a former psychiatric nurse, was elected to the Dáil in 2002 on a hospital protest vote; while Sinn Féin's Caoimhghín Ó Caoláin, who had also campaigned on the hospital issue, topped the poll.

The cynical use of politics in the run-up to local elections has made communities exceedingly wary of government promises. In April 2004, for example, Fianna Fáil councillors in North Monaghan threatened not to stand in the local elections in June unless they received satisfactory assurances on the future of Monaghan General Hospital. Lo and behold, on 21 May 2004, they got a letter of comfort from Micheál Martin, which he then followed with an official announcement on 29 September 2004—his last day as Minister for Health—promising a CT scanner for the hospital. It has yet to materialise.

Nevertheless, the effectiveness of public and political pressure has been shown in the reprieves for Nenagh and Roscommon Hospitals—probably no more than temporary in the minds of current government and medical strategists. Interventions made by former Minister Michael Smith and Deputy Michael Finneran had their effect. A number of communities are considering fielding candidates in the upcoming general election. Former Chair of the Health Services Action Group Dr John Barton has already declared his candidature: he is running for Fine Gael on a hospital ticket in Galway East.

Since the 2002 election, it has become increasingly clear that the North East, in general, and Monaghan, in particular, has been selected to drive the centralisation agenda forward. In theory, the *Hanly Report* was to be piloted in the Mid-West (Ennis and Nenagh Hospitals) and in Dublin's east coast (Loughlinstown and Dún Laoghaire). Instead, for political reasons, it now seems certain that *Hanly* was, and is, being piloted in Monaghan. Since 2001, the hospital has been systematically stripped of its services in the teeth of community opposition, while Ennis Hospital continues to survive on the two-year stay of execution it got on its A&E in 2004. But the electoral picture in Monaghan is very different. As Ceann Comhairle, Rory O'Hanlon does not have to contest the next election. Fianna Fáil believes, rightly or wrongly, that its second seat in the constituency is a certainty, although at least one prospective candidate threatened not to stand unless he got substantive guarantees on the hospital's future.

Interestingly, Fianna Fáil's current stance on centralisation represents a 180-degree shift from its previous position. The party came to power in 1977 on a promise to continue to provide the 'necessary level of services to the local community'. Will Fianna Fáil revisit this pledge in the run-up to this year's general election?

IV Medicine Inc.

Chapter 11

Corporate Love Affair

A MARRIAGE MADE IN HEAVEN

One of the enduring mysteries over the past couple of years has been what exactly the Government means when it talks about developing 'a world-class' health service. But an early pre-election broadcast, courtesy of our national broadcaster, shed some light on this mystery. Speaking on the *Late Late Show*, Ms Harney expressed admiration for Sloan-Kettering, which she visited in 2005: you got the feeling that, if only we could have ten Sloan-Ketterings, losing Monaghan General (and the other twenty-two monaghans) would be a small price to pay for such excellence.

Memorial Sloan-Kettering Cancer Center grew out of an alliance between the Sloan-Kettering Institute and New York's Memorial Hospital. The Institute began life in 1948, dedicating itself to 'innovative basic science research'; the New York Cancer Hospital, founded in 1884, later morphed into Memorial Hospital; and the Institute merged with Memorial in 1960, hence s-k's claim to be the oldest as well as the largest private institution in the world dedicated to cancer care. While its main campus is in Manhattan's Upper East Side, s-k has a number of other sites in Long Island, New Jersey and Sleepy Hollow. Sloan-Kettering also leads the way in pet health care, research and education, running a not-for-profit hospital 'specialising in more than 20 areas of [pet] medicine and surgery'.

If you go there, you will live longer, s-k hints. But its website no longer mentions an article published by the *Journal of the American Medical Association*, claiming 40–80 per cent lower death rates for cancer patients in hospitals 'that had the most experience performing particular surgical procedures'. Sloan-Kettering's world-class services are available only to paying customers who hold high-end private health insurance plans. Another point to note is that s-k is now a partner in a major pharmaceutical research initiative.

For the wealthy, s-k offers every service that you can imagine in both in-patient and out-patient cancer care. Its clinics read like a list of New York millionaires, bearing such names as Rockefeller, Lauder, Kimmel and Guttman. Its outpatient centres offer 'integrative medicine', providing a dazzling array of complementary therapies, such as acupuncture, Reiki, massage, hypnotherapy and nutritional counselling. Long Island residents have the Suffolk Outpatient Center in their own backyard, along with two other 'community-based' clinics that deliver comprehensive cancer treatment, including genetic counselling. Local technology available to paying Long Islanders includes CT (computer tonography) and MRI (magnetic resonance imaging) scanners, digital X-ray facilities, conventional and stereotactic mammography, ultrasound, radiation oncology, a CT simulator and 'state of the art' linear accelerators. On the complementary health side, spiritual healing, meditation, guided imagery, visualisation, t'ai chi, Swedish massage, art and music therapy are all on offer.

At a price. A visit to the s-k website offers a crash course in managed health care, American-style. The site warns patients to get prior authorisation, in writing, from their health insurer for each procedure or service, and for every admission. Authorisation is required because insurers may declare a procedure medically unnecessary; these procedures include mammography, biopsy and MRI scans. Overall, the amount of cover varies with the insurer, with the employer, and with the policy. s-k says that individual insurers will be able to provide details 'about your in-network and out-of-network coverage for care' as well as 'what your financial responsibility will be'. Out-of-network coverage means you pay. Patients are warned that, even for those who hold private insurance, Sloan-Kettering services may not be covered. Many insurers limit payments to 'medical providers' using their own fee schedule of *usual, customary and reasonable* allowances. No fee schedule appears on the s-k website, but balance billing is clearly envisaged: 'You will be responsible for the payment of any fees not covered by your plan, including any balances.' s-k has managed care contracts with a number of insurers, but these contracts apply only if employers have purchased such plans and only if they have been bought for you.

Exclusions seem to be more common than cover. One insurer offers care in New Jersey but not in New York, although most cancer surgery is done at Memorial Hospital in Manhattan. 'Deductibles' are also payable. Sloan-Kettering says that it is 'covered' by standard Medicare insurance, a us government insurance programme that covers the over-65s and the disabled. But Medicare here means having to pay 'co-insurance'—a percentage of the total cost of your care. This may be as high as 20 per cent *after* paying 'deductibles', the annual amount payable for health-care 'expenses', before your insurer begins to pay. Such 'cover' is not unlike the 'scholarship' offered to young hopefuls from Ireland by a New York school of acting: this involved handing over $18,000 to the school in order to 'win' a 'bursary' of $2,000.

Although the Sloan-Kettering website is silent on fees and other deductibles, it is remarkably forthcoming about private health insurance. The tone is upbeat: 'Memorial Sloan Kettering Cancer Center's financial counsellors are committed to working with you, your physician and your insurance company to help you access our services. These counsellors are available to help verify your coverage.' In 'Steps To Take If Denied Coverage', the news is relentlessly good: insured cancer sufferers have the right to have their grievance heard within forty-eight hours by their insurers, if a delay constitutes a risk to their health. Assuming you live long enough, and you are denied coverage, you could try the following: learning about your insurance plan, your illness and your 'treatment options', getting your employer or union rep to intervene on your behalf with your insurer, filing a grievance or appeal with your insurer or a complaint with the New York State Insurance Department. (Half of all consumers in New York win their appeals against insurers, apparently.)

But perhaps the most interesting aspect of the billion-dollar operation that is s-k is its sweetheart deal with Pharma. The world's leading cancer treatment centre has now signed a contract making it eligible for bonus payments if it meets drug sales targets. The private hospital-clinic complex is a shareholder in a company that specialises in buying intellectual property rights in biotechnology. (Instead of having to wait a decade or more to collect royalties, Royalty Pharma offers cash upfront to 'institutions, inventors and life science companies' in exchange for 'royalty interests'.) On 22 June 2004, MSKCC bought $7 million worth of Royalty Pharma shares. Reciprocating the gesture, Royalty Pharma bought a portion of S-K's patent in two cancer drugs, Neupogen and Neulasta, for $263 million upfront, plus certain additional payments if annual sales of these drugs (developed by Sloan-Kettering) in Memorial Hospital and its network of clinics exceeded 'certain agreed sales hurdles'.

Neupogen is a genetically engineered version of a naturally occurring protein that is the body's primary defence against bacterial infection; the product was launched by Amgen in 1991. It is 'indicated' for use in some cancer patients who are already getting chemotherapy or who have had bone-marrow transplants. The cost of these drugs is unknown. Royalty Pharma—together with Sloan-Kettering—owns rights in nine 'leading marketed biopharmaceuticals', including drugs made by companies with a substantial base in Ireland, such as Eli Lilly and Pfizer. In 2002, Sloan-Kettering announced plans to raise $1 billion over five years.

One of its most recent achievements was to develop a vaccine for dogs suffering from advanced melanoma, based on DNA: research on nine pets showed that the vaccine tripled survival times. Instead of dying on average after ninety days, the canines survived for 389 days. Open around the clock, 365 days a year, the pet hospital deals with 60,000 'patient cases' every year.

A SEASON IN HELL

In her book, *A Season in Hell*, author Marilyn French talks abut the unaffordability of private health care in New York. Then suffering from cancer of the oesophagus, which had spread to other sites by the time it was diagnosed, Marilyn French got most of her treatment at Sloan-Kettering. In her memoir, she explodes the myth of 'the best' hospital in the world. All the nurses are marvellous, she says, but only some of the doctors are. French almost never sees her main oncologist: he is too busy developing cures and travelling the world. The 'best' cancer hospital in the world has good public waiting areas, but bad food, apparently, poorly cooked and of inferior quality.

Marilyn French nearly died in the best hospital in the world. They gave her the full works: chemotherapy and radiation simultaneously;

her body responded by going into a coma that lasted for two weeks. Yet, in the best hospital in the world, she was given no explanation for her post-coma condition, no prognosis and no apology. When she confronted her oncologist about her condition, he refused to talk to her and summoned a psychiatrist to speak to her.

As well as killing the cancer, the treatment destroyed her spinal column and the peripheral nerves in her hands and feet; left her with severe urinary tract and kidney problems; damaged her soft tissue, particularly her salivary glands. Later, having suffered a heart attack, she discovered that the cancer treatment had left her with half a heart. She now walks into walls, because s-k left her with irreversible brain damage. Six years on, she is suffering from osteoporosis, arthritis and diabetes, and spends over $1,000 a month on medication—none of it covered by insurance—and half of that again on alternative treatments.

She does not blame the medical establishment—what she calls that 'huge, indifferent machine; it is just that cancer treatment is barbaric. 'I no longer think in terms of recovery, but only of small gains and getting through. She counts her blessings: 'I even have moments without pain.'

French felt that the medical staff were over-specialised. Nobody, she complains, saw the whole picture. She found the care fragmented and depersonalised: 'Everyone just dealt with their bit'.

Money cannot buy a private room at s-k: these rooms are reserved for people getting bone-marrow transplants. Marilyn French comments that the private rooms at St Luke's Roosevelt Hospital in New York are so expensive that they lie empty. A private room there costs $500 a day extra, on top of the $2,000 daily charge for semi-private accommodation, and this is before medication or treatment. The author's care plan would pay only $80 of this.

So who can afford this level of private for-profit care, if a wealthy, bestselling author cannot?

GLOBALISATION

Globalisation has always been a force in health. Even before the term was invented, the medical profession networked globally, through conferences, journals, textbooks, schools. The active management of labour provides an early example of globalisation: it has been exported as a system all over the world and can be found not only in Britain, Canada and the us, but also in Chile, Bolivia, Nigeria and Singapore.

Over the past thirty years or so, the conditions under which health-care policy is made and services delivered have changed radically. Corporations now have some measure of control over governments. Since 1973, when the Organisation of Petroleum Exporting Companies (OPEC) was formed and oil prices surged, governments have embraced market solutions that emphasise economic freedom for individuals and corporations and limit the role of government. By the early 1990s, neo-liberalism had installed itself as the prevailing economic orthodoxy. The 1948 General Agreement on Tariffs and Trade (GATT) had already liberated corporations from their birth places, enabling them to roam freely, without incurring 'punishing financial penalties'. The World Trade Organisation (WTO), set up by governments in 1993, with Irishman Peter Sutherland as its first director general, was mandated to enforce GATT standards and also to set new rules that would block government regulations suspected of restricting international trade.

Deregulation affects how health care is provided. For example, in November 2006, an account appeared in a British midwifery journal of an Israeli trial on women of a new 'computerised labour monitor-ing system' manufactured by an Israeli corporation. To work the monitor, you clip two electrodes to the woman's cervix during labour, screwing a third onto the baby's scalp; ultrasound waves then chart the opening of the mother's cervix and the descent of her child's head. The machine is being promoted in Europe and the US as an examination-free way of assessing a woman's 'progress' during labour; this suggests that it would be particularly useful in countries where there is a short-age of midwives. Debbi Gedal-Beer, an Israeli midwifery education coordinator, wrote: 'This product takes advantage of and potentially harms women and their babies in labour, all for the purpose of eco-nomically profiting a biotech company.' 'How can we stop the march of this machine?' she asked.

Could such a machine be banned in Europe? Governments today are bound by WTO rulings. The organisation has, on numerous occasions, required governments to change or repeal laws designed to protect the public interest. Recent WTO decisions indicate that human health may take second place to corporate interests. A European Union ban on producing and importing beef from cows treated with synthetic hormones, for example, was deemed to violate WTO standards.

In his lucid and illuminating book, *The Corporation*, Canadian Professor of Law Joel Bakan says that the twentieth century was unique in its belief that 'democracy required governments to protect citizens' social rights and meet their fundamental needs'. Institutions essential to human health, development and safety, such as water, welfare, schools, colleges, courts and prisons, were removed 'beyond the corporation's exploitative grasp'. Health services were among those protected. Today corporations increasingly encroach on public services. Governments have handed over every element of what was once believed to belong to the public sphere. Water, power, police, prisons, fire and emergency services, schools, universities, genes, airports, parks, research—all have been, or are about to be, privatised in different countries.

The influence of corporations on health care has never been higher. In many countries across the world, health has become a commodity to be traded.

Private health care is now more developed in the US than in any other country in the world. Health care there is more costly and of lesser quality than in those countries where for-profit health is less salient. Even health entities that are not run for profit in the US are frequently controlled by chains. This topic will be returned to in the next chapter.

Even in Europe, market forces are beginning to dominate health care, ousting the social model of health that prioritised patient care over profit making. In Britain, for example, every hospital and every service is being privatised. 'Our foundation hospitals are now established in law as private corporations. There is no accountability, except through a regulator,' Professor Allyson Pollack told a health-care conference on privatisation, in Dublin, in November 2005. Hospitals are increasingly coming under corporate control. Large American chains, she says, are now breaking into Europe in an attempt to increase market share: 'Ireland, France, Spain and Greece are now going down this route.'

But corporate influence over health does not stop with McMedicine. Joel Bakan describes WTO as a 'powerful, secretive and corporate-influenced overseer of government's mandate to protect citizens and the environment from corporate harms'. The same observation could be made about the World Health Organisation (WHO). In 1982, more than half the WHO's budget came from six leading drug corporations in the United States, West Germany, Japan, France, Britain and Italy. Fifteen years later, WHO's biennial budget was $1.7 billion; it had loans of $2.5 billion from the World Bank, giving the agency a controlling voice in its affairs.

The WHO was established in 1948. It focused initially on the health of troops in North Africa and the Pacific. At that time, malaria and yellow fever represented a significant obstacle to European economic interests in Africa, India and South East Asia. The WHO's focus on eradicating smallpox and malaria benefited US corporations: 60 per cent of exports from the US were to countries with malaria that also supplied 40 per cent of American imports.

The late Joan Donley, a New Zealand writer, believed that WHO's promotion of less technological and more community-based medical care, in the early 1970s, reflected the increased industrialisation and economic exploitation of the Third World. 'As the World Bank pointed out, where there is an infinite supply of cheap labour, there is little incentive to supply curative medicine. The premature death of workers is preferable to morbidity and absenteeism, which has a greater economic impact.'

As far as health care is concerned, pharmaceutical corporations are the puppeteers of the world. Pharma, for example, routinely sponsors both national and international health care conferences, agencies and organisations. The International Confederation of Midwives (ICM) has long been a target of such companies. Its 1997 conference in Jakarta, on health promotion, was the first to involve the private sector. Participants included Johnson & Johnson and SmithKline Beecham (plus its NGO) as well as Coca-Cola and Guinness. Some delegates at the conference felt that 'WHO had pushed ahead, driving the agenda of private sector *partnerships* [emphasis added] with little consultation or analysis of the implications'.

But why should midwives be targeted by multinationals? A subsequent ICM congress in the Philippines gives a clue: midwives there discovered that they had been renamed *reproductive health workers*. Joan Donley believed that this had been done to facilitate the delivery in developing countries of injectable contraceptives, such as Depo-Provera—long banned in the Western World—and Norplant. Whether or not this is true, there is no doubting the existence of a veritable population control industry, and its sustained targeting of countries such as India, China and Brazil, to name but three. The

WHO has been one of the industry leaders since 1985.

Corporate interests may also overlap with professional agendas, as in the use of ultrasound technology in childbirth. Electronic fetal monitor manufacturers funded a WHO meeting to develop guidelines for the use of these machines on women during labour. The WHO insisted that scientific evidence did not justify their routine use. The meeting was organised by the Féderation Internationale des Obstetricians-Gynecologues (FIGO), a body that is reportedly committed to the expansion of this technology in the labour ward. Today, these machines have been installed in every delivery suite in the industrialised world; British obstetricians believe that they are the main driver of Caesarean section rates in Britain.

BIG PHARMA, BIG PRESENTS

Ireland is widely acknowledged as one of the most open economies in the world; it is also the biggest net exporter of pharmaceuticals. In 2005, the industry accounted for 44 per cent of Irish exports.

How does this influence the delivery of medical services? Curiously, drugs are much more expensive in Ireland than they are in many other European countries. The state does a deal every year with the pharmaceutical companies, which appears to be far more advantageous to the industry than to the taxpayer. The use of expensive, branded drugs is a continuing problem in Ireland. Since 1992, GPS have been encouraged to prescribe generic drugs for their public patients; nothing has been done to curb the market for drugs for private patients, although these, too, are partly refunded by the state.

Industry links with medical journals are strong. The pharmaceutical industry adopts the same promotional strategies in Ireland as it does in other countries; and it gets results. Take statins, for example. In recent years, companies have heavily promoted these drugs to control cholesterol; statins have now become the strategy of choice for many doctors for lowering patients' cholesterol levels. Authors' corporate ties are frequently undisclosed.

In Britain, pharmaceutical 'perks' for doctors have famously included trips on the Orient Express. In Ireland, pharmaceutical companies, also in the name of 'education', organise medical junkets in leading hotels, such as the Four Seasons, the K Club and Markree Castle. Luxurious, all-expenses-paid soirées and weekends have become the norm. Annual bashes guaranteeing corporations access to top medical decision-makers in our hospitals have now become part of the social calendar for doctors and their families. In September 2004, for example, Novartis footed the bill for two nights in the K Club for child psychiatrists to listen to lectures on 'hyper-activity' encouraging them to prescribe a drug similar to cocaine, branded as Ritalin, manufactured—surprise, surprise—by Novartis. Also in that year, Pfizer brought sixty Irish doctors to a rugby match in France.

Such is the unquestioning acceptance of the 'gift culture' in Irish medicine that companies routinely target entire public hospital departments without fear of challenge. Formula milk companies are ubiquitous here: they frequently violate the WHO code governing the marketing of formula by giving 'free' samples to health workers. Corporations seem to find it remarkably easy to penetrate the public sphere in Ireland. Infant formula manufacturers have been allowed to give 'lectures' in 'nutrition' in UCD to public health nurses, for example, while a leading formula manufacturer, SMA, sponsored the Rotunda Hospital's 250th anniversary conference for midwives.

No one knows just how much money companies in Ireland spend on wooing the medical profession. No questions are asked, no tabs kept. Unlike civil servants, who are forbidden to accept gifts of more than nominal value, doctors and nurses are free to accept presents of unlimited value from corporations manufacturing or distributing drugs, medical devices or other supplies that health professionals may have a role in selecting for their hospitals or their patients. This evident conflict of interest has gone virtually unquestioned not only by the profession but by the media. UCC academics are now beginning to study these trends. But while doctors maintain that their choice of drug or device is not influenced by such inducements, no one knows for sure to what extent, if any, medical decision-making has been, and may continue to be, corrupted by the intimacy of the profession's tango with the pharmaceutical industry.

A pharmacist's report gives us a rare glimpse into the industry's infiltration of our hospitals. Company representatives, if they 'work' hard enough, may significantly increase the use of a particular drug. The antibiotic chemist noted that the use of a broad-spectrum antibiotic, Tazocin, had increased by a whopping 73 per cent at the hospital in one year. This drug, classified as 'undesirable' (presumably on the grounds that broad-spectrum antibiotics contribute to the growth of superbugs) had been 'actively promoted' by the company rep. You may wonder, as I did, how the rep actively promoted the drug, but while the health services employ 145,000 people, not one of them is charged with investigating just how pharmaceutical companies promote their products and how this relates to doctors' prescribing patterns.

The organs controversy provided another glimpse of the cosy relationship between medicine and the pharmaceutical industry in Ireland. Up to thirty-two hospitals in the state harvested pituitary glands to enable pharmaceutical companies to manufacture growth hormones. These organs were taken without consent from dead patients during post-mortem examinations; the practice ceased only in the mid-1980s when a synthetic hormone became available. The glands were effectively gifted to the companies by the hospitals.

PATIENT GROUPS

Pharmaceutical companies have now developed a new strategy. Not content with love-bombing doctors, they have now turned their attention to patients. Many see industry 'sponsorship'—masquerading as 'education', whether directed at doctors or patients—as marketing in disguise. In Ireland, as in other European Union countries, advertising drugs directly to patients is prohibited. Companies have now become more audacious in their attempts to circumvent this ban and recent advertising has, unusually, drawn fire from the medical profession.

Patient groups are now being enlisted in this endeavour. According to UCC social scientist Orla O'Donovan, the industry is increasingly funding—and founding—health advocacy organisations. Pharmaceutical companies, she says, have generally succeeded in defining themselves as a philanthropic force in Ireland. 'There is a growing tendency among Irish health advocacy organisations to frame pharmaceutical corporations as their friends and allies.' Patient groups believe that they can protect their independence by properly managing their relations with pharmaceuticals. This belief, as Orla O'Donovan sees it, mirrors the medical view that clinical decision-making is uninfluenced by pharmaceutical gifts.

Her study of 112 advocacy groups revealed that almost half were getting money and/or support in kind from the industry, usually for 'educational' purposes. Groups tended not to disclose this funding. Leading organisations, such as AWARE, the Irish Cancer Society, the

Asthma Society, the Diabetes Federation of Ireland and Fighting
Blindness have formed an umbrella organisation to promote and
source funding for biomedical research; the group now sits on the
Health Research Board and has recently launched a joint funding programme for research into rare diseases.

'CITIZENSHIP'

In 2000, I attended a conference on maternity care, in Nantes in
France. The conference was entitled 'Citizenship and Birth', and I was
curious to know how notions of citizenship had come to be entwined
with ideas about improving the services for birth; I came home none
the wiser. Since then, I sometimes wondered about the proliferation
of 'citizenship', how it seemed to have become the new stock in trade,
replacing other 'ships' and 'isms', such as regionalism and nationalism.

Years later, I discovered that citizenship was now being invoked to
promote consumerism, especially in health. How to make the citizen
a better consumer of health services and medical supplies is a
question that has been preoccupying corporations for years. The
industry has developed a 'battle plan' to employ 'ground troops in the
form of patient support groups, sympathetic medical opinion and
health-care professionals'. Private citizens, voluntary organisations
and public institutions, including the European Union itself, have
become the new corporate targets. According to activist Susan
George, there are over 100,000 corporate lobbyists in Brussels at the
present time.

Under the banner of 'corporate social responsibility', corporations
are now planning citizen 'partnerships' actively promoting the
privatisation of public services. But while corporate social responsibility may have only recently been discovered by Bono, this particular
chestnut has been around since after the First World War, when
corporations first strove to make themselves look socially responsible.
Joel Bakan points out that corporate social responsibility, if genuine,
is actually illegal: corporations are legally obliged to put shareholders'
interests above all others.

Like the medical profession, corporations utilise the building
blocks of knowledge, research and reports, as well as the social
currency of seminars and conferences to foster their global interests.
The sixth international seminar on corporate social responsibility was
held on 30 June 2006 somewhere in Europe, at a secret location, with

an undisclosed programme and unlisted speakers. For those delegates lucky enough to be invited to attend, it was an all-expenses-paid conference. Its aim? To build relationships between citizens and private companies. Voluntary groups in every EU Member State, including Ireland, were offered funding to attend, the sole requirement being that 'representatives' identify, and invite one or two corporate dancing partners in their country of origin. The event was organised, apparently, by a group calling itself the 'Active Citizens Network' (ACN).

This network has no members, only floating 'partners'. It was founded by an Italian group, CittadinanzAttiva, in 2001. CittadinanzAttiva is openly dedicated to the privatisation of public services across the European Union, particularly in health. Deregulation is another objective. The Berlusconi-backed group supported a Forza Italia candidate in a recent municipal election in Italy. In Ireland, CittadinanzAttiva's partners have included the Irish Patients' Association Ltd, Dublin City University and Age Action Ireland.

Funded by some of the biggest corporations in the world, General Electric (Medical Systems), Merck Sharp and Dohme and Bristol Myers Squibbs, CittadinanzAttiva has scripted a 'European Charter of Patients' Rights', which is being actively promoted all over Europe. Liberalisation and privatisation of public services, the party says, require a new definition of 'patient rights'.

The charter was initially discussed in Rome on 7 September 2002, at a meeting attended by, among others, Stephen McMahon, chair of the Irish Patients' Association Ltd. His company subsequently commissioned the School of Nursing and the School of Law and Governance at Dublin City University to review the charter's 'ethical foundations' and its 'standing in Irish law'. The Irish Patients' Association Ltd funded this review with assistance from Merck Sharp and Dohme and Pfizer. The report, published in April 2005, was launched by the Minister for Health, Mary Harney, and co-authored by a member of the Health Service Executive's governing body, Professor P. Anne Scott, Professor of Nursing at DCU.

Corporations are now working through patient groups, such as the 'Chronically Ill Associations Coalition'—another group with links to CittadinanzAttiva—which campaigns for free prescription drugs for all chronically ill people, forever. Such campaigns help mobilise support for legislative change. Drug companies, and others, hope one day to see legally enforceable entitlements to their products. This is the long-term goal.

To this end, CittadinanzAttiva aims to construct what it terms 'a European citizenship' to influence policy-making in health and other public services. The group is dedicated to building partnerships between the private sector and international agencies. It now hopes to get money for its enterprises from the European Commission's public health kitty.

The Berlusconi-linked organisation focuses on areas of particular interest to corporations—the zero costing of new drugs for certain chronically ill patients, transplantation surgery and radiotherapy. Its tactics include setting up—or infiltrating—patient organisations and forming alliances with family practitioners and hospital doctors, and honing in on niche markets, such as home-care services, 'the surgical path', pain therapy and oncology services.

CittadinanzAttiva is currently demanding 'an enrichment' of the concept of subsidiarity in the European Union to include the relationship between institutions and citizens, '*in order that institutions favour the free initiatives of citizens, both as individuals and as organisations* [emphasis added]'. Its followers hope to get EU funds to extend the *monitoring* of their charter to twenty-eight countries, including Ireland.

The group may be pushing an open door. The European Commission is currently funding citizenship projects: DG EAC 18/06 has called for proposals to grow 'Active European Citizenship'. Like the European Charter of Patients' Rights, this can, presumably, be expected to act as a growth promoter of multinational interests in Europe.

Chapter 12

McMedicine

Ask yourself, how would Neiman Marcus run a hospital? How would Nordstrom operate a skilled nursing facility? How would Tiffany & Company serve customers of a home care agency? These companies all share three things: top-line service, quality products and higher-than-average *[emphasis added] prices.*

Author and health marketing guru, John O'Malley, urging for-profit hospitals and home-care agencies to think retail, not health

The idea of medicine as a for-profit enterprise has always been with us, ever since doctors charged private fees for their services. This they have been doing since time immemorial. In the community, doctors traditionally formed partnerships with other doctors, companies limited by guarantee, where the owners were the managers. But today, these partnerships have been supplanted by another model, the corporate model, where the company is owned by investors, and the owners are no longer the managers. Successive American governments have allowed corporations to trade patients as commodities since the mid-1960s, at least. Today the US has the biggest private health care industry in the world.

US hospital chains have recently begun targeting Europe, where, with the rise of neo-liberalism, the idea of health as a social good is beginning to decline. In Britain, hospitals are increasingly coming under corporate control: for-profit consortia are also running general practitioner and other services. In Ireland, over the past decade, the Government has promoted private for-profit health to a degree unprecedented in our history. Cancer sufferers, for example, are now treated as a 'market' by both government and state. Markets are created with one object in mind: to make money.

What happens when health care facilities are handed over to for-profit companies, to own or to manage? Is for-profit health care more 'efficient', as is often claimed? Less costly? Better quality? The US health care scene offers us a glimpse of the future, a picture of Ireland in twenty years' time, if current government policies in health are implemented.

The corporate model of health care, the one we are on the point of importing, has been tried and tested in the US for nearly forty years. So, by now, the original design should be wrinkle-free, with any remaining creases ironed out. But what the US experience shows is that giving market forces free rein in health care has been an unqualified disaster: corporate health care has signally failed to deliver on equity, quality, efficiency, and cost control. There is a massive crisis today in patient access, quality of care *and* public funding. Recruiting and retaining doctors, nurses and managers has also become a problem. Professional indemnity is another difficulty, especially in high-risk areas such as obstetrics.

The US health care system—if you can call such a fragmented array of services a system—is now one of the costliest in the industrialised world, and, rated by health outcomes, one of the most unimpressive. The current system is increasingly attracting criticism, however, and awareness of the need for health care reform is growing.

Four years ago, the corporate model looked as though it might be in trouble. A wave of bankruptcies had hit the private nursing-home sector, and the private hospital industry was reported to have declined since 1997, the year the FBI raided hospitals in Texas. Industry commentators said that hospital mergers had failed to deliver the hoped-for efficiencies. Bear Stearns analyst Jason Gurda summed up the view from the markets: the hospital sector, he said, had been 'hurt by soft volumes and an increasingly large amount of bad debt expense due to rapid growth in the number of uninsured patients'. 'Soft volumes' referred to unused bed capacity, a feature of many US hospital chains. The average bed occupancy for the third biggest hospital corporation in the US, Triad, for example, is only around 50 per cent, roughly half that of most Irish public hospitals. The 'bad debt expense' derived, and derives, from the industry practice of treating uninsured patients, who cannot pay the money for their medical care. Hospitals then seek to recover from the patient; after a certain time has elapsed, the debt is classified as bad.

Today, however, the us health care business is booming as never before: profits of the top 100 publicly traded health-care corporations currently stand at over $103 billion. Soaring profits have made for uncontrollable costs, however. Far from capping costs in health care, the market is actually fuelling medical inflation. The hospital industry has had two consecutive years of record profits, $22.6 billion in 2003 and $26.3 billion in 2004.

Market mechanisms have failed spectacularly to stem rising costs or to ensure uniformly high-quality care. As always, escalating drug costs are part of the problem. Although Medicare costs have fallen somewhat in line with increases in fraud detection, medical inflation continues to rise inexorably. Many hospitals in the us are losing the battle with pharmaceutical companies, medical suppliers, health insurers and others to control expenditure.

The rising cost of medical services and treatments is making health care increasingly unaffordable for many. Health insurers have yet again raised their premiums; double digit increases—now being seen in Ireland—are becoming the norm in the us. Health care costs, in consequence, are rising—for employers, state agencies and taxpayers. Government insurance schemes have cut back on payments. Medicare, for example, has begun to change its paying practices, paying per diagnosis rather than per treatment. Some firms have scaled back on health plans for their employees, and this has swelled the ranks of the uninsured. The national health spend is one of the highest in the industrialised world: in 2003, health consumed 15 per cent of America's national income, nearly double the oecd average of 8.8 per cent. Despite this, for ordinary Americans, access to health care is a growing problem. The us system, while one of the costliest, is also one of the most unequal. Almost 46 million Americans are now uninsured. Many uninsured and underinsured people are in full-time employment.

So why are costs rising so uncontrollably? Overcharging is one factor pushing health care costs out of control. An uninsured person who becomes ill is forced to go to a hospital a&e department. This is the most expensive of all forms of care. Hospitals then shift the cost of that care on to insurers, by charging as much as they can for operations, drugs and medical supplies. This creates a vicious circle: as the services become more costly, care is cut back, health insurance premiums rise, and fewer people can afford them.

Private for-profit hospitals in the US have been shown to charge those who pay them—insurers and patients—a multiple of what it costs to provide a service. Staggeringly high mark-ups have become the norm in the hospital industry across the board. Evidence of blatant overcharging by pharmaceutical companies, private hospital owners and operators has now come to light. A pioneering study of over 4,000 hospitals has revealed how the top forty most expensive hospitals in the US make their money. These hospitals charge an average mark-up that varies from a low of over 1,000 per cent for surgical procedures to a high of over 5,000 per cent for medical supplies: the drugs mark-up stands at over 2,300 per cent.

The study, carried out by the Institute for Health and Socio-Economic Policy in California, showed that pricing in hospitals affiliated with chains, such as Triad and HCA, was consistently higher than in hospitals that were not managed or owned by conglomerates. Its authors concluded: 'The anticipated reduction in charges from building economies of scale has not occurred.'

FRAUD

Fraud is also fuelling health care costs in the United States. The hospital industry is not only one of the largest industries, it is also one of the most corrupt. Nursing homes bill Medicaid for supplies that were never bought. Doctors bill Medicare for diagnostic procedures they never performed. The largest single Medicare fraud settlement was made by a pharmaceutical company, TAP. It paid the government $875 million to settle criminal charges and *qui tam* lawsuits; the government alleged that TAP had paid illegal kickbacks to doctors to prescribe its prostate-cancer drug, Lupron.

Qui tam lawsuits are whistleblower actions taken under the False Claims Act. This act empowers citizens to take lawsuits on behalf of the US government in cases where they believe fraud has been committed. The government is free to join the action, or not. For a variety of reasons, some of which may have little to do with the substance of allegations made, the government may elect not to join a particular *qui tam* action; this is no indication of its worth. The US government took five years, for example, to decide to join the

Alderson suit: it turned out to be the biggest fraud in health care in American history. If the case succeeds, the state collects a chunk of the monies recovered; the relator, as the *qui tam* complainant is called, is also entitled to a share. Far from being motivated by greed, as corporations occasionally suggest, *qui tam* complainants are generally impelled by a sense of outrage at what they perceive to be fraud against taxpayers.

The false-claims legislation has been remarkably successful. Since the act was introduced in 1986, the American government has recovered nearly $18 billion in corporate fraud; health care corporations usually top the list of payers.

Whistleblower law firm Phillips and Cohen has detailed some of the scams that have been uncovered under the False Claims Act. Its website shows that the scope for fraud in the health care industry is limited only by the imagination of the fraudster. A state-owned hospital in Iowa, for example, billed for ventilation of all intensive-care patients, regardless of whether or not they had been ventilated. Two sisters in Maine, both supervisors in a residential-care facility, stole money by creating phantom employees and phantom contractors whose salaries and expenses were included in the cost reports submitted to Medicaid. A Georgia nursing home and clinic owner defrauded Medicare by billing for personal expenses, such as jewellery, cars, vacations and the costs of show dogs, disguised as employees' salaries. The company paid over $1 million to settle criminal and civil fraud charges.

Sadly, the medical profession has proved itself to be corruptible. A New York radiologist billed Medicaid for thousands of medically unnecessary, forged and duplicate sonogram tests. His Medicaid claims increased from $8,200 to more than $2.2 million in two years and involved huge kickbacks to more than fifty 'salesmen'. He was sentenced to up to three years in prison and barred from state health care programmes for ten years. An Iowan anaesthetist routinely billed Medicare an extra hour-and-a-half for every open-heart operation in which he took part. A Californian orthopaedic surgeon billed for services performed while he was out of the country. A Maryland ophthalmologist billed for laser surgery when all he did was remove stitches post-operatively.

Corporate fraud in health is a huge problem: 5–10 per cent of the national spend on health is swallowed up in fraud, or wasted in some other way. In 1996, for example, health fraud cost the US government an estimated $127 million. Medicare and Medicaid, the government insurer for the poor and other federal programmes have lost billions of dollars in fraudulent claims.

Many, if not most, of the biggest health care corporations in the US have been indicted or convicted of fraud. Multi-million-dollar settlements of fraud charges have become the norm. Fraudulent billing practices and corrupt physician relationships are widespread. Top executives in one of America's biggest health care companies were recently convicted of fraud on a scale that approached Enron. Chief financial officers at HealthSouth, a Texan health care company, pleaded guilty to a multi-billion-dollar fiddle. CEO and company founder, Dr Richard Scrushy, a hospital physician, was accused of orchestrating the $3 billion fraud. Five financial officers who served under Scrushy testified that their CEO was aware of the scam. The prosecution alleged that Scrushy had funded a luxurious lifestyle from the sale of shares that had been artificially inflated. Company accounts from 1996 to 2002 showed mythical profits, allegedly at his behest, with the company claiming non-existent assets of $2.7 billion. Selling these shares, the prosecution said, netted the former CEO more than $200 million, funding Scrushy mansions, Scrushy yachts and Scrushy classic cars. After a four-month trial in Birmingham, Alabama, the jury deadlocked. The impasse lasted twenty-one days, broken only by the arrival of a new juror. Scrushy walked free, having been acquitted on thirty-six charges. He had been charged under new corporate disclosure laws requiring chief executives to certify the accuracy of financial statements; the state failed to prove beyond reasonable doubt that he had knowledge of the fraud. *The Financial Times* commented that Mr Scrushy combined his training in 'respiratory therapy' with an 'entrepreneurial spirit'.

In November 2006, Scrushy and HealthSouth were reported to have settled claims against each other arising from the company's accounting fraud. HealthSouth wanted Scrushy to return $48 million in bonuses, while the former CEO demanded that the company foot his $21 million defence bill. Scrushy apparently agreed to return $21 million in bonuses paid to him by HealthSouth from 1997 to 2002. Sixteen former HealthSouth executives were convicted of criminal charges in connection with the fraud conspiracy.

Fraud is almost endemic in the private sector. Nor is it confined to for-profit entities: many not-for-profit facilities have fallen prey to management by big us health care chains in recent years. Some of them have proved to be a hugely corrupting influence on doctors, administrators and others. During the 1980s and 1990s, and continuing to the present day, hundreds of not-for-profit hospitals owned or managed by health care corporations became enmeshed in fraud. Witness the Catholic and Lutheran hospitals that were owned and/or managed by Columbia/hca, a corporation that perpetrated the biggest health care fraud in American history.

Such is the scale of fraud in American health care that it almost defies the imagination. In 2001, for example, the Justice Department recorded, 465 defendants were convicted of health care fraud crimes; federal prosecutors filed 445 criminal indictments in these cases. In that year, there were 1,746 civil actions pending, while 188 civil cases were filed. Medicaid fraud control units collaborated with state licensing boards to combat swindles in 2001; it was a record year for health insurance bans. In that year, 3,756 individuals and companies were barred from participating in federal health insurance programmes. Most of those who were disqualified had been convicted of crimes relating to Medicare or Medicaid, of patient abuse or neglect, or had had their licences revoked.

KENTUCKY FRIED HEALTH CARE

The Healthcare Company of America (hca) was one of the first health care corporations in the us. Its successor, Triad, has recently entered the Irish market. Recent us Senate Majority Leader, Bill Frist, who plans to run for the Republicans in the next presidential election, has strong ties with hca. The company was founded in 1968 by his father, Dr Thomas Frist, and brother, both us senators.

hca merged with a much younger corporation, Columbia Healthcare, in 1994, when Columbia was just six years old. Columbia was founded by a Kentucky Fried Chicken founder, Jack Massey, and lawyer, Richard Scott, backed by a group of 120 doctors.

Columbia promoted a McMedicine model of care, modelled on McDonalds and Wal-Mart. Market analysts later described Columbia/hca as an 'acquisitions machine'. The company's spend on marketing was enormous; in some years, its pr budget in the us exceeded $100 million. Columbia/hca was widely criticised for its aggressive business tactics. These included attacking not-for-profit hospitals in the media, portraying them as 'social parasites' and 'economic dinosaurs', before gobbling them up. These takeovers were reported to have taken place in secret: hospitals sold at below market value, with hospital board members and executives allegedly profiting financially from the sales.

Non-profitable hospital services were quietly terminated prior to sale. Companies that buy hospitals are legally obliged to continue to provide pre-existing hospital services, but Columbia/HCA was not in business to provide unprofitable or costly services.

After HCA merged with Columbia in 1994, Richard Scott became company president and CEO, with Thomas Frist Junior MD as vice-chair. The corporation moved to Nashville, Tennessee, in 1995. In that same year, it bought HealthTrust, which had been formed in 1987 when HCA spun off 100 hospitals. HealthTrust was also based in Nashville. By 1996, the health care leviathan was the ninth largest non-government employer in the US, employing about 285,000 people. At its height, Columbia/HCA operated over 400 hospitals, 500 health care agencies and numerous other health care facilities in at least thirty states.

By 1996, Columbia/HCA was embroiled in controversy: it stood accused of tactics that have now become synonymous with the US private hospital industry: cherry-picking profitable admissions, cream-skimming wealthy patients; patient dumping; overcharging; operating unsafe staff–patient ratios; and providing only lower-cost services.

Of course, in refusing to provide costly services, HCA was only doing its duty to its shareholders. Corporations are legally obliged to make as much money as possible for their stockholders, and nothing, as Joel Bakan explains, can be allowed to stand in the way of profits. For a hospital corporation to rank patient safety, for example, above profit would arguably be illegal.

Columbia/HCA policy was to get doctors to buy stakes in its hospitals. This was a strategy that was to get the company into trouble with the federal authorities. American law prohibits hospitals from claiming from Medicare for items ordered or treatment provided by doctors who have an 'improper' financial relationship with the treating hospital. Dubious recruitment practices were also alleged; Michael Wynne, a surgeon in Brisbane, Australia, who monitored the group's activities, relates how the corporation regularly gave assurances to doctors that they would put competitors out of business.

The corporation offered financial incentives to doctors in the community. This led to allegations of illegal kickbacks, of hunting and fishing trips in Texas, Mexico, the Caribbean and Alaska; of bribes to induce doctors to refer their patients to company hospitals. Exactly the same allegations had been levelled at another major US hospital chain, Tenet, six years previously.

Company billing practices were alleged to be dishonest. Columbia/HCA routinely engaged in 'aggressive' billing, such as 'upcoding', inflating the seriousness of a condition, such as pneumonia— a code used to classify 100 illnesses. But hospitals could charge only $3,150 for 'simple pneumonia', whereas 'complex pneumonia' brought in $6,800. With hundreds of hospitals across the United States generating thousands of cases of pneumonia, upcoding was a seriously profitable business.

Columbia/HCA duly ran into trouble with Medicare and other government insurers. Michael Wynne reports that HCA paid its first fraud settlement in 1993–4, to the state of Texas. Whistleblower lawsuits began.

The first such court action was taken in the early 1990s, against a hospital in Montana owned by HCA and managed by Quorum, formerly HCA Management Company. (Quorum was spun off as a separate company in 1989.) The whistleblower was James F. Alderson, a former chief financial officer employed by Quorum. Alderson refused to operate company accounting procedures that involved preparing two sets of accounts, one for insurance purposes and the other for company purposes; he also refused to operate company billing practices (involving Medicare claims) that he believed were wrong. Fired by Quorum in 1993, he subsequently took a *qui tam* action against his former employer. Little did he know that the suit would take ten years to resolve.

Columbia/HCA and Quorum were accused of defrauding Medicare, Medicaid, and other public insurers, claiming for non-allowable expenses, such as advertising and legal bills, wrongful physician billing, manipulating costs and keeping 'improper statistics'. Official investigations into the companies peaked in March 1997, when the FBI raided hospitals in El Paso, Texas.

On 11 May 1997, before the second FBI raids, the *New York Times* summarised Columbia/HCA's enormous financial success by saying: 'At the heart of that achievement is an aggressively competitive vision of medical care, one that applies the practices of corporate America to an industry still dominated by not-for-profit institutions.' That competitive vision translated into 'in-your-face marketing', as well as 'hospital takeovers, cost-cutting and layoffs, volume purchasing, complex pricing strategies and large monetary incentives for managers who meet financial targets.'

Faced with spiralling investigations, CEO and chair Richard Scott continued to insist that Columbia/HCA had done nothing wrong; he was removed in 1997, and walked away with a severance payment, topped off with $324 millions' worth of shares and a large mansion. In 1997, Dr Thomas Frist Junior was brought back out of retirement. He took the helm once again as company chair and CEO, adopting a new role as crusader against corporate corruption. Michael Wynne found this ironic; he points out that HCA's first pay-out in 1993 was to settle fraud allegations that related to the period 1984–93 when Frist was chair and CEO.

The FBI raids had a major effect on the company's plans for expansion. Having bought a managed care company in Britain, Columbia/HCA bid for two US insurance companies, Blue Cross and Blue Shield. This led to a public outcry: the corporation was accused of anti-competitive practices, of trying to become a health insurer while remaining a health care provider. It relinquished its insurance ambitions. The corporation's plans to penetrate Europe and Australia were similarly dented. Columbia/HCA's bid to buy the big French chain, Général de la Santé Internationale, was foiled; and it was also forced to back off from the Australian market. In both countries, surgeon Michael Wynne reported, medical organisations were well informed about the corporation's activities.

From April 1997, numerous class actions and related lawsuits were filed against HCA and its current and former directors, officers and/or employees. These lawsuits alleged 'improper and fraudulent billing, overcharging, coding and physician referrals, as well as other violations of law'. Some were conditionally certified as class actions.

Criminal and civil lawsuits against the corporation opened in October 1998. Over thirty whistleblowers led to as many court actions; the government intervened in eight of these. In October 1998, five years after Alderson had blown the whistle, the Justice Department took its own case against both Columbia/HCA and Quorum. The case came to court in July 1999. By then, as in the Enron case, the government was drowning in a tsunami of paper. Over 2,400 cost reports alone were submitted in the case. Over 400 hospitals across the US were accused of routinely preparing two sets of accounts, one for reimbursement by government health insurers, the other, the 'reserve' accounts, for concealment from government auditors. From 1985 to 1999, the fraud was systemic, the state maintained. The government's case was that, in 1975, HCA Management Company had issued a memo that required 'aggressive' cost reporting to Medicare and other insurers. A follow-up directive in 1980 stipulated that monies were to be set aside to cover only the cost of those items which, if discovered by Medicare, would 'probably' be rejected.

All 200-plus hospitals owned by HCA, all 179 hospitals managed by Quorum (previously HCA Management Company), plus a further thirty-four facilities owned by Quorum stood accused. Quorum's management services included preparing cost reports to federal and state authorities. The scam, according to the state, involved no fewer than four government insurers, Medicare, Medicaid, Tricare (a scheme for the military) and the Federal Employees Health Benefits Programme (for civilians).

Two Columbia/HCA executives were found guilty of fraud. Michael Wynne also reported that some executives were jailed in December 1999.

Frist was forced to break up the company, spinning off about a third of its stock to fund its legal battles and pay its fraud fines. These sixty-four hospitals—dubbed 'the baby Columbias'—were spun off into two companies, Lifepoint, in Brentwood, Tennessee, and Triad in Dallas, Texas. The old Columbia purchasing system, described as 'the nation's largest integrated delivery network', re-emerged in Nashville as HealthTrust Purchasing Group. Columbia/HCA was forced to change its name to HCA—the Hospital Corporation of America. In December 2000, HCA entered into agreements with both the criminal and civil divisions of the Department of Justice and various US attorneys' offices. The corporation agreed to pay $745 million to resolve Medicare fraud allegations and a fine of $95 million against two of its subsidiaries; it paid $95.3 million to settle criminal charges and pleaded guilty on several criminal counts. These settlements did not, however, resolve the cost report or physician kickback issues, nor did they deal with the *qui tam* actions. In 2001, Frist was replaced by Jack Bovender Junior. According to Michael Wynne, Bovender had been a top executive in Columbia/HCA, when it was under FBI investigation.

The probe dragged on until 2003, when HCA made a final settlement with Justice. Quorum was detached from the action, and the
cases against it were advanced to active litigation. The (draft) legal
agreement between Justice and HCA listed twelve whistleblower
actions, including James Alderson's. HCA was to pay $631 million to
cover the 200-plus HCA hospitals that, according to the Justice
Department, had engaged in fraudulent insurance claims and
physician kickbacks. The Justice Department alleged that HCA had
paid 'remuneration to physicians intending that remuneration to
induce ... referrals in violation of the Anti-Kickback Statute'. Entering
into the agreement, however, did not constitute an admission or
evidence of liability or wrongful conduct.

The agreement also incorporated a corporate integrity agreement
made in 2000, binding not only on HCA but on its successors.
On 26 June 2003, HCA duly paid $631 million in civil penalties and
damages to resolve Medicare allegations, $250 million in settlement
with Medicare and Medicaid units, plus $17.5 million to resolve
Medicaid claims.

Between them, the various settlements—dealing with both criminal
and civil charges—ultimately amounted to $1.7 billion. It was the
biggest health care swindle in US history, perpetrated by America's
largest health care corporation. James Alderson was justly rewarded:
the government decided to give him a particularly generous portion of
the $1.7 billion settlement, in recognition of his exceptional commit-
ment to the case, and the heavy cost to his family and finances that it
represented.

Triad's 2002 report notes that HCA was under formal investigation
by the Securities and Exchange Commission (SEC) for 'anti-fraud,
insider trading, periodic reporting and internal accounting' breaches
of federal securities laws. The report also revealed that HCA had been
implicated in felony charges to which another company had pleaded
guilty. In July 1999, an unrelated corporation, Olsten, and its subsidiary, Kimberly, agreed to pay $61 million to settle allegations that
they had defrauded Medicare. Kimberly, in pleading guilty to felony
charges (conspiracy, mail fraud and violating the Anti-Kickback
Statute), cited the involvement of another corporation. This corporation, HCA admitted, was itself or one of its subsidiaries.

Since 2003, when it paid almost $900 million in settlement to the
government under the False Claims Act, HCA has been experiencing

something of a downturn. On 25 July 2006, the *Wall Street Journal* reported that HCA was again planning a buy-out, this time for $21 billion, 'plus as much as $16 billion in new debt'. The deal initially collapsed—stockholders rejected the $37 billion bid from Merrill Lynch and others as too low—but it later went through. One of those who bought a $50 million stake in HCA through Merrill Lynch in the recent buy-out was an Irish businessman from Clare. The total debt of America's largest hospital chain—owner of 182 hospitals and ninety-four day-surgery centres—then amounted to $23–27 billion.

The ripple effect of the Columbia/HCA debacle spread to KPMG, Columbia/HCA's accountants. The Justice Department joined a whistleblower suit against KPMG, accusing the company of helping a client to defraud government health care programmes by submitting bogus expense claims. On 28 February 2003, *Forbes* reported that KPMG had paid the government $9 million to settle the action. The payment had been made twenty months previously, on 23 October 2001. It was the second time one of the so-called 'big five'—accountancy giants—had been indicted by government. The KPMG settlement topped the $7 million pay-out paid by Arthur Anderson four months previously.

In June 2006, a watchdog group, Public Citizen, called for an investigation into Senator Bill Frist's blind trusts for potentially illegal stock trading. He was reported to have sold all his shares in HCA just before the stock took a nose-dive in 2005; an SEC investigation into this transaction is continuing. Until the late 1990s, at least, the Frists were major investors in HCA. Bill Frist's nephew, Thomas F. Frist III, is a director of Triad.

TRIAD-QUORUM

Triad was created on 11 May 1999, when HCA divested itself of its Pacific Group, spinning off forty-two hospitals to stockholders. Most of Triad's senior management today, including its Chair and CEO, Danny Shelton, who led the spin-off from HCA, are former HCA or Columbia/HCA executives. None of them, the company stresses, has ever been found guilty of wrongdoing.

In 2001, the federal government insurance agency, CMS, notified Triad that it intended to re-open files on Medicare and Medicaid cost reports filed by fourteen of Triad's current and former hospitals, including two hospitals formerly owned by Quorum. This investigation

ended in 2003, when HCA made its final settlement with the Justice
Department.

Triad bought Quorum in April 2001 for $2.4 billion in a deal that
saw one former HCA company buy its brother corporation. Described
as 'the biggest deal of the year', the merger netted Triad a further
twenty hospitals, making it the country's third-largest investor-owned
hospital company, earning more than $3 billion in revenue.

Over half of its hospitals are in Alabama, Indiana and Texas.
Quorum Health Resources (QHR) is Triad's management arm, just as
it was once the management arm of their parent company, HCA. QHR,
a wholly owned subsidiary of Triad, is responsible for the liabilities of
HCA Management Company, as well as being its successor in interest.

After the merger of the two brother corporations, Burke Whitman,
then Triad's chief financial officer, explained that the plan was to
integrate Quorum with Triad, 'to combine the cultures, the policies,
procedures, the infrastructures and the strategic planning'. Triad's
operations were now structured in two segments: the first, hospitals
owned by Triad; the second, facilities *managed* by its subsidiary.

In October 2000, Quorum paid $95.5 million to settle two *qui tam*
lawsuits, one of which related to the Alderson complaint. Also in
October, Quorum, together with Flowers Hospital, paid $18 million to
settle a Medicare case taken by the US government. The following year,
Quorum paid $87.5 million to settle cost report allegations, again
relating to the Alderson suit.

On 27 April of the same year, Quorum was served with two *qui tam*
lawsuits taken against it under the False Claims Act, involving one
owned and two managed hospitals. Triad reported that Quorum had
'accrued the estimated liability on these items prior to the merger'.
The 2002 report also notes that the government had requested
Quorum to conduct a self-audit in relation to one of the managed
hospitals and three other issues. The government, Triad said, had also
stated that 'it intends to investigate certain other allegations'. In
respect of the Quorum-owned hospital, Triad reported that it had
paid $427,500, plus interest and whistleblowers' legal costs, on 15
January 2002, in settlement of alleged violations of the False Claims
Act; the case was dismissed with prejudice.

In July 2002, HCA paid Triad $4.5 million in part settlement of a
False Claims Act case settled by Quorum prior to merger. Triad's
accounts for the first six months of 2002 reveal the existence of two

whistleblower actions for claims involving three Quorum hospitals, one owned by QHR, and two managed by them. According to Triad, 'Quorum accrued the estimated liability on these items' prior to the merger.

Triad also related that, in June 2002, Quorum had settled an action by its stockholders who alleged that Quorum had breached federal laws by materially inflating its net revenues, Enron-style; Quorum's liability on this had been accrued prior to the merger.

On 9 September 2003, Triad was served with a *qui tam* suit in relation to a Mississippi hospital managed by its subsidiary; Quorum was also named as a defendant in the action. On 18 May 2004, Triad was served with further proceedings alleging false claims at two Georgia hospitals formerly managed by Quorum. This case is under appeal. On 26 April 2005, Triad was notified of yet another whistle-blower action against one of its Quorum-managed hospitals, this time in Pennsylvania.

In February 2006, in a renewal of this *qui tam* suit in Pennsylvania, Quorum was accused of perpetrating swindles that involved false and fraudulent claims to government health insurers over a twelve-year period, from January 1994 to February 2006 inclusive. Distressingly, fraudulent cost reporting over a period of years seems to be a recurring allegation in lawsuits taken against Quorum.

The corporation also stands accused of paying kickbacks and 'illegal remuneration' to doctors and others, and of entering into 'prohibited financial relationships' with physicians to induce them to refer patients to its hospital. Six doctors are named as co-defendants in the action. Triad has said that these allegations appear to be groundless and will be vigorously contested.

Only a month previously, Quorum had had to contend with US government charges. On 19 January 2006, the federal government filed a lawsuit against Ohio Valley General Hospital in Pittsburgh, accusing it of submitting false claims for more than $2 million in Medicare reimbursements. The action, filed by the US Attorney's Office on behalf of the Department of Health and Human Services, could result in civil penalties of more than $6 million. The government is also seeking $2 million in damages. The hospital is under Quorum management.

In its 2005 report, Triad told stockholders that the revenue service had disallowed deductions for payments made in 2001, 2002 and 2003 by Triad to the federal authorities arising out of three *qui tam* actions brought against Quorum. Triad jointly owns, or owned, hospitals in which Quorum held a majority interest in 1999, 2000 and 2001. In 2004 and 2005, Triad paid $5.9 million to settle charges.

Quorum faces heavy damages if found guilty of defrauding government insurance schemes. While fines range from $5,000 to $10,000, the damages payable are equal to three times the financial losses sustained by government. If HCA is unable to discharge its Quorum liabilities into the future, Triad will become liable for Quorum's charges.

In its 2005 report, Triad repeated its warnings to stockholders of the potential harm to the company of 'government investigations, known and unknown'. The corporation cautioned that it could be the subject of future, additional investigations alleging violations of law: 'Triad may not know about those investigations.' If Quorum hospitals were found to have violated federal or state laws, Triad said, it might be forced to pay substantial fines, civil and criminal damages and legal fees. Triad also cautioned that it could find itself excluded from Medicare, Medicaid and other government health insurance programmes.

In its 2005 report, Triad also disclosed that it owns facilities that, prior to spin-off, belonged to HCA or its subsidiaries. Triad lists on its website fifty-three hospitals and twelve ambulatory surgery centres. Some of these hospitals have been named in False Claims Act proceedings; others appear in draft fraud settlement agreements. Government fraud proceedings issued in 1999 in the Alderson case name Quorum hospitals owned today by Triad. The draft legal agreement, dated 26 June 2003, under which HCA paid the Justice Department $631 million, names 200-plus HCA hospitals, grouped according to charges. Around one-third of Triad's hospitals appear on this schedule. Fraudulent cost reporting and physician kickbacks were the main charges levelled against them. The schedule includes hospitals formerly owned by Triad, such as Mission Bay and San Leandro in California.

Chapter 13
Health for Sale?

THE BUSINESS OF HEALTH IN DUBLIN

'Agree the allocation of risk,' the speaker advises. 'If everything that is planned gets built, there is a medium-term risk of over-supply. Tax, legal, accounting, build, design and banking, these are the inputs you need,' she told her audience. The inputs listened intently: they included financiers, management consultants, bankers, solicitors, accountants, architects and engineers. Welcome to Ireland's 'inaugural' private health-care conference, 'The Business of Health', partnered by the Health Service Executive and Eircom, and sponsored by General Electric, VHI, Ulster Bank and 'The Health Partnership'.

I missed the opening address by the Tánaiste, Minister for Health Mary Harney. This is an environment, I quickly realise, where pharmaceutical companies, such as Pfizer, may share tables with professional medical bodies, such as the RCSI; health bureaucrats may mingle with private health-care companies; public relations executives chat to private health insurers; recruitment agencies tick-tack with nursing homes; and private facilities talk to private not-for-profit hospitals. I am interested to see the Coombe Women's Hospital among the delegates.

We are seated in a large room in the Grosvenor Suite in Dublin's Berkeley Court Hotel, under six cut-glass chandeliers, their stems tastefully wrapped in burgundy velvet. The walls are yellow damask.

Marbleised pillars frame ivory-panelled mirrors. Pin-head down-lighters illuminate the ceiling; snow-white damask covers the tables. Dining chairs in bright-red burgundy velour hold 276 bottoms, some ample (often male), some slender (mostly female), all suited, darkly, all listening intently to Gemma Lynch, health care team head at Ulster Bank (Corporate Banking).

She talks about 'a significant increase in the pool of private equity since 2002'. They note her complaint about 'a lack of transparency on the cost of different [medical] procedures'. Her colleague, Barry Lynch, talks about 'strategic control', envisaging a 'handback' of 'assets' to the state in thirty years. (He must be talking about thirty-year leases, a dream scenario for the private sector in Britain.)

But public–private partnership bids are not for the faint-hearted, or for the shallow-pocketed. The cost of 'the full process', Barry says, is between €1 million and €5 million.

I study the conference packs, which are among the most elaborate I've seen: black *faux* leather, heavily stitched, with a sharp-looking letter opener—courtesy of Ulster Bank—in stainless steel and black rubber. Perfect for this conference.

There seems to be a lot happening in the private health care scene that has gone unreported in the Irish media. The Northern Ireland public–private partnership (PPP) health division, for example, has announced 'deals' on 'up to' twelve private hospitals and health care projects. The 'RoI deal', costing in excess of €400 million, includes four large cancer treatment units: cancer patients are now being traded as commodities on the open market in the Republic. The guy from the Northern Ireland health division stands up to correct what has been said about there being £2 billion in the NI 'environment'. 'It's actually in excess of three billion,' he says, 'for infrastructure in Northern Ireland.'

General Electric, one of the largest corporations in the world, is to present at the conference. I think of all the major breaches of law involving this highly respected company in recent years. In addition to soil, air and water pollution—repeatedly contaminating the Hudson River, for instance—the litany includes: design flaws and safety breaches at nuclear plants; inadequate testing of aircraft parts; money laundering and fraud in connection with the illegal sale of fighter jets to Israel; defrauding and overcharging government in defence contracts; discriminating against employees who report safety breaches; chemicals dumping; asbestos contamination; worker safety violations; overcharging on mortgage insurance; unfair debt collection practices; and misleading advertising. All this and being ordered to pay damages for two airline crashes in just twelve years, from 1990 to 2001.

Before I can work out the equivalent of these breaches in the health care industry, the General Electric video begins. It is awesome. 'How do we define illness?' a male voice asks. 'Imagine if we could treat illness *before* it appeared.' We gaze, stupefied, at a snowstorm of molecules. The voice is commanding, authoritative; it tells us that 'protein purification technologies' will help us to 'discover Alzheimer's or Parkinson's *prior* to onset'. 'We are helping to re-imagine health care,' the narrator concludes.

Dan O'Connor doesn't quite have the charisma to follow *Imagination at Work*. No mortal could. General Electric, he reminds us, made America's first jet engine. Now it has a machine that can image the heart in *five* seconds. Medical imaging, he predicts, will 'give us a focus on early health'.

This focus on early health is rudely disturbed. The air is suddenly foul: stink bombs explode. Two young Ógra Sinn Féin men in suits are addressing the audience. 'Health for People, Not for Profit,' they chant, before being carted off. Dan resumes smoothly, effortlessly, as though the spectre of health for people, not for profit, had never entered the room.

The second speaker from General Electric, Paul Morton, talks about 'a massive increase in patient expectations', 'difficult choices' and 'future-proofing'. I think of the design flaws in nuclear plants for which the company was fined $80 million in damages in 1992, in Pennsylvania. Hotel employees, meanwhile, are proofing the air, opening windows.

Ivory nets sway, distractingly. The patient, we are told, is 'moving through the system faster than the information'. There is a solution to this problem: outsourcing. But outsourcing is no longer what it used to be. The old approach, a 'device and maintenance contract,' Morton explains, 'has now been replaced by a collaborative approach, where we help you to design your facility to take advantage of the technology.' This collaboration sounds like an arranged marriage: 'GE becomes your partner.' Even the dowry is taken care of: 'GE will arrange your funding for you.' Corporations dream of monopolies. GE's vision is to have 'one integrated supplier of technology services'—on a thirty-seven-year contract.

The nets over the French windows billow in the cold spring breeze as Morton talks about 'transferring the risk of technological obsolescence'. 'MRI and ultrasound technologies are changing very fast,' he emphasises. But maybe obsolescence isn't such a risk after all: technology is not getting dearer. Morton forecasts that, in 2010, scanners will cost about the same as they do today, 'but there will be many more of them'. A CT scanner, he tells us, costs €500,000–800,000, while an MRI scanner comes with a tag of €1–1.5 million.

Only Vincent Sheridan, the CEO of VHI Healthcare and a director of FBD Holdings, plc, sounds a note of caution: 'I ask what all this will cost.' For him, one of the key questions is: to what extent will the public health system 'outsource' to the private sector?

Touchstone Healthcare Group CEO Joseph Hoban sports a deep 1980s Marbella tan. Touchstone, he says, is 'for people who walk in off the street, who are ambulant'. Joseph thinks the focus should be on primary care. He describes 'the ideal': 'Compressed morbidity: it means you will stay as well as possible for as long as possible, then you go to hospital for as short as possible, then you die.' Joseph describes the family doctor as the greatest single resource in the Irish health care system, 'only they don't have the tools.' Touchstone aims to give them the tools; the company owns a string of pharmacy/general practitioner outlets in the Republic. 'You could put in twenty-four different services [into primary care],' he suggests, 'like community health nursing, diagnostics, home nursing, home helps.' Just like the state, in fact, except that for-profit community services come with a price tag.

The star of the show, unquestionably, is Nations Healthcare CEO Jerry Mansmann. Nations is based in London, but Jerry has done 'a lot of work' in Ireland. Modest Jerry is not: Nations, he claims, has been 'very successful' in the 'independent treatment sector'. ('Independent' in health care is American for 'private'.) General Electric is one of Nations' partners; Barclay's does some of Nations' funding. Bradford (hospital), Jerry says, was built on the US model; this was the first ISTC—independent sector treatment centre—to open in Britain.

Jerry gives us a bird's eye view of just how to build an American-style health-care facility: 'You just put a consortium together, with Nations at the centre.' Then, to neutralise the opposition, you enlist a prestigious American university. 'We recognised that there would be a lot of *pushback* from clinicians,' Jerry explains (this is his word for 'opposition', I gather). 'So we went to Johns Hopkins University: they were able to deal with any changes that would be necessary in clinical practice, for example, in day-care cases.' (Johns Hopkins, I recall, is listed as having paid $2.6 million in 2004 in a settlement under the False Claims Act in the US, for failing to comply with federal regulations governing research. Many American universities have made such settlements with government, particularly departments of medicine.)

Jerry, an American lawyer and 'health care adviser', is large, upbeat, buoyant and expansive: 'We do not just provide the infrastructure, but also, for the first time in history, we provide the clinical services,' he says, proudly. The ultimate aim of the NHS, Jerry reckons, is to move 'from being a payer-provider to being a payer only'.

Nations Healthcare aims 'to create accountability in the market'. 'The word *competition* is not appropriate.' Nations' dislike of the term 'competition' may, I muse, be related to its ambition to become a near-monopoly provider. For Nations, if not for NHS patients, the future is bright: 'There will only be four or five players in this market, in the long run, with consolidation,' Jerry predicts, confidently.

Elective surgery, diagnostics, cancer, chronic diseases—these are the areas to target, he advises his rapt audience. 'We formed strategic alliances with, for example, the University of Pittsburgh Medical Centre.' UPMC has a presence in Ireland already, according to Jerry, with American Health, one of the biggest 'players' in long-term care.

Enthusiastically, Jerry identifies the stepping stones that paved the way for turning the British NHS into a vehicle for corporate health care: the introduction of private finance initiatives (similar to PPPs); the establishment of foundation trust hospitals 'that would have the ability to control their own destiny'; and LIFT, which Jerry describes as 'a programme for GPs outside the NHS'. (LIFT, he could have added, is a government programme, designed to grow consortia at local level involving corporations such as Nations, general practitioners, the NHS and other state bodies in private for-profit health care ventures.)

The British government, according to Jerry, has committed 15 per cent of the nation's total health budget to the 'independent' sector. Privatisation comes in 'waves', apparently. In Britain, the first wave is costing the state £1.6 billion, while the second wave, for 'incumbent private health providers', will cost £4 billion plus. The waves are huge, a surfer's dream: waves one and two involve contracts potentially worth up to £15 billion. Jerry is jubilant, and understandably so: 'Every patient has five [care] options, one of which has to be an "independent" provider'. When Nations entered the market, the NHS gave it 'guaranteed revenues'.

> *Even if those patients did not show up, you would be paid for them.*
> Jerry Mansmann, Nations Healthcare CEO, on the corporation's
> sweetheart deal with Britain's NHS

But there was more icing on the cake: 'If they [NHS] didn't renew the contract after five years, they would buy it back.'

In Britain, Nations has gone from winning an initial £320 million contract to being shortlisted for an NHS contract worth £1 billion. How did they do it? Jerry is nothing if not frank about the various strategies Nations employed in managing its entry into the NHS. The company set out to make private for-profit health care more acceptable by identifying 'needs' in 'local health economies'. Nations also got 'strategic health authorities' to be funded centrally, not locally, but he did not elaborate on how, in a democracy such as Britain's, an Australian–American corporation managed to secure such a major shift in public health-care funding. There was a 'pushback', he admits. 'But we got it [privatisation] through without too much opposition from the unions.' 'Early consultation', it seems, was a key factor in neutralising the trade union movement. Performance management is another tool used by Nations 'to make it easier for the public sector to participate'. 'We have key performance indicators, like cleanliness. It's very, very important to put these into the public domain,' he stresses.

He then takes the discussion to another level. Speed is of the essence, he advises: 'The process has to be fast-tracked. Do it in a year or eighteen months. You also need an outsider in a [state] department to push the agenda,' he underlines. '[In the UK] we developed a commercial directorate—we picked a UK citizen raised in Texas! You can't get a more aggressive person than a Texan! He really pushed it [the corporate agenda].' How Nations managed to influence the internal workings of the British health care system by putting an industry representative into one of the top jobs in the NHS was left unexplained.

In addition to fast-tracking the process and infiltrating the state bureaucracy, Jerry advises poaching doctors from the public sector. 'Additionality doesn't work,' he says firmly. This is his term for independent recruitment, where the for-profit sector sources its own staff.

Jerry's advice is succinct: 'You're better to have the NHS doctors than having to recruit internationally.'

He finishes his talk with a brief look at the nuts and bolts: 'You need a length of contract, five or seven years or more. You need to make the programme an integrated part of the health economy. You need courage, because there's gonna be a lot of pushback.' On that cheery note, Jerry finishes his talk.

The future certainly looks rosy for the corporation: Scotland has now committed to a Nations project, Portugal has invited the company to tender for a ten-year contract, France is 'looking' at a possible project and Nations is 'in discussions' with Wales.

In Ireland, Jerry complains, there has been no policy decision taken by government as yet 'as to whether there will be a public–private relationship and if so, what that will be.' But, ever the optimist, he reckons that medical consultants in Ireland will be 'more entrepreneurial [than their British counterparts]'. A combined North–South initiative would be needed, he thinks, to make it worth Nations' while. Working with the public sector, Jerry points out, would make it more 'sustainable', 'as long as they knew the rules of the game going forward'.

One of the final speakers at the conference, John O'Brien, Director of the HSE's National Hospitals Office, is clearly 'going forward' on privatisation: 'There is a role for the private sector to respond very aggressively to what's coming into the hospitals at the front end,' he says, but it isn't clear whether he's referring to people with chronic care conditions or to women having babies.

> *We are exploring cross-relationships.*
> John O'Brien CEO of the National Hospitals' Office, on the forthcoming marriage in Ireland between the public health system and the private for-profit sector

O'Brien seems enthusiastic about the opportunities that exist for privatising health care. 'The notion that there is not a partnership between the public and the private is misplaced,' he insists. He admits that public–private partnerships in health have been slow to develop: 'We've not been as agile as other departments.' But all of this is about to change. On 'social infrastructure,' he predicts, we will see 'a big drive on this, going forward, in social partnership'.

Two months after John O'Brien predicted a surge in what he termed 'social partnership', Irish unions dropped their opposition to the outsourcing of core public services, paving the way for cross-relationships to fuel growth in for-profit health care. The Irish trade union movement had now apparently accommodated itself to neo-liberalism. The definition of core public services included health: this represented a policy shift which, in twenty years' time, could see Ireland's health care landscape closely resemble America's. As long as the money was on the table, who cared?

HOSPITALS INC.

There is serious money to be made out of health. In 2005, the Department of Health spent €2 billion in public-sector contracts. In 2004, for instance, pre-tax profits at the Mater Private rose by a whopping 74 per cent. Today, even religious orders turn a profit in health. The nuns once ran a not-for-profit hospital system. Until the 1980s, private hospitals run as for-profit entities were rare. Now, the good nuns have joined the ranks of those—property developers, investors and doctors—who make money from the sick, the aged and the vulnerable. In 2003, for example, the Sisters of Charity made a tidy profit of €5.4 million from their three Dublin hospitals, St Vincent's public, St Vincent's private and St Michael's. In 2004, although pre-tax profits were down, the Sisters' revenue jumped by over 30 per cent, boosted by a generous—if involuntary—donation of €147 million from the taxpayer. Of course, legally, once you plough the money back into the business, it's classified as not for profit; more importantly, as a charity, you have no tax liabilities.

Private nursing homes have mushroomed and private for-profit hospitals have proliferated. Jimmy Sheehan, surgeon and owner-developer of the Blackrock and Galway Clinics, was one of the country's first medical entrepreneurs. He claims credit for the extreme generosity shown in the 2001 Finance Act to medical investors such as himself: 'I went to Charlie McCreevy and I lobbied him,' Jimmy proudly told local authority councillors at a conference on for-profit health care in Ennis, Co. Clare, on 19 May 2006. Tax breaks for building or refurbishing private and public hospitals and nursing homes were introduced by the Government in 2001. Initially for non-profit hospitals only, the tax concessions were extended to for-profit investors a year later. This was a watershed in hospital history. Only eight years previously, the Department had expressed serious concern over the proliferation of private hospitals run as 'business entities', purely for 'commercial profit'. Now, McCreevy's tax breaks opened the floodgates to all-comers in a private hospital environment that was totally unregulated. Vincent Sheridan, CEO of VHI, would later describe government policy of growing for-profit hospitals without the controls of a licensing system as 'madness'. Within months of the 2002 Finance Act passing into law, US hospital chains, such as HCA, gravitated towards the pot of gold now on offer from the Irish taxpayer. Even the Sisters of St John of God in Kilkenny yielded to the temptation to sell off their hospital, Aut Even, to a for-profit company formed by cardiologist John Clarke and former independent hospitals group head, Micheal Heavey.

Four years after the act was introduced, the investment of choice for the wealthy was a nursing home rather than a golf course. Since then, showing a healthy growth rate of 10 per cent per annum, private nursing homes have proliferated. By the end of October 2004, there were 427 private nursing homes in Ireland with a total of 16,461 beds. The 'crossover' from holiday homes to nursing homes is one now being made by many investors. With chilling realism, the southern nursing home group, Golden Meadows, for example, describes its main business as 'real estate management'. Nursing homes have become the latest in tax-fuelled investments, rivalling hotels, holiday homes and inner-city developments. More recently, mental health facilities have been included in the tax breaks.

Private consortia are finely tuned to take maximum advantage of these business opportunities. Mowlam Health Care, for example, brings together private investors who club together to 'buy' a nursing home for ten years. (To qualify for a tax write-off, you must 'invest' for a decade, at a minimum.) Mowlam—largely owned by Limerick property developers John Sheehan and Joseph Hanrahan—finances and builds the development, which it then leases and operates as a nursing home business; after ten years, Mowlam buys back the property.

IN THE COOLEY MOUNTAINS

'Delivering Healthcare Solutions for the North East', the expensive-looking, turquoise-shaded A5 prospectus proclaims. Nature has been enlisted in the enterprise: 'The natural landscape ... allowed to flow, apparently uninterrupted, towards and under the new *intervention* [emphasis added]....' The new intervention is 'a pristine modern building form, appropriate to the scale and ambition of the health care facility required'. Welcome to the Ballymascanlon Clinic, in the foothills of the Cooley Mountains. At a conference in Ennis on private health care, in May 2006, Mary Grehan, a Dundalk GP, explained how the hospital came about: 'I have put in a million, my husband has put in a million, and that's our contribution to health care in Ireland.' There are two other investors in the project.

The clinic was then awaiting planning permission. It planned to sell cardiology, obstetrics/gynaecology, IVF, radiology, general and vascular surgery, ear, nose and throat (ENT), general medicine, rheumatology, neurology, pain, dermatology, cancer, ophthalmology, psychiatry, haematology, pathology, orthopaedics, sports medicine and urology services. 'Eminent' medical consultants, who are likely to be gainfully employed already in public hospitals in the North East, have 'committed' to the project, according to the brochure.

It was not slow to exploit the craters left in the public health system by two decades of under-funding. 'There is a major shortage of an urgent nature of medical care facilities and hospital beds in the country as a whole and in the north-east region in particular,' the prospectus declared. 'The region is devoid of specialist services. This means that patients have to travel to Dublin for treatments.... In 2004 in excess of 600 round trips were made to Dublin by volunteer drivers from the North Louth hospice alone, transporting patients to Dublin for treatment. The waiting list for in-patient hospital services in the North Eastern region is considerable ... the largest proportion of cases fall within the specialties of general and vascular surgery, orthopaedics, ENT, ophthalmology and cardiology.'

The Ballymascanlon Clinic is but one of a number of private hospitals mushrooming all over Ireland. In 2005, Goodbodys Stockbrokers listed eleven private hospitals in planning and two under construction. A procurement process is under way for a further ten for-profit facilities. Can Ireland sustain all twenty-three of them?

Any anxieties these private hospital developers may have will be allayed by the existence of a national kitty, the National Treatment Purchase Fund (NTPF). Private hospitals depend on public monies for viability and the NTPF is a mechanism for using public monies to treat public patients privately. The NTPF acts as a growth promoter of private medicine, stimulating both individual private practice and the private hospital sector. The fund was created by government in 2002, ostensibly to shorten public waiting lists.

If you are a public patient, the NTPF sounded good: twelve months (now three) on a waiting list for an adult, six months (now three) for a child, and, bingo, you can phone the fund; they will organise and pay for your treatment in a public or a private hospital, in Ireland or Britain. At a macro level, however, the NTPF has been a disaster, in the view of many. The fund puts cash into private pockets, cash that could be used to build up our public hospital system, which is being denied the resources it needs to enable it to function. Instead, thanks to NTPF monies, consultants are being paid to treat their own public patients privately. So the taxpayer is now paying twice for their treatment, once through the usual hospital funding, and once more through the NTPF. How much the fund is paying for these procedures is a closely guarded secret: the Department of Health claims that this informa-tion is 'commercially sensitive'.

Official figures show that the fund is actually a gravy train for some consultants. An audit done by the Comptroller and Auditor General shows that 36 per cent of all treatments paid for by the fund were carried out in the same hospital on whose waiting list the patient had been waiting for twelve months or more. The same report showed a staggering range of fees for the same procedures, suggesting not just massive overpayment by the fund, but rampant overcharging by some doctors. A scandalous waste of public monies was the general verdict in some quarters. The NTPF experience also showed that, if some consultants worked harder, more patients could be treated in an acceptable timeframe. The question that was left unanswered was: why did it take money to buy access? How come public patients who had been scheduled for a particular procedure could suddenly be treated by the same consultants on whose waiting lists they had been left to languish for a year or more?

LOCATION, LOCATION

'That golden blend between public and private where everyone benefits' was now invoked to solve the A&E crisis. By mid-2005, the Government had decided to embark on the biggest public–private partnership in the history of the state: in health. On 15 July, 2005, the Minister for Health announced a new initiative to provide 'an extra 1,000 acute hospital beds' in 'major hospitals' across the state, through procuring the building of private hospitals on public hospital sites. The public hospitals to be chosen for this honour would be those with the biggest number of private beds.

Far from seeking to remove that drain on the public purse, the public–private mix, the Minister now sought to embed it even more deeply, in building contracts and service agreements, through co-location— the siting of private hospitals on public hospital lands. Although Ms Harney repeatedly denied it, co-location *is* a form of privatisation. Indeed, co-located hospitals are often referred to as 'private wings', so symbiotic is their relationship with the nearby public hospital on which they batten. Put simply, co-location involves inviting private investors to build an extension to a public hospital, defraying half the cost of the build, allowing the new private wing to be staffed with medical consultants poached from the public hospital, and guaranteeing the viability of the enterprise—and the profits of investors—by enabling streams of public patients to be rerouted from the public hospital.

Hospitals scheduled for co-location include Tallaght, St James's, Beaumont, Limerick Regional, Our Lady of Lourdes Hospital, Drogheda, Cork University Hospital and University College Hospital Galway. By May 2006, this figure had jumped to eleven. The Lourdes Hospital was later dropped from the list, after the publication of the *Teamwork Report* recommending its demise. More recently, tenders for Galway and Letterkenny had to be re-launched after initially interested bidders withdrew.

Ironically, one of the arguments used by *Hanly* to close smaller hospitals around the country was that Ireland had 'too many' of them, and that this was resulting in a 'costly duplication' of services. Now— two years later—the Government proposed to build no fewer than ten new small hospitals on public hospital sites. 'Viability' for the new hospitals was defined at eighty-plus beds.

Clearly, there had been a shortage of small hospitals all along. There was no talk now of costly duplication, although the new private hospitals would offer to precisely the same population exactly the same medical services, in many cases, as their public hospital neighbours. Competition was the name of the new unspoken game, the creation of an internal market. (This is a strategy in Britain that has brought hospitals to their knees, in hock to hospital chains.) But, for some reason, the Government failed to spell out the rules of the new game. Not for the first time, taxpayers found themselves in the dark.

Dr John Barton was, and is, highly critical of the new scheme: 'The Minister's plan will boost a system that gives a perverse incentive to doctors to fast-track their private patients,' he says. The Health Services Action Group chair pointed out that the vast majority of the 1,000 private beds would remain private. 'Private patients who take up public beds in public hospitals are generally very ill. Private hospitals will not look after these patients,' the Galway physician commented, continuing:

> The mix of private and public medicine in our public hospital system has led to a two-tier health service, with the private patient within that system being accorded greater importance, not because doctors in general favour greater access to treatment for private patients, but because the system of remuneration encourages doctors to secure quicker access and treatment for private patients. This discriminatory system of remuneration encourages differences in approach by consultant doctors to private and public patients. This in-built discrimination between private and public patients will now be exacerbated by government and state policy favouring greater involvement of the private sector, if consultants contracted to work in public hospitals are allowed to work at unregulated times in these new private facilities and, indeed, to invest in these same facilities.

There was every danger that the Minister's plan would bring even more chaos into the public system. How would consultants organise their consultations, their treatment and their surgery? Would they operate in the middle of the night and see patients at weekends in these private hospitals? Or would they simply go AWOL from their public hospitals during normal working hours?

One thing was clear: the new private hospitals would be for profit. The HSE was reported to be looking for 'expressions of interest' from investors; their proposals would have to meet 'a range of criteria'. These criteria were publicly unspecified, save one: public hospitals would be selected for privatisation only 'where consultants accept that there would be no question of having to be compensated for the transfer of their private beds to the private facility' and where they agreed 'to work in teams'.

But consultants were already working in teams, weren't they? And only a minority of beds were to be transferred; the rest could stay where they were. Consultants would be able to keep 60 per cent of their private beds in public hospitals, it later emerged. This meant that another layer of dysfunction would simply be added to the mix. The separation of the public from the private was nowhere in sight.

Getting consultants' agreement to the plan was vital to the success of the Minister's enterprise: beds needed to be seen to move, at least on paper. The PR paid off: IHCA assistant general secretary Donal Duffy welcomed the imaginary 1,000 public beds, but said that they fell far short of what was needed. The INO, portrayed by the Minister as the sole union representing nurses in the private sector, also welcomed the plan, but questioned how the beds would be staffed. Only the IMO president, Asam Ishtiaq, expressed concern that the 'development of for-profit private medicine in Ireland might not be in the best interests of the long-term future of the health service.'

Five months later, the number of private beds to be liberated from public hospitals into private wings had apparently doubled, with *The Irish Times* reporting plans for 'the transfer of over 2,000 existing beds for fee-paying patients in public hospitals to the proposed private centres.'

HOW PPPs WORK

'A very nice little number for the private sector' is how Anne Counihan, then CEO of the National Development Finance Agency, describes public-private partnerships (PPPs). Originally designed for road-building in Britain, PPPs are now used in Ireland for roads, bridges, and schools, to name but three. And, now, hospitals. Ireland has a 'very clear' policy on PPPs, according to Counihan. 'Under the National Development Plan, from 2006 to 2010, we are spending €43.5 billion, plus €5.5 billion on PPPs, plus further PPPs funded by, for example, tolls.' Now three years old, the agency was founded to give advice to state and semi-state bodies on 'all projects with a value of over €20 million'.

The procurement process in PPPs is very different from the traditional tender. In this, the state draws up the project design and issues contract documents to tendering firms, who then submit their prices for the job; the most economically advantageous tender, usually the lowest, is supposed to win the contract. (In Ireland, however, unlike other countries, tenders are not binding: builders can up the price *after* the project is completed and the finished hospital, or extension, often comes in at double the price.) But in the case of PPPs, such as the 'competitive dialogue' process being used for the co-located private hospitals, the starting point is often a blank canvas, itself a potential drain for state monies; it begins at a much earlier stage, sometimes before the process has formally opened, over lunch, perhaps, in Patrick Guilbaud's, maybe. Secondly, with no design or contract to restrain them, corporations are free to write their own script, often based on the golden formula of 'design, build, finance and operate'. Thirdly, the winning company secures the contract on grounds that may never be discovered. That's right: commercial sensitivity. Such contracts, shrouded in secrecy, are shielded from public view. The payback to investors varies from project to project; this is worked out as part of the deal. In Britain, in the NHS, for example, very long leases have become the norm, guaranteeing investors handsome rental returns on their money for thirty, or even sixty, years. 'There's very little risk in this for the private sector,' Counihan observes.

Ten months later, co-location was presented as a native plant, grown on the 'realities' of Irish health care, using a time-honoured planting method, the public–private mix. As well as making us feel safe by appealing to tradition, Harney appealed to feelings of insularity, reminding us that that 'mixed system of financing and providing hospital services' was not only centuries old; it was ours. And ours alone, she might have added. This was the mix, after all, that could have been described as 'utterly unique in the developed world': one that 'promoted private practice in medicine at the expense of the less well off'; a 'perpetual drain on the public purse' that 'cried out to be abolished'.

A TENDENCY TO JUMP

The Minister's costings now appeared to be somewhat elastic. On 15 July 2005, Eithne Donnellan reported that the price of a new bed (build) was 'up to' €500,000. But by 4 May 2006, construction costs had apparently doubled: each hospital bed, the Minister declared, cost 'approximately €1 million' to build. The Minister seemed to be referring to the cost of building a public hospital bed. But the average cost of a public bed several years earlier had been a fraction of that figure. In 2002, according to an official report, the cost to the state of building a hospital bed directly was just €125,000. Now the Minister was quoting €1 million for the same bed. This was a pole-vault of nearly 900 per cent, unequalled even by new houses in millionaire estates over the same period. No explanation was forthcoming for this extraordinary leap in building costs. Was it possible that the Minister was confusing (cheaper) direct public building with (dearer) public-private trickle-downs? A year previously, the Department of Finance estimated that the cost of subsidising James Sheehan's Galway Clinic (€20 million) would result in twenty 'public' beds at a cost to the state of €1 million each. Could this have been what the Minister was thinking of?

Hospital running costs showed the same distressing tendency to jump. In July 2005, a hospital bed was reported as costing 'about' €300,000 a year to staff and run'. By May 2006, according to the Minister, that cost had soared to €400,000. But, with inflation running at 3–4 per cent, it was difficult to see just where that increase of 33 per cent in running costs had come from. Taxpayers could still relax, however, because, according to Mary Harney, 'private developers' would be 'bearing this cost under the plan'.

But would they? As in Britain, the plan was for the state to buy health services from private operators. This was hinted at, discreetly, by the then Tánaiste, who said it would be 'open to the HSE and the National Treatment Purchase Fund to buy services for public patients from the private facilities'. Would this really be an option or would it be a non-option? The Department of Health planned to build just 450 hospital beds from 2006 to 2009, when 3,000 were needed. Starved systematically in this way, the public system would soon find itself forced to buy core hospital services for public patients from private conglomerates. The vista of General Electric, one of the biggest multi-nationals in the world, caring selflessly for cancer patients, suddenly came into view. (General Electric is the 'diagnostic imaging partner' of the Northern Ireland Cancer Centre, in Belfast.)

The Government's shifting, chameleon-like scheme, with its wildly fluctuating cost base, was presented as a win-win: on the taxpayers' side, there was that tantalising—if false—prospect of €0.5 billion just waiting to be saved; overstretched public hospitals were promised additional specialists; and time-poor consultants would 'save time travelling between public and private hospitals'. (The Minister omitted to mention the salient fact that, in the newest incarnation of the parallel public–private universe, public hospital consultants would now be given a perverse incentive to absent themselves from their public hospital duties, because, by so doing, they stood to make a vast amount of money.) Diehard socialists were also offered a carrot/stick or two: 'some' consultants might 'in future be asked to take on public work only', a suggestion later roundly rejected by medical unions. Finally, the Minister indicated that plans to charge private health insurers 'the full economic cost' of a hospital bed would end the state subsidy of private practice in public hospitals.

The Minister neglected to spell out the plan's advantages for private corporations, developers and investors: their capital costs almost halved; their specialists ready for poaching from a public pool of highly experienced doctors; their market guaranteed by a state willing to pay significantly over the odds for core patient services, such as radiology or dialysis. Those who had most to rejoice in were not the cancer sufferers or the diabetics in our midst; they were the millionaire builders, bankers, developers, investors, financiers, advertisers, auctioneers, solicitors and PR consultants, who needed no reminding of their excessively good fortune. Meanwhile, the 2002 Finance Act would ensure that investors' investment in the new private hospitals would be gifted to them by the serf taxpayers (assuming that these investors were themselves taxpayers, in the first instance, of course).

IMAGINARY BEDS

For public patients, the outlook was poor. In an opinion piece in *The Irish Times*, John Barton wrote: 'While the Minister claims these hospitals will reduce pressure on the public system, the Canadian Health Services Research Foundation in Ottawa has described such claims as "mythical".' An OECD study showed 'adverse effects' on waiting lists for surgery when parallel private hospital systems were introduced in countries, like Ireland, where consultants were in short supply and where they were allowed to practise privately in this parallel universe.

'Mary Harney says these for-profit hospitals will have to reserve 20 per cent of their beds for public patients, and that these patients will then be taken off waiting lists, via the National Treatment Purchase Fund,' Barton wrote. But Australian research shows that building private hospitals side by side with public facilities actually leads to an *increase* in public waiting times.

In a report on the effect of private money on public health care in five OECD countries, he continued, 'Carolyn Hughes Tuohy, Professor of Political Science at Toronto University, said there was "no ground" for believing that a parallel privately insured system reduces waiting lists or waiting times for public patients. "Private alternatives are not the solution," she concluded.'

This cast serious doubt on the notion that 1,000 (of the 2,500 minimum) beds currently 'set aside' for private patients in public hospitals would 'be clawed back by transferring private patients who use them to new private hospitals which will be built by investors'. Looking at the realities of Irish hospital care, the claw-back, in any case, was a myth. Department of Health statistics showed that 71 per cent of all hospital in-patients were admitted through A&E. 'The plan will not materially improve A&E,' John Barton concluded, 'as all urgent cases— public and private—will still have to go to the public hospital.'

For-profit hospitals cream off the simpler cases; they don't 'do' A&E. There was no question, ever, of 'springing' 1,000 beds in public hospitals out of private commission and into public use. Even if, as Myles na Gopaleen suggested in *The Third Policeman*, a man might, over time, fuse with his bicycle, patients were not bonded, molecularly, to their beds. The Minister's plan was a mirage: hospital beds, like hotel rooms, are occupied on a rotating basis. Most of the 1,000 beds under the ministerial gaze were occupied by patients who had been admitted as emergencies and could not, therefore, be 'transferred' to private hospitals: for-profit hospitals don't have the staff to care for the diverse needs of such patients. Casualty is too costly to be profitable. When private hospitals have emergencies themselves, when their patients become very ill, they transfer them, speedily, to public hospitals, where they can be looked after by specialist nurses and doctors, who are employed in sufficient numbers to provide round-the-clock attention.

So the Minister's plan, at best, would yield only about 290 additional beds. No one said anything; civil servants cannot publicly contradict their ministers.

The Opposition failed to challenge the Minister's figures effectively, although most people knew that if you were really sick, a private hospital or a private clinic was not the place to be. The case of a mother of three who had become seriously ill after an operation at a new private hospital in the west had been widely reported. A 34-year-old mother of three, she slipped into a coma shortly after a routine procedure at the Galway Clinic; she was immediately transferred to University College Hospital Galway, where she remains in a persistent vegetative state at the time of writing (February 2007).

CHEAPEST OR DEAREST?

The Minister claimed her scheme was 'the fastest and most economical way of meeting the need for extra public beds'. Fastest, perhaps, but cheapest? Far from 'saving' money, taxpayers were being asked to pay out far more than they would otherwise have done, had these beds been built by the state. Writing in *The Irish Times*, Harney claimed that her policy 'saves taxpayers €520 million in capital costs and substantial running costs'. The Minister planned to co-fund the building of these private hospitals; co-funding was presented as 'saving' taxpayers money. 'If the private sector builds the new facility,' she argued, 'the capital cost to the Exchequer is reduced to a maximum of 48 per cent, with full capital allowances being used.' What the Minister didn't say was that, in order to 'save' money, the Government would first have to sign away well over €0.5 billion, at least, in tax revenue, to help finance facilities that would belong entirely to their private owners, in perpetuity.

Looking at the Minister's own figures, it became very clear that her plan would cost taxpayers more, not less. Speaking at the private health care conference, Anne Counihan, then CEO of the National Development Finance Agency, accepted that PPPs in health entailed *additional* costs for the state: 'As we see it, the transfer of risk away from the public sector is what makes it [the investment] worthwhile.' No one asked her the obvious question: where is the risk in building a public hospital bed?

In May 2006, the Minister indicated that she was prepared to compensate the ten public hospitals selected for lost income. This was a new twist: when the plan was first announced in 2005, Harney had maintained that the 'benefit' of gaining extra public beds would be 'sufficient compensation' to public hospitals for their losses. For their 2,500 private beds, these hospitals stood to lose €220 million annually from private health insurers, such as VHI, VIVAS and the rest. To offset their drop in income, the Minister now promised to give public hospitals €145 million based on 'full economic charging' for private beds. Adding the cost of compensation to the price of the beds—48 per cent of €1 billion—would bring the Exchequer's contribution to this particular public–private partnership to €625 million, at least. Even on the Minister's figure of €1 million per bed, her plan would cost the general taxpayer about €300 million *more* than if the state itself had built the 290 beds, even after allowing for increased charges for private beds the plan might free up in public hospitals.

Moreover, the Minister's figures were completely notional: they did not allow for cost over-runs. Over-runs on the roads had cost the Exchequer a staggering €7 billion. Massive cost over-runs in health have been logged in Britain.

And there was another hidden extra: the cost of consultants' indemnity. By then, the Government had agreed to foot the insurance bill for consultants, in high-risk specialties, who worked *solely* in private hospitals. Why these facilities could not be required to pay indemnity insurance for their medical staff as they do in other countries was a question left unasked. By then, the private sector was being portrayed as vital to the overall health economy: the public and the private were both now 'interdependent' and 'complementary'. The climb-down on insurance was a further sign of the Government's commitment to private medicine by protecting it from having to bear some of the more onerous costs of running a business.

Co-location is a woodworm that eats its way into the nerve centre of the public system, stripping it systematically of its most crucial assets—staff and patients. It is central to multinational strategies for market penetration. Nations Healthcare CEO Jerry Mansmann cites Nations' medical facility in Buxton—co-located on an NHS site—as an example of Nations' success in the marketplace. Also co-located on an NHS campus and run by Nations Healthcare is Nottingham NHS Treatment Centre, which is cheek by jowl with one of the biggest teaching hospitals in Europe, the Queen's Medical Centre. (Hospitals are now increasingly referred to as 'medical centres' to facilitate and conceal the fragmentation that privatisation brings.) With 150,000 outpatients and an output of 24,000 procedures annually, this is the biggest for-profit treatment centre in Britain, according to Mr Mansmann.

In Ireland, the Minister's plan for co-location will almost certainly add a further 1,000 beds to the for-profit sector. (With bids costing up to €5 million, the possibility that the independent not-for-profit sector might become involved is remote.) Adding the thirteen pre-existing tax-fuelled, investor-owned hospitals to the pot, assuming— with one exception—an average of 100 beds in each, the proportion of money-making hospital beds in Ireland, excluding psychiatric and long-stay, is set to rise to 42 per cent, nationally, minimum.

However it was presented publicly in Ireland, co-location—the word was never mentioned—was far from being an Irish solution to an Irish problem. By the time Ms Harney announced her plan to bring co-location to the nation, she was flying in the face of over-whelming evidence. From North America, Australia, and Britain, the message was clear: Ireland was about to replicate a discredited system.

BEACON

The Minister's plan for co-location may well extend the influence of corporate health care in Ireland. Corporations are already involved in the provision of cancer-care services in the south-east. If large con-glomerates succeed in their bids for a chunk of Ireland's hospital assets, we may expect to see major changes over the coming years in the way hospital care is delivered in Ireland. These changes are unlikely to be for the good of patients.

Bidding for the co-located hospitals is under way at the time of writing. One of the bidders for six of the co-located hospitals is the American chain, Triad Inc., which is already running a private hospital in south county Dublin. The Beacon Clinic is Triad's first venture in Europe, although its parent company, HCA, reportedly has hospitals in England and Switzerland.

Triad's partner in Ireland is the Beacon Medical Group, founded in 2002 by cardio-thoracic surgeon Mark Redmond and businessmen Michael Cullen and Paddy Shovlin. The group's business comprises the Beacon Consultant Clinic, Beacon Dermatology, Beacon Renal and Beacon Hospital (which has 183 beds).

Beacon's partner, Triad, owns and operates hospitals in seventeen states in the US. Three-quarters of its hospitals are located in small cities with populations below 150,000; they are usually either the only hospital or else one of two or three hospitals in a community. Triad's wholly owned subsidiary and brother corporation, Quorum, is also based in Plano, Texas. The largest hospital management company in the US, Quorum manages over 200 private hospitals and health sys-tems in forty-three states. These hospitals are generally located in non-urban areas: two-thirds have fewer than 100 beds.

Triad is a for-profit corporation that is listed on the New York Stock Exchange. It has not yet paid a dividend to its stockholders, not because it is a not-for-profit corporation, as Mr Redmond suggested in *The Irish Times*, but because it is restricted from doing so by indebtedness covenants.

Although not marketed as such, Beacon is a Triad hospital; the company does not believe in branding, preferring to retain the name under which the hospital is known locally. As Burke Whitman, its former CEO, explained, this gives the local community a sense of ownership in what is really their hospital. Triad has entered into an agreement to lease the hospital; the lease was reported as running from the fourth quarter of 2006. Triad will receive a percentage of the profits, and it has also entered into an agreement to manage Beacon, installing its own CEO and chief financial officer there, in a formula typically used by Quorum in its network of managed hospitals in the US.

Deborah Brehe, Beacon's newly appointed CEO, spent twenty years at Mission Bay Hospital, working her way up to the top; when Triad closed Mission Bay in November 2000, the corporation offered her a similar post at San Leandro Hospital. Her former colleague there, Mark Hoffman, has also been appointed to Triad's Dublin hospital as chief financial officer. Just how much autonomy the team will have is unclear; in an agreement that runs until May 2008, Triad's company of origin, HCA, is contracted to provide Triad with 'financial, clinical, patient accounting and network information services'.

The lack of regulation of health care in Ireland will come as an unexpected bonus to multinational health care operators. US chains, such as Triad, will be surprised by the absence of regulatory controls in the Republic: health care in the US is much more highly regulated than it is here. Conglomerates will be amazed to discover that while you need a licence to operate a car wash in Ireland, you don't need one to run a hospital. American corporations, in particular, will be pleased to learn that practices that are unlawful in the US are lawful in Ireland.

The forging of strong financial links with the medical profession, which is such a feature of American corporate hospital culture, is a case in point. Triad, for example, has continued the policy of HCA, its parent, in this area. The 'primary number one' aspect of Triad's corporate strategy, according to Burke Whitman, has been the building of 'strong, robust physician relationships'. Every Triad hospital in the US has its 'physician leadership group'; most doctors are self-employed. Triad offers financial inducements to doctors to set up in practice in the catchment areas of its hospitals. The company supplements doctors' incomes for one year, through loans and income guarantees, while physicians establish themselves in private practice; in return, doctors undertake to remain in practice in that community for three years. Triad records these payments to physicians as an 'other asset'; a number of doctors appear to be in debt to the corporation. As of 31 December 2005, unpaid physician income guarantees amounted to $64.9 million. While giving doctors financial and other inducements may not be legal in the US, such arrangements are probably perfectly lawful in Ireland.

Triad also has a policy of offering medical staff who work in their hospitals a beneficial interest in their ownership. Such gain-sharing is generally not lawful in the US, but, in Ireland, of course, there is no prohibition on doctors holding stocks in hospitals. Ireland, unlike the US, prefers to turn a blind eye to the clash of interests that exists between the doctor-as-healer and the doctor-as-shareholder. The Beacon Consultant Clinic is reportedly structured as a 'partnership'.

Another important difference between Irish and American law is the prohibition on benefit where a financial stake is involved. No such ban is in force in Ireland, in relation, for example, to the National Treatment Purchase Fund. The 'moral hazard' is much greater in Ireland than in the US where, as we saw in Chapter 12, a huge incidence of fraud and of false claims has added heavily to the costs of the American system and to the burden on the public purse.

Johns Hopkins Medicine International has signed an agreement with Beacon at its East Baltimore campus to provide 'educational and consulting services' to the new hospital. The Minister for Health was heralded as attending the signing ceremony on 9 May 2006. The south Dublin facility opened in October 2006 at a reported cost of €183 million, raised mainly through private investment. Investor tax breaks for this American hospital will cost the Government an estimated €71 million over ten years. On 6 January 2006, the US chain announced that after-tax losses from Beacon for 2006 would amount to $4 million, but that, by mid-2007, the Dublin hospital would be making money.

Beacon Medical Group, in association with Triad, has been longlisted for six co-located hospitals in Dublin, Cork, Limerick and Waterford. It also has ambitions to enter the primary care 'market'. According to Johns Hopkins Medicine International, 'the Beacon philosophy for the advancement of health care in Ireland is to develop the interface between primary and secondary health care, both on-site and nation-wide.' Beacon also intends to build a new maternity, women's and children's hospital in Sandyford, Co. Dublin.

Extreme generosity on the part of the Irish people towards for-profit health care operators looks set to continue, thanks to the Government's decision to pick up the bill for all insurance claims in excess of €0.5 million incurred by consultants working wholly in the private sector in specialties carrying a risk of brain damage. Taxpayers will now pick up an open-ended tab for any personal injuries claims made 'going forward' into the future, claims that properly belong to these hospitals' private owners.

Maternity care is a sector where experience in Ireland has shown that—stemming from the industrial practices of active management—personal injuries claims often succeed. With a bill of €400 million outstanding for past claims in obstetrics, and cerebral palsy awards running at around €5 million, serf taxpayers have little to be cheerful about.

Chapter 14
Corporate Raiders

Two months after John O'Brien, the National Hospitals' Office CEO, predicted a big drive 'going forward' in privatisation or 'social partnership', as he preferred to call it, the trade union movement dropped its opposition to the outsourcing of core public services, hitherto an impediment to Mr O'Brien's 'cross-relationships'.

Co-location is one particularly invidious form of cross-relationship—that arranged marriage between corporation and state that comes with such an unaffordable dowry. Investment advisers classify co-location as the first step—in an eight-point scale—in privatising a nation's health care system. Like snakes and ladders, this particular board game allows governments to jump forwards and backwards. You might start with option number two, move on to four, jump back to three, then land on one, like Ireland. If co-location is the first step, 'outsourcing' secondary services, such as laundry and catering, is the second. This has been happening in Irish hospitals for nearly two decades, without fuss, without debate. As O'Brien has pointed out: 'There is a huge amount of outsourcing, particularly in what are loosely called the "hotel services".' Next on the scale of privatisation we find the buying of 'clinical support' services, such as radiology, from the corporate sector. Plans to 'offer' cancer sufferers private radiotherapy services, most notably in Waterford, caused outrage. The Government intends to build six oncology units at a cost of €550 million in capital costs, plus €72 million annually in running costs. Since July 2005, the National Development Finance Agency has been given additional powers 'to procure and deliver projects', 'to deliver back the linear accelerators, for example to HSE'.

The fourth step in privatisation is the outsourcing of core patient services, such as hip replacements. In Ireland, core patient services are outsourced through the National Treatment Purchase Fund, set up for this purpose. 'Private management of a public hospital' is the fifth step. This has happened in Australia, where the government has handed over public hospitals to private companies for a period of years, usually several decades, to be managed. The sixth is a now-familiar PPP scenario, 'private financing, construction and leaseback' of a facility, seen to salutary effect, cost-wise, in Irish road-building. Under New Labour, the leaseback of privately built hospitals has become a feature of the now debt-crippled NHS in Britain. The seventh step in privatising a country's health system gets closer to the edge; this is where private corporations finance, build and operate new 'public' hospitals.

Here, as well as owning the building, conglomerates have a monopoly over providing services; the state's role, as always, is to pay up, to 'reimburse the operator annually for capital costs and recurrent costs for services provided'. Armageddon finally dawns: 'Sale of public hospital as going concern'. Again, this has happened in Australia, where public hospitals for the elderly were sold off. But even in this scenario, the state still continues to pay 'the operator for clinical services'; the corporation's role is now to 'operate' the facility 'as a public hospital under contract', while the state 'monitors compliance', on paper at least. Governments, like Ireland's, who decide to trade health as a commodity, typically employ some or all of these privatisation strategies.

The ultimate aim of corporations is to blend the public with the private to the point where they become so enmeshed, contractually, that they can no longer be extricated from each other, or at least until companies have made their money. But like Siamese twins joined at the hip sharing vital organs, the weaker will sicken and may even die.

Debate over privatisation is currently raging in Canada, a country whose health system was, until very recently, one of the leaders in the developed world. But under a Conservative government privatisation has proliferated. In every province in Canada, since September 2004, for-profit ventures in health have flourished.

Australia has one of the largest private health sectors in the OECD, apart from Ireland. In 1996–7, 29 per cent of all hospital beds in

Australia were private. By 2001–2, this had risen to almost 35 per cent. Large corporations, religious orders and private insurers run these hospitals. More than three in every ten hospital admissions in Australia are private, as is one in four hospital days.

The Australian government, looking for capital to grow private health care, encouraged multinational corporations to enter the 'market'. These attempts were initially unsuccessful; American health care chains, such as Columbia/HCA, who pleaded guilty to corporate crime in the United States, were initially prevented from coming into Australia. More recently, lured by the lucrative prospect of co-location, large for-profit corporations have succeeded in rooting themselves in the health care landscape. The trend is for such for-profit hospital groups to form monopolies, killing off competition to become 'dominant players' in the market. In 1998, nine major private hospital groups controlled 45 per cent of Australia's private beds.

Is Ireland, rampant with new money, ripe for such conglomerates? The private nursing home experience suggests that chains, in health care, as in fast food, may gobble the market. One of the biggest nursing-home chains is Mowlam Health Care. In 2001, Mowlam had only three such facilities in its portfolio, but, by 2005, the company had ten nursing homes, in Limerick, Galway, Dublin, Kilkenny, the north-west and the midlands. Recently, Mowlam built a 'retirement village' in Moate, Co. Westmeath, at a cost of €12 million. The village was opened in May 2005, by the then Minister for Finance, Brian Cowan. Another private nursing home chain operating in the south is Golden Meadows; First Care, a Dublin chain, has four such properties, while another, Silver Stream, has built in Dublin, Galway, Meath and Tipperary. The trend towards nursing-home conglomerates is set to continue in Ireland: Sonas Healthcare, for example, plans to spend €100 million developing 'retirement care centres' across the country, with wealthy private investors providing cash that they will then recoup in the form of tax write-offs and hefty charges for care.

BAD FOR YOUR HEALTH

In an opinion piece for *The Irish Times*, Dr John Barton made the important point that involving for-profit companies in health care is bad for patients. The Australian Senate had recently reported that public–private partnerships had resulted in inferior care for the elderly and the chronically ill. And research on patient care in the United

States in for-profit hospitals is consistently negative, he said. American studies show that investor-owned facilities result in poorer quality health care. Patients in for-profit hospitals and dialysis centres fare worse than those in not-for-profit facilities: death rates are higher, surgical complications more frequent and 'preventable adverse incidents' more common. Profits in health, John Barton comments, are made at the expense of the sick; for-profit nursing homes have been shown to skimp on nursing care, for example. Overall, for-profit facilities provide less care for more money; they spend more on administration, and pay beefed-up bonuses to senior executives. The Dutch experience of for-profit care is similar: a report carried out for the Dutch Board for Hospital Provision found that public–private partnerships in health had resulted in too much cost-cutting at the expense of patient care.

In May 2006, stung by repeated public allegations of worse care in private hospitals, the Minister for Health said that there was no evidence that private hospitals in Ireland provided care that was less safe or of worse quality than public hospitals. There was no evidence because there was no information. Nothing is known, publicly, about Irish private hospitals, their patient outcomes, their patient–staff ratios, their costs. Asked why it had never monitored any aspect of their activities, the Department of Health said that it was not part of its remit. But the Departmental gaze is exceedingly narrow: there is no inspection of short-stay public hospitals, either, except in the psychiatric services. Recent evidence of sub-standard patient care in private for-profit nursing homes—a sector that is subject to some state supervision—is worrying.

Evidence given to the American Senate Industrial Relations Committee on the subject of patient care in for-profit hospitals was not reassuring. On 15 January 2003, Tom Moore told senators that some patients in for-profit hospitals were admitted unnecessarily and kept too long; given laboratory, radiology and other tests they did not need; had seen specialists they did not require; and, a final horror, had been subjected to 'questionable surgical procedures'.

The cost to patient health is not difficult to imagine: all surgical procedures and most medical tests carry some margin of risk.

POOR PATIENT CARE

Evidence of sub-standard patient care in the private for-profit nursing-home sector in Ireland has recently come to light. Leas Cross was the second private nursing home to close its doors in Ireland in 2005. It did so following a raft of allegations of poor patient care. A ninety-bed home in north Co. Dublin, Leas Cross was one of hundreds of private nursing homes 'midwifed' into being by the 1997 Finance Act. *Prime Time* catapulted the Swords residence into public consciousness in May 2005. Footage secretly filmed by a journalist posing as a care worker apparently showed an older resident being restrained in a chair against her wishes, whilst another was depicted as being harassed by a care worker.

Citing 'the poor standard of nursing care' and 'grave concern' for residents' safety, the HSE subsequently decided to remove all public clients from the home, and advised private residents to move elsewhere. Their own inspectors had voiced reservations about the home in 1999, it later emerged. After the television screening, Leas Cross claimed it had been approved by the HSE as a nursing home, but this was denied. Following 'site visits', the HSE declared, Leas Cross had been deemed unsuitable as a residential-care facility, and, after a three-week investigation, the HSE decided to close the home. Some residents had been there for seven years and found the enforced move distressing.

A report released in autumn 2004 had criticised standards of care in Leas Cross, noting an unusually high number of deaths in patients transferred to the home from a nearby psychiatric unit. No explanation was given as to how psychiatric patients came to be referred to an unauthorised nursing home, or how the state came to contract public beds to a step-down facility that it subsequently said did not have its approval. A number of patients were reported to have died in hospital shortly after being transferred from Leas Cross. A subsequent report, commissioned by the HSE from consultant geriatrician Professor Desmond O'Neill and published in November 2006—following a lengthy delay—was severely critical of the level of care at Leas Cross. He indicated that his overall assessment was 'consistent with a finding of institutional abuse'. The report also strongly criticised the regulatory process overseen by health authorities. It warned that, given the lack of engagement by these authorities and the Government, it would be a major error to believe that the deficits in care shown in Leas Cross represented an isolated incident. Aspects of the report's findings were disputed in some quarters.

Mr Aherne, proprietor of Leas Cross, had previously offered to bail out Tullamore General Hospital during a beds crisis in late 2004. Seeking tenders from the private sector for step-down facilities for older patients discharged from acute hospitals is central to the Minister for Health's plan for 'solving' the A&E crisis.

American research shows that some investor-owned nursing homes skimp on nursing care. When the HSE began to look for alternative homes for the seventy Leas Cross residents, it found that staffing levels in other for-profit facilities in the Dublin area were even lower than those in Leas Cross, which was reported to have had a night-time nurse–patient ratio of 1:30. On 28 June 2005, the health board said that seven of the thirty homes operating in its jurisdiction had failed to meet standards during the first six months of that year; staffing levels were one of the main areas of concern, along with infrastructure. Outside Dublin, there was also evidence of low staffing levels and poor hygiene in some private nursing homes.

If high-quality care is not necessarily guaranteed in the for-profit sector, neither is continuity. Private for-profit nursing homes may simply withdraw from the market, leaving their elderly residents high and dry. Occupants of a 'retirement village' in Co. Offaly had to be rescued by the state after its owners, citing financial difficulties, requested the HSE to remove its residents. On 27 June 2005, Tullybeg Retirement Village Ltd informed the HSE that it had ceased to have any involvement in, or responsibility for, its clients. A nine-hole golf course adjacent to the Rahan nursing home also closed. The thirty-six residents were subsequently transferred, to the disappointment of many, to other nursing homes in Offaly, some of them 28 miles away, in Clara and Birr. The Tullybeg directors claimed that 'insufficient numbers of clients' and 'financial issues' had led to the closure; they were, they said, 'unable to sustain losses'. Staff at the nursing home had not been paid for three weeks prior to the closure.

One of the nursing-home directors had been arrested in January 2005 after a large amount of money was found in his garden. Ted Cunningham, one of three directors of Tullybeg Retirement Village Ltd, was released without charge following a money-laundering investigation in Cork. Gardaí had found a sum of €2.3 million composting in a green bin in his garden. Another prominent figure in the Co. Offaly retirement village, Cathy Armstrong, was also arrested during the same search. Senior gardaí linked the money to the Northern Bank raid in December 2004, which was alleged to have been the work of the IRA. Tullybeg Retirement Village was the first of the nursing-home boomers in Ireland to close.

Adverse effects have also been seen in other areas. Private firms have been brought in to run some services previously run by hospitals themselves. Outsourcing has become widespread: areas such as catering, laundry, cleaning and security are often farmed out to private companies. Private firms are now targeting other areas of hospital activity for business, particularly in the area of information technology. But outsourcing hospital catering and cleaning has led to problems, international experience shows. Quality suffers and disease spreads, as we saw in Chapter 3.

MEDICAL INVESTORS

In recent years, both consultants and family doctors have entered the private hospital/nursing-home business. Village Care Ltd, for example, is owned by a west of Ireland medical practitioner, Dr Hassan Bhatti. Surgeon Jimmy Sheehan co-owns both the Galway and Blackrock Clinics. Dr Mary Grehan is one of the main investors in the Ballymascanlon Clinic.

Professor Risteárd Mulcahy is a longstanding and vocal opponent of for-profit medicine. For over thirty years, he has actively opposed the turning of health into a business; he sees the trend towards corporate health care as being inimical to patient welfare, and cautions heavily against the involvement of doctors in for-profit health ventures. 'For-profit hospitals fuel new conflicts for health professionals,' he says, firmly. 'Doctors and nurses find themselves caught between the patient's need to be cured and the investors' need to make a profit.' 'American doctors were banned for a period of time from owning health-care facilities, such as day surgery centres,' adds John Barton. Here, the Government has no plans to ban doctor-owned hospitals or nursing homes.

FAILING TO DELIVER

Public–private partnerships in Britain have created an inequitable system designed 'to exclude the poorest and the sickest'. 'Certain groups, such as refugees and the elderly, are now excluded from NHS

entitlements,' Professor Allyson Pollack says. Some are being denied
operations in an attempt to ration health services. Obese people, for
example, are now being denied hip replacements on the NHS.

Co-location will not improve waiting lists, Australian research
shows. Research done by Professor Stephen Duckett at La Trobe
University, Melbourne, demonstrated that public patients waited
longer in public hospitals after private hospitals had been built in their
grounds. In Britain, privatisation has led to sharp reductions in access
to hospital services, for both public *and* private patients. Every single
public–private partnership in the NHS, Professor Pollock says, has led
to cuts in hospital services, staff reductions and bed closures.

While public patients will suffer most under the planned acceleration
of the two-tiered system in Ireland, even those who hold private
health insurance stand to lose. The boom in for-profit health care
means more tests, more procedures, and more 'bed nights'. More
costs, in a word. Subscribers will inevitably face bigger premiums;
private hospitals rely heavily on private health insurance funds. In
Australia, for example, in 1996–7, 71 per cent of private hospital
revenue came from insurers. Insurance premiums rose as private
hospitals mushroomed. From September 1996 to September 1997, the
cost of private health insurance in Australia rose by 20 per cent.
Subscriptions dropped.

Will Ireland see similar increases in price, and similar drops in take-
up? Insurance premiums are already set to rise, following the
Government's decision to charge insurers the full economic cost of
private beds. There are at least 2,500 private beds in public hospitals:
costs will rise steeply with the removal of the existing 40 per cent-plus
subsidy on these beds. If the additional costs and increased consumption generated by new for-profit hospitals are factored in, the effect on
private insurers' costs over the coming years will be catastrophic. And
if companies pass even a proportion of these cost increases on to
subscribers, some subscribers will be unable to pay.

If subscribers dwindle, will hospitals flee? Less than two years after
Burke Whitman told journalists: 'We may own the bricks and mortar,
but our hospitals really belong to their communities', Triad closed a
hospital in California. On 11 July 2003, the *East Bay Business Times*
reported that Triad had closed Mission Bay Hospital in San Diego. Its
San Leandro Hospital was sold off a year later, in July 2004.

THE MYTH OF REGULATION

Governments promise that they will protect the public interest, by regulating corporate activities, when they privatise important public services such as health care. But compliance can be very hard to monitor, even when the political will is present. When the political will is not present, companies can run amok. In the American meat-packing business, during the Reagan years, for example, a typical American plant could expect a visit from a health and safety inspector once every eighty years.

There are other problems. Companies lie: congressional hearings during 1987 heard that Iowa Beef Packers kept two sets of logs, one for official consumption. Health agencies also lie. In Britain, an independent investigation by *Health Which* into the performance of the ambulance services revealed that many NHS trusts had lied systematically about their ambulance response times.

There is also the problem of 'information asymmetry'. Even Competition Authority economists have admitted that there are serious difficulties with the state regulation of private companies, not least because of the information imbalance between the two sides.

There are also limits to regulation: regulators have only the powers given to them by law. Or they may find themselves overruled in court by a judge who takes a different view, as happened in a recent case in Ireland. Bridget Seepersad, a nurse, successfully challenged the HSE's refusal to register her Co. Meath nursing home. The authority had alleged that Seepersad had failed to appoint an 'appropriate person' to manage the home. Judge John Brophy disagreed; the HSE's refusal to register Hill View was overturned in the District Court on 13 July 2005.

> *The roads have been very successful.*
> Barry Murphy, Head of Structured Finance, Ulster Bank (Corporate Banking), speaking at a private health-care conference in Dublin

A DRAIN ON THE PUBLIC PURSE

Private hospitals can drain public purses. In the US, Triad, for example, is heavily dependent on government insurance schemes. Medicare and Medicaid payments amounted to 39 and 38 per cent of total patient revenues for the six months ended 30 June 2002 and 2001, respectively. Triad also has a continuing problem of spare capacity. Its bed occupancy rates across its entire US network stood at just 52 per cent in 2005, down from 54 per cent in 2001. Many public hospitals in Ireland have double these bed occupancy rates.

Cost control is weaker in for-profit hospitals, John Barton maintains. American research, he says, shows consistently that investor-owned facilities result in more costly health care. Professor Allyson Pollack goes even further than John Barton: she says that it is 'ludicrous' to suggest that the private sector can deliver services and hospitals more efficiently than the public system. The for-profit sector, Pollack maintains, 'cannot deliver as efficiently because it is operating ... on market lines'. She underlines the additional costs faced by the sector, in billing, marketing and paying shareholder dividends. Describing public–private partnerships in health as a 'dream scenario' for the private sector, she says that, for the NHS, such 'partnerships' have been a 'nightmare'. As in Ireland, PPPs in health were touted as delivering 'value for money'. New Labour promised that they would result in hospitals being built 'on time and on budget'. But at the Health Services Action Group conference, the message was stark: PPPs cost more. Cost over-runs in Britain have been significant. With over-runs of up to 200–300 per cent in the NHS, the conference heard, 'the amount of money spent on servicing debt has spiralled out of control'. British hospitals, Pollack says, are in increasing crisis. Soaring debts have forced service cutbacks.

Charting in minute detail the effect of public–private initiatives on the NHS, Allyson Pollack concluded that they have cost the state far more than the amount that would have been involved in borrowing the money—at preferential rates—to build directly. The NHS now leases back buildings and services from private companies at a cost 'far greater' than the amount the state would have needed to borrow to design, build and operate these hospitals itself.

Why does privately provided health care cost more? Investors have to turn a profit, Barton points out. For every €75,000 invested in the for-profit sector, investment promoters forecast a profit of €62,760. This is an extraordinarily high return, almost 84 per cent. Private health care *is* hugely profitable: Croft Nursing Home in Inchicore, Dublin, for example, made a profit of €350,000 in 2003.

How can private health care be so profitable, when public hospitals are so deeply in debt? Part of the answer lies in cherry-picking. IMO

President Christine O'Malley says that for-profit hospitals focus on high-tech surgical patients, leaving public hospitals to provide care for the very ill, and for emergencies. A&E costs.

Earlier we saw evidence presented to the US Senate of 'utilisation manipulation'—the over-supply of medical treatment—in the for-profit sector. Apart from the enormous cost to patients' health from the adverse effects of medical treatment, over-supply has huge implications for cost control. Investor-owned hospitals in the United States cost 19 per cent more to run than not-for-profit facilities.

> *It made breakfast at the Berkeley Court look like good value.*
> Cork mother Máire O'Regan, on the price of rashers and eggs at the
> Mater Private Hospital

Overcharging, as we saw in the last chapter, is how America's most costly hospitals make their money. The cost of bed and breakfast at the Mater Private Hospital was aired on *Liveline:* one listener recounted how having had a heart operation, she had been treated, post-op, to a breakfast of rashers and sausages that cost over €6,000. At a conference on health in Ennis in May 2006, Professor Risteárd Mulcahy told delegates that the cost of dialysis services for public patients at the Beacon Clinic, Sandyford, Co. Dublin, was around €70,000 annually, per patient—two-and-a-half times the cost of the same treatment in Germany.

A FUTURE THREAT
For-profit health care threatens the sustainability of national health care systems. Allyson Pollock says that privatisation has led to the 'disintegration and fragmentation' of the National Health Service in Britain. Departments are closing, beds lie empty and staff are being made redundant. Hospitals now find themselves with crippling annual charges; one hospital which had previously spent 7 per cent of its budget on capital costs now spends 33 per cent of its annual allocation servicing debts. 'With bankers, builders and shareholders to be paid every year, there is less money to pay hospital staff,' Pollack observes.

In Australia, the government has done everything in its power to fuel the private sector, seeing it as a way to fund health services. Now, in an implicit acknowledgement of failure, even its own website carries a warning 'that healthy people may opt out of private health insurance'. What has happened in France has happened in Australia: there has been a drift to the private sector. Those holding private health insurance tend to choose the private sector over the public. In Australia, for example, from 1997 to 1999, public hospitals' share of the private patient market was 19 per cent, down from 36 per cent in 1993–4.

Subscribers saw private health insurance as bad value for money. In December 1998, in an attempt to boost the market, the federal government passed legislation giving a 30 per cent rebate on private health insurance. This carrot was followed by a stick: four years later, the government introduced financial penalties for all 30-somethings 'for every year they delayed joining a [private health insurance] fund'. Unsurprisingly, the take-up in private health insurance rose to 45 per cent. But this increase, from a low of 31 per cent in 1998, has generated a significant rise in demand for private hospital services. The government has now warned that claims are rising from 'new entrants', that this will drive up the cost of premiums, and that demand for private insurance may decline. This, in turn, will adversely affect private hospitals, which are 'heavily reliant' on private health insurance coffers.

The same trend can be seen in Ireland. The equation is identical: the cheaper a health insurance premium is, the more people will buy it and the more likely they are to avail of medical treatment. But the more people are treated privately, the more it costs the insurer; and the more likely it is that insurance premiums will rise. According to Vincent Sheridan, CEO of VHI Healthcare, 52 per cent of the Republic's population now hold private health insurance: 'This is higher than any other country that I am aware of.' In recent years, particularly, the demand for medical goods and services in Ireland has far outstripped supply. But this 'under-capacity', as Sheridan calls it, has helped to limit consumption. Keeping consumption down controls costs; this is what made private health insurance in Ireland relatively affordable. 'The relatively low cost of health insurance is linked to control over capacity,' he explained to conference delegates in Dublin's Berkeley Court.

All that is about to change: there has been a 67 per cent increase in the volume of claims for which VHI pays. Private health insurance currently supplies most of the revenue to the private sector. 'As capacity ceases to be a limiting factor, we're going to have to find some way of limiting consumption,' he warned. As an insurer, he sees the writing on the wall: 'The mechanisms to control people's consumption are very limited.' Particularly in the for-profit scenario, he might have added. He identifies 'huge' cost drivers in Ireland: affluence, demographics, technology, and 'unprecedented new capacity'. Other factors also contribute to rising costs, such as obesity and consumer 'education'.

What happens when costs are uncontrolled? Could private health care topple the public system? Last year, PricewaterhouseCoopers predicted that most public health systems would be 'totally insolvent' by 2015–20. Will Ireland be among them?

Making profit the aim of health care warps the system, according to a Harvard professor. Steffi Woolhander says that for-profit hospitals usher in 'a new value system that severs the communal roots and Good Samaritan traditions of hospitals, makes doctors and nurses the instruments of investors, and views patients as commodities.' us Congressman Pete Stark, who introduced the anti-fraud legislation known as the Stark Statute, was less kind: 'The for-profit chains have the minds of piranha fish and the hearts of Doberman pinschers.'

V Futures

V Futures

Chapter 15
Coup d'Etat

U nderlying the current debate on health in Ireland are global issues: neo-liberalism, with its fetishism of competition and the 'free' market; the role of corporations and their growing influence over health care; the dominance of pharmaceutical companies and their potentially harmful relationship with medicine; the pre-eminence of insurers and their control over the content of patient care; the power of medicine to expropriate health and its disabling effect on people's ability to cope.

In Ireland, three-quarters of a century of political stagnation has led to what we see now: a sprawling, chaotic, fragmented, divided, inequitable, and unsustainable health system that has finally spiralled out of control. Decades of under-investment and administrative inertia have finally worked their way through to the steps of A&E. Meanwhile, the medical profession has been extremely active in pursuing its own interest, growing the professional project incrementally, year in, year out.

How can the chaos be reduced to some semblance of order? How can the dysfunctional trends we saw earlier be reversed, the vicious circles broken?

WHAT'S WRONG?
One consequence of political failure is lack of regulation. Corporations seeking to establish themselves in Ireland found that, in some cases, they were entering a regulation-free zone. Those who

came to pursue genetic engineering interests, for example, found a dream scenario: pots of state money with no strings attached. Human cloning, for example, is legal in Ireland, a Catholic country with a constitution that enshrines a pro-life amendment. Political cowardice, electoral gain and moral indifference have combined to leave more than one regulatory crater in the reproductive health industry. After more than twenty years of egg fertilising, freezing and injecting, of sperm collecting, freezing and banking, the human egg and sperm industry in Ireland remains in regulatory freefall, guided only by the prayers of the Medical Council (enshrined in its ethical code). Decades of the same laissez-faire approach in the wider health arena have left us the unwilling inheritors of a chaotic, crumbling, vested-interest-riven system. Only by regulating the system adequately can we hope to unravel the knots.

Lethargy pervades state administration, particularly in health. Policy-making is completely stagnant in some areas. National maternity care policy, for example, has not been reviewed since 1976. As a result, women in Ireland have less choice in maternity care than women in virtually any other country in the European Union. In some areas, the pace of administration has been glacial. The Nurses' and Midwives' Bill, for example, has been in the pipeline for eleven years, the Medical Practitioners' Bill for thirteen.

Medical scandals inevitably resulted from the lack of regulation, the absence of oversight. The scandal of tainted blood was the biggest in the history of the state. Greed, parsimony, incompetence, lethargy, arrogance and unaccountability combined to contaminate over 1,600 women with Hepatitis C; most were mothers in childbirth. Other victims contracted HIV/AIDS. Today, MRSA and other superbugs seem set to lead the field in terms of iatrogenic injuries and deaths. Hospital-acquired infection may well, in time, become the biggest health scandal of all.

Meanwhile, we have two other contenders: one a private non-profit hospital with a very special department; the other a medical specialty, a number of whose practitioners believed that their Catholic faith should inform their medical practice. In the former case, over a thirty-year period, the obstetrics department of the Lourdes Hospital performed over 150 Caesarean hysterectomies, nearly all of them needless. But the second biggest scandal in the history of the state must surely be Irish obstetricians' revival of symphysiotomy, an operation long discarded in the developed world because of its dangers to mothers and babies. From the mid-1950s to the early 1980s, up to 500 mothers in hospitals across the country were denied a Caesarean section, condemned by their doctors to a life of pain, incontinence and impaired mobility. Only a public inquiry into the practice of symphysiotomy will lance this particular boil. Private inquiries, as in the Caesarean hysterectomy scandal, offer few learning opportunities. And obstetrics, with its €400 million bill for past negligence and malpractice, is one specialty that is in particular need of public scrutiny.

Consultant bodies and private non-profit hospitals in this country ruled for 200 years before the foundation of the state, a state of affairs that, in the case of medical training bodies, continues largely unchanged. While the state has, to a degree, since the 1990s, sought to curb the powers of the Dublin voluntary hospitals, the medieval powers of the royal colleges have survived, unrestrained and unquestioned. Nor have those eighteenth-century powers ever been challenged, publicly, until very recently. Hospitals in consequence have tended to gobble up the health budget; specialist hospital medicine developed at the expense of primary health and community care. This imbalance needs to be corrected.

The relationship between government, the state and doctors has been fruitful for medicine, if not for health. Medical law in this country has largely been written for the benefit of the profession, not of the people. Today, it is very doubtful if, anywhere in the industrialised world, the medical profession enjoys privileges equal to those carved out by consultant bodies here. Until 2004, however, there was some notion, however woolly, of the checks and balances needed in a democracy. Today, that concept has disappeared.

Organised medicine has brought careerism and elitism. Today, grafted onto the technocratic agenda is another form of greed— a greed fuelled by the prospect of tax breaks and land deals, a greed nourished by decades of speculation and re-zoning. The scope for private enrichment in the hospital sector under current government plans is massive. Stand-alone specialty hospitals slated to close will be sold off to the highest bidder, just as acute hospitals were during the 1980s. Developers, particularly those close to the heart of the current government, must be waiting with bated breath for such bounty. Present Fianna Fáil/Progressive Democrat plans will also unleash an enormous hospital building boom. Existing hospitals chosen for expansion will require vast extensions to increase their current capacity. Banks, property developers, builders, auctioneers, solicitors and others stand to make millions from this bonanza. Then, on top of this, there is yet another honey-pot: co-location.

As in Britain, the Government is now looking to the private sector to provide solutions to shore up the potholes in the public sector left by the parsimony of decades. But making health into a commodity—a shoppers' paradise for consumers who can afford to buy—is not the answer. Public–private partnerships in health are not the same as public–private partnerships in, say, road-building. In health, what are being traded are not materials such as concrete, but human beings at their most vulnerable. The bodies of the sick, the elderly and the dying are today being turned into trading commodities, in our name, without debate. By developing cancer services, through public–private partnerships for example, the Government has made cancer services into an investors' market, a money-making enterprise.

Through the generosity of its tax breaks, through its policy of co-location, the Government has now succeeded in attracting into Ireland hospital corporations, such as Triad, to run private for-profit hospitals in this country, just as they do in the United States. But the regulatory environment here is infinitely weaker than it is in the US. There they have a senate that has the power to conduct investigations; here we have an upper house that is virtually toothless. Reform in this area could help improve patient safety: we need an American-style senate to investigate abuses in health care as well as in other areas.

MAKING HOSPITALS SAFER

Consultants' independence in treating the sick has not always been for the good of the patient. Their clinical autonomy—written into their contract of employment—has on occasion constituted a direct threat to patient welfare. The reign of Caesarean hysterectomy in the Lourdes and the latter-day revival of symphysiotomy both testify to the dangers of untrammelled clinical autonomy. Poor outcomes are inevitable in a system where medical practice is a matter of personal predilection rather than evidence. Patient safety suggests that some limits need to be put in place. Unnecessary medical treatment is another manifestation of clinical autonomy that places patients in jeopardy. This results partly from the practice of defensive medicine. Two of the most common operations in Ireland, Caesarean section and hysterectomy, both leading causes of litigation, are frequently performed without good reason. More clinical accountability and improved hospital management—both topics to which we will return—would help bring about the change in culture that is needed. Expanding the birth reporting scheme to include induction and acceleration of labour, as in Sweden, for example, would be a first step in reducing the very high rates of intervention in our hospitals.

Hospital culture needs to change. Few today wish to work within a nineteenth-century hierarchical model of management. Modern norms of management apply right across the public service, with one exception: public and private non-profit hospitals. There, what the Nursing Commission memorably described as that 'semi-militaristic medical hierarchy' still rules, to a degree. Consultants need to be brought within the management loop.

Consultants are legally entitled to delegate any or all of their work to another doctor. This is another feature of the common contract that needs reform, as it is conducive to absenteeism, and absenteeism has led, and continues to lead, to poor outcomes. Lack of supervision of junior hospital doctors and others has been identified as a factor in patient death and injury. Our system of using trainee doctors, nurses and midwives as frontline staff needs to be reformed.

Increasing the numbers of clinical staff in our hospitals should be a priority, as staff shortages in many areas are acute. A specialist:trainee ratio of 1:1 has been recommended. More fully qualified specialists are needed to comply with the work-time directive; this would help to raise the quality of hospital care, reduce public waiting lists and help keep small hospitals viable, as we will see.

Plans for hospital services to be provided around the clock by hospital consultants should be reconsidered. (With current employment contracts being what they are, this is a sure-fire recipe for bankruptcy.) Even Germany, with its expensive health-care system, does not have a model of care that requires all hospital services to be provided 24/7 by consultants. This is an unnecessarily expensive way of providing hospital services. Hospital health care should continue to be consultant-led, as it is at present, not consultant-provided. 'The hospital by day is different to the hospital by night,' John Barton observes.

Consultants cannot, simply by their presence, ensure the safety of hospital services. Safety is multi-layered: it depends on adequate staffing levels, good laboratory facilities and proper equipment. Computerised ordering systems, for example, reduce medication errors; palm pilots obviate the need to rely on notes or memory. Safety also requires evidence-based medicine, risk management—the reporting of poor or unexpected outcomes—and a credible scheme of competence assurance.

Investing in the public health system is the only way to solve the A&E bottleneck. Funding more hospital beds and employing more medical specialists will reduce waiting lists—the promised 3,000 extra beds must be delivered *in the public system*, not reneged on, as we have seen over the past five years. Greater productivity would help, and more day surgery. Improvements in hospital efficiency would mean fewer trolleys. More step-down facilities would ease the pressure on beds. We need to find—and fund—new solutions to old problems. In Cornwall, for example, specialist community matrons carry caseloads of chronically ill patients, working with GPs and hospital staff, cutting emergency admissions by half. General practitioner services need to be genuinely available out-of-hours: the huge GP co-ops set up in part to deal with this problem are failing to deliver an adequate 24/7 service.

The government failure to provide adequate funding for our public health system is costing lives. The state must spend the money that comprehensive patient isolation costs. Noël Browne isolated TB patients in the 1950s, as part of a successful strategy to eradicate that disease. Yet, today, at a time when Ireland is immeasurably wealthier as a nation, and superbugs are rampant in our hospitals, the best the Minister for Health can offer is to underline the importance of hand-washing.

Infection control costs: refusing to spend the money on specialist staff and facilities simply piles on the cost elsewhere—in litigation, for example. As well as the misery for the individual patient, an infected patient occupies a hospital bed that might otherwise be availed of by an A&E victim, or by someone waiting for surgery. This is yet another example of a vicious circle: overcrowding contributes hugely to hospital infections; yet the Government's refusal to spend money on beds means that hospital infections cannot be dealt with effectively. Meanwhile, every patient who has contracted an invasive infection costs a multiple of a non-infected person. Up to 5 per cent of total hospital budgets goes on treating infections that patients catch in hospitals. In 1999, for example, hospital infections cost the NHS in England alone an estimated £1 billion. Effective infection control could save up to €50 million annually in Ireland. Enough to buy 50–100 beds, or more, depending on how they are priced.

Generations of doctors, both in hospital and in the community, have wrongly prescribed antibiotics (among other drugs), fuelling the growth of superbugs. Measures need to be taken to combat inappropriate prescribing. All existing beds in public and voluntary hospitals should be designated as public, for infection-control purposes. It is unethical to reserve single rooms for private patients when they are so sorely needed to prevent cross-infection. Finally, the outsourcing of hotel services, such as cleaning and catering, in our hospitals, should be ended. Contract cleaning has manifestly failed to ensure clean hospitals, although there have been some improvements. Every hospital in Northern Ireland, bar one, has now switched from outsourcing cleaning to employing staff in-house. We should follow suit.

ACCOUNTABILITY

As the recent health scandals show, the present imbalance of power between doctor and patient, medicine and society, threatens public safety. Ours is a system without locks, a model of care that allows hospital consultants to run their medical practices as independent fiefdoms, largely unfettered by public controls. National or local systems of surveillance in health hardly exist. Only the most meagre hospital statistics are in the public domain. Had the Lourdes Hospital not ceased to publish its statistics in the late 1980s, Alison Gough, and others, might have been left with their bodies intact. In an era of 'transparency' and 'accountability', hospitals, regulatory and other health bodies, such as the Medical Council, continue to operate as closed systems, impervious to the public gaze. All is secrecy, and secrecy is all. New York State has legislation requiring maternity hospitals to publish their rates of intervention. Not Ireland. Dutch hospitals are inspected. Not ours.

Hospitals must be exposed to greater scrutiny: in a climate where clinical independence is so fiercely protected, patient safety *will* be compromised. The failure of the medical profession to audit its outcomes in any systematic way is matched only by the failure of the state to compel—and fund—outcome-oriented research, locally, regionally or nationally. This has led to a huge deficit in vital information in our health system. Here, only the big Dublin maternity hospitals publish annual clinical reports. National enquiries into maternal deaths, still-births and deaths in infancy—routine in Britain—are urgently needed. All hospitals should be legally required to publish statistics on medical procedures and their outcomes. This would enable comparisons to be made between hospitals, and—if they were broken down by doctor—between consultants. In 2005, Scotland became possibly the first country in the world to publish death rates by doctor in surgery. While producing mortality and other statistics has to be done with great care, there is no doubt that putting this kind of information in the public domain would do much to improve the quality of hospital care.

In order to publish statistics, you first have to collect them. Audit needs to become the norm. Many hospitals in our 'knowledge economy' still depend on hand-collated records. Information technology is a vital area that needs a huge injection of funds and—after the PPARS debacle—expertise.

We need to regulate hospital (and nursing home) care more closely, to draw up regulations incorporating standards that are clear and unambiguous. With staff shortages being what they are, there is a real danger of de-skilling. The use of care assistants needs to be regulated. Legislation preventing care assistants from carrying out invasive procedures or administering drugs, passed in California some years ago, may also be needed. We need a licensing system backed up by an inspectorate for all of our hospitals, public and private, not just psychiatric hospitals. Privately owned hospitals and nursing homes should be subjected to the same controls as restaurants.

Another aspect of quality assurance is competence assurance. The Medical Council is now, belatedly, piloting 'professional practice review': small numbers of medical colleagues, non-medical colleagues and patients—all selected by the doctor in question—will be surveyed about doctors' medical practice. This kind of review brings to mind the old question: who polices the police? Coming as it does in the wake of the *Harding Clark Report* on the Lourdes obstetric unit, this review process will do little to restore confidence in the profession. Even if the respondents were randomly selected, there are no national standards in place against which a doctor's performance can be measured. Surely something more robust yet fair could be devised. The New Zealand College of Midwives has developed an approach to standards review that is a model of it kind. To protect public safety effectively, the review process needs national standards, independent assessors and transparent processes. It should be run by the training colleges, not the regulator: fairness demands that review processes be kept separate from fitness-to-practise machinery.

A final point on accountability: the IHCA is lobbying for the introduction of a 'no fault' compensation scheme specifically for babies brain-damaged during birth. Reform is needed, but seeking to draw a veil over medical negligence or malpractice is not the way forward. While there is a need to address the issue of continuing care, parents must be able to find out what happened to their child. The lack of accountability inbuilt into no-fault compensation is a major issue, particularly in Ireland where accountability mechanisms are so weak. The right to resort to litigation is an important one.

SUSTAINABILITY

Staff shortages in areas such as midwifery and nursing are threatening public safety. Our dependence on developing countries to plug the gaps in our health services may not be sustainable over the coming years. Something that could make a difference here is legislative reform. The new Nurses' and Midwives' Act needs to reflect the needs of midwives as well as nurses, if the current haemorrhage is to be stemmed. Midwifery legislation in New Zealand and Canada, countries that have seen a renaissance in midwifery since the 1990s, offers a model for progressive legislation in this area.

Tom Nolan, a Clare GP, suggests one strategy to deal with the current manpower shortage: compulsory public service for all medical graduates trained in the state. Public service employees who graduate at the state's expense have long been required to serve for a period of ten years, or else repay the cost of their education. Again, this would help to reduce the manpower crisis, as would flexible retirement. Already available to other public servants, it should also be introduced for health professionals.

There is an urgent need for new hospital specialists in the public service. These appointments require a new contract: we simply cannot afford to continue the swiss-roll model (see below). A public-only contract is the only contract we can afford; such a contract is essential if we are to meet the work-time directive. The present public/private arrangement, John Barton says, is 'an egregious system that provides doctors with perverse incentives to give quicker access to care for the privately insured.' The IHCA has resolutely opposed a public-only contract, as has the IMO. But no union should be allowed to dictate the future terms of a contract that might be offered to employees for a job that has not even been advertised.

Swiss Roll
The Irish hospital system is a swiss roll: private beds in public hospitals are one of the main ingredients of the sponge; the jam is the clause in the common contract that allows doctors to treat private patients during public working hours. Both have combined to create a parallel public–private universe in our hospitals. One consultant in every three holds a contract allowing them to leave their workplace during working hours in order to do private work off-site. The swiss-roll system is one that pays consultants twice to treat the same patient—in the case of a private patient—one payment by the state, and a second payment by a health insurer or by the patient.

Not alone are doctors paid twice to look after the same patients, but they run their private practices at little or no cost to themselves. Yet private practice can be extremely lucrative: in millionaire specialties, such as obstetrics, private incomes average around €500,000, annually, in addition to public salaries. Private practitioners in other fields bear the entire costs of running their practices, including insurance, themselves. The serf taxpayers have, until now, paid 40 per cent of the total cost of private for-profit activity in public hospitals. This subsidy should be withdrawn and the money saved ploughed into the public system. In order to develop the public system, we must first pluck the private system out of its heart.

Indemnity insurance is another ingredient in the swiss roll. Until recently, the state paid 80–90 per cent of the cost of consultants' insurance. Then along came enterprise liability, so they were covered 100 per cent for their work, whether public or private, in public hospitals. The state believed it would be reasonable for consultants in full-time private practice to cover themselves. But by then, after a quarter of a century of the common contract, greed had become institutionalised; millionaire consultants threatened to strike over the state's alleged 'failure' to cover their private practice in private hospitals. The state crumbled, as always, in the face of IHCA demands. Serf taxpayers now foot the malpractice bill for medical consultants in the private sector. No other profession in Ireland enjoys this level of state subvention; it should be withdrawn.

In its current GUBU form, the public–private mix is the nettle that no one has been willing to grasp. If our health services are in difficulty, one of the reasons is that almost 70 per cent of our publicly employed consultants are legally entitled to practise privately in their place of work, at taxpayers' expense, while the other over 30 per cent may lawfully practise privately off-site, wherever. This is an arrangement that has no parallel in any other country in the world. If secondary teachers in public schools were allowed to take private classes during the school day, the inherent contradictions, vested interests, potential abuses, inequitable outcomes and unfair costs would be visible for all to see. But like fish, who can't see water, we seem to be unable to grasp the need for root-and-branch reform. The entitlement to private practice is one that must be allowed to wither away. All new contracts issued to consultants should be public only.

In the meantime, existing consultants should be required to pay a contribution for the use of public facilities to treat private patients, as they do in some EU countries. Charges should be levied for the use of publicly funded facilities, such as nursing and midwifery time, diagnostics, technology, drugs, theatre time, intensive-care time, and so on. This is part of what is bleeding the public hospital system to death. If the full economic cost of these facilities were borne by private health insurers and consultants, there would be at least 40 per cent more to spend on building up the public system. Equity also demands the introduction of a common waiting list. People should be treated on the basis of need, not income.

Most analysts believe that reforming the so-called common contract is key to the future of Irish hospital health care. The new contract should clearly spell out a doctor's duties and obligations, such as taking part in audit, in terms that are enforceable. John Barton believes that a forty-eight-hour commitment should replace the current thirty-three-hour week. Finally, secretaries of state departments serve for a period of seven years; specialists should be asked to do no more. Permanent contracts should be a thing of the past at the top of the hierarchy. However, this is likely to be resisted: medical unions, such as the IHCA, can hold the country to ransom any time, simply by threatening strike action. One way of reducing consultant bargaining power would be to enlarge the specialist workforce in our hospitals. The IHCA has indicated that new consultants cannot be appointed without its say-so because it will block the interview process. But the NCHD label also includes fully qualified specialists who, under the present system, are simply left to languish on short-term temporary contracts, despite being on the register of medical specialists.

Giving these—and other new recruits—a three-year contract as hospital specialists—creating, in effect, a new public-only grade of consultant—would offer a possible solution to the current impasse. And while every care needs to be taken to ensure continuing high standards in hospital medicine, recruiting specialists from other countries should not be too difficult, given the extraordinarily attractive salaries that apply in Ireland. This would also alleviate manpower shortages in the different specialties, redress the imbalance between consultants and NCHDs and help compliance with work-time legislation. Maintaining the current system of five-star generals, backed up by a vast pool of non-commissioned officers, is no longer a viable option.

Organised medicine is not unlike a corporation. Both are long-standing institutions of considerable power; both have come under fire in recent times. Their power is not a constant—it depends on public support. If that support wanes, the power of the institution will fade. It is unlikely that there would be much support for a strike by consultants, many of whom are millionaires, particularly if its objective were to block the appointment of badly needed hospital specialists, whose employment would shorten waiting times for beds and procedures.

TOTALLY INSOLVENT
Last year, PricewaterhouseCoopers predicted that most public health systems would be 'totally insolvent' by 2015–20. Ireland will be among these unless we halt the current government drive towards privatising our health services. *Everyone* needs a decent public health system—it's the only one available if you have a serious accident, or suffer a heart attack or a stroke.

For-profit health care raises very serious issues for us as a society: anywhere you look, for-profit care has failed to deliver accessible, high-quality, cost-effective care. Allowing market forces to determine the shape of the health services, far from increasing public access to health care, actually reduces it. We have now opened our doors to corporate health care. But the needs of the market will always be at variance with the health needs of patients. Canadian law professor Joel Bakan maintains that for a hospital company to rank patient safety above profit would be illegal.

Research carried out on for-profit facilities is predominantly negative on quality of care and value for money: services run for profit are less safe and more costly than those that are not. Death rates are higher in private for-profit hospitals. The profit motive in medicine leads to over-testing and over-treatment, increasing risks for patients.

Private sector efficiency is a myth: US hospital chains, such as Triad, run at around 50 per cent of in-patient capacity. Cost-effectiveness is an even bigger myth: for-profit care costs more. Administrative costs, for example, are higher. Canada estimated that converting half of its non-profit hospitals to money-making entities would increase overall hospital costs by $3.6 billion annually. We should do a similar calculation here before it's too late. New Labour proved this point spectacularly in Britain. As in Ireland, the plan was for the private sector to finance, design, and build hospitals and, latterly, to operate patient services. Today, with schools and hospitals contracted to private maintenance companies that charge up to €200 to change a light bulb, the NHS is on the verge of bankruptcy. Over sixty hospital services are slated to close as NHS hospitals struggle to pay spiralling debts to for-profit corporations.

Market mechanisms have also failed utterly to stem rising costs or to ensure uniformly high-quality care. Escalating drug costs are part of the problem. Overcharging, not efficiency, has been shown to be key to profits in health care in American hospitals. Could the same be true of Ireland? Few know what the charges are in Irish private hospitals, however. Is the price of bed and breakfast at the Mater Private Hospital, reported to be around €6,500, in line with industry standards? One way or another, surely it amounts to overcharging?

Finally, the shadow of fraud looms large. In the US, involving private for-profit companies in health has led to wholesale fraud, bribery and corruption, on a scale that is almost unimaginable.

We should learn from these experiences and end state subsidies of for-profit hospitals, nursing homes and psychiatric facilities, terminating the tax breaks for building them. Equally—if not more—

injurious to public health is the government policy of co-location. These policies, taken together, will irretrievably alter the character of Irish hospital care for the worse.

A Trojan Horse

Co-location coupled with investor tax breaks is a lethal brew. If all twenty-three hospitals planned by developers are built, the proportion of private beds in Ireland (excluding psychiatric and long-stay accommodation), will grow from 33 to 42 per cent minimum of the total stock. We will then have more than three times as many for-profit hospital beds (as a percentage of total beds) as the US and France, and seven times as many as Austria. Moreover, the trend, worldwide, is for for-profit hospital groups to form monopolies, killing off competition to become 'dominant players' in the market. Here, the private nursing home experience suggests that chains, in health care, as in fast food, may soon gobble the market. One major and acquisitive US hospital chain, Triad, is already operating in Ireland.

A massive bonanza for the private sector, co-location is a particularly invidious form of privatisation, a life-long marriage from which there is no escape. Creating exactly the kind of internal market that has brought the NHS to its knees, co-location embeds the private with the public, in building contracts, service agreements and thirty-year leases. The new alliance will be based on competition: co-located hospitals will, if built, offer exactly the same services in many cases as their public hospital neighbours—to the same population. Co-location is a Trojan horse that batters the public hospital system, leaving it wide open to incursions from private corporations. Since July 2005, the National Development Finance Agency has been given additional powers 'to procure and deliver projects', including, for example, delivering linear accelerators to the HSE. These powers should be rescinded in respect of the health sector.

Co-location is not the answer to the nation's health service problems. Building private hospitals will do nothing to solve the beds crisis. Instead, the Government's plan is far more likely to lengthen hospital queues as consultants cross the lawn to their private clinics.

Private for-profit hospitals cherry-pick, treating only less costly and more profitable patients, creaming off lucrative services, such as selected day surgery, and avoiding costly, unprofitable services, such as 24/7 A&E. These services, like unprofitable bus routes, are left to the state to run. Nor will co-location liberate 1,000 private beds in public hospitals for public use, as the Minister for Health has claimed. Very sick patients take up almost three-quarters of these beds, patients who came in through casualty and who cannot be looked after in for-profit hospitals, which do not provide 24/7 A&E. Mary Harney's plan is a mirage: it will give us about 290 extra beds, at best, which will not belong to us, and these beds will cost us €300 million more than if we had built them ourselves.

But this is not the worst feature of the plan; the mayhem in A&E is set to continue. The parallel public–private universe in our public hospitals already gives doctors what John Barton describes as 'perverse' incentives to treat private patients before public ones. Co-location will make things worse, giving many consultants new shiny, high-tech, private for-profit wings, linked by a corridor, perhaps, to the public hospital—wings in which it will be lawful for them to invest. Public waiting lists will rise, not fall, as a result, and this has been confirmed internationally, again and again. Co-location does nothing to improve waiting times for public patients. Public patients may wait longer because co-located hospitals poach consultants from the public system, reducing access to specialists, increasing patient dissatisfaction, lowering demand for public services and placing the public institution in jeopardy. The co-location plan should be reversed.

NTPF
Those planning to develop co-located hospitals hope to get patients on a plate, under the National Treatment Purchase Fund. A mechanism for outsourcing patient treatment, the fund treats relatively small numbers of patients at greater cost to the taxpayer, giving consultants a perverse incentive to keep their public patients waiting, by paying substantial fees for those who have waited three to six months for a procedure. The fund puts cash into private pockets that could, and should, be used to build up our public hospital system, to enable it to function properly. Consultants are paid twice to treat their public patients privately; and taxpayers pay twice for the privilege, once through the usual hospital funding, and a second time through the National Treatment Purchase Fund. So poor is the value for money that details of the cost of different procedures in different hospitals have not been made public. This information should be released, the fund abolished and the monies saved reinvested directly in the public health system.

The proposed privatisation of VHI and its break-up into a number of 'competing' entities should be rejected. As a society, we do not need multiple health insurers. In fact, one would be ideal. The Government promotes the fiction that insurers compete with each other, but the reality is that different insurers offer the same packages, more or less, at roughly the same prices, to subscribers, while, euro for euro, offering the same fees to consultants. But their very existence gives the illusion of something that, in a consumerist society, has been elevated to a religion: 'choice'. Government policy forcing VHI to 'compete' with VIVAS is misguided. Its plan to turn VHI into a commercial entity should be abandoned; VHI should remain an undivided public non-profit company.

Growing private health insurance also grows the market for medical services, but as the Australian experience shows so clearly, this is a growth promoter no country can afford. As many as 52 per cent of people in Ireland pay for private health insurance; if we continue on our current privatisation path, premiums will rise steeply in the coming decade. This will put them out of reach for some. This is exactly what has happened in Australia and in the United States. There, health premiums are becoming increasingly unaffordable.

So, the issue of risk equalisation is important, to ensure that VHI does not collapse under the weight of increasing claims. Risk equalisation is a payment to be levied on insurers to compensate VHI for the fact that the vast bulk of *its* subscribers are older and are more likely to need greater care in the coming years. In 2006, the Supreme Court found that the Government had the right to impose risk equalisation. The payment is not unfair; companies who recently entered the market have made enormous profits, taking in vast sums of money in subscriptions, and paying out relatively little in claims from younger subscribers.

Doctors should have a single paymaster. The present system of payment, where there are two paymasters, the state and the private insurer, is leading to abuses. John Barton believes that the current two-tier system puts the public hospital patient at a disadvantage and leads to higher costs: 'a fee-for-service system is very costly: it incentivises doctors to over-treat patients and leads to an over-supply of medical treatment. Having a single payer would end this costly over-supply. Consultants should either be paid through insurance or by the state.'

Widening the Gaze

Ireland has always had a considerable number of private non-profit hospitals: we now have a growing number of the for-profit variety. Nothing is known here publicly about these hospitals in Ireland, their patient outcomes, their patient–staff ratios. The Department of Health has always taken the extraordinarily blinkered view that for-profit hospitals are outside its remit. The idea seems to be that, because these hospitals are not funded directly by government, the state has no role in overseeing their operations. But as Joel Bakan underlines, 'the corporation depends entirely on government for its existence, and is therefore always, at least in theory, within government's control.' The Department urgently needs to widen its gaze: public safety demands a modern regulatory framework that encompasses all hospitals.

In 1895, Sir John Moore appealed for regular inspection and licensing of private hospitals (and nursing homes) by public health authorities. Over 100 years later, there is still no licensing of nursing homes, while private hospitals continue to operate under cover of darkness. We urgently need a licensing system. The Minister's recent decision to exclude private hospitals from the remit of the Health Information and Quality Authority (HIQA)—except where they provide a service on behalf of the state—does not inspire confidence in the Government's determination to regulate the private sector.

Private non-profit hospitals should be brought under public ownership. They are now funded almost entirely from the public purse, yet some, such as the Dublin maternity hospitals, continue to behave as though they were independent fiefdoms. The Medical Missionaries of Mary sold their unwanted hospital in Drogheda to the local health board in 1997. Today they could have sold it to a private corporation for up to €200 million. We need legislation governing the sale of private non-profit hospitals, to block their conversion into for-profit entities. In Kilkenny, the nuns sold their hospital, Aut Even, to the highest bidder, for profit. We should also take steps to ensure that these hospitals cannot be handed over to private hospital management chains, as has happened in California.

CURBING CORPORATIONS

The Government has now taken significant steps to corporatise health services in Ireland. But again, the checks and balances that obtain in other countries do not exist here. US hospital companies operating in Ireland have a policy of offering the medical staff in their hospitals a beneficial interest in their ownership. Such gain-sharing is unlawful in certain states in the US, but in Ireland, of course, there is no prohibition on doctors holding shares in hospitals. Ireland prefers to turn a blind eye to the clash of interests that exists between the doctor-as-healer and the doctor-as-shareholder. As cardiologists Risteárd Mulcahy and John Barton have tirelessly pointed out, there is an inherent contradiction between the two. Doctors should be legally prohibited from investing or holding shares in for-profit hospitals, as they are in many US states.

US law prohibits hospitals from claiming from Medicare for treatment provided by doctors who have a financial relationship with the treating hospital. The Stark Statute prohibits hospitals from billing Medicare for items or services referred or ordered by doctors with whom the hospitals have an 'improper' financial relationship. Similar legislation is needed in Ireland, to protect VHI and the NTPF, if it continues. We also need anti-kickback legislation to prohibit financial associations between private hospitals and doctors in private practice in the community: in the US, this has led to referrals motivated not by the best interests of the patient, but by kickbacks or benefits in kind to the doctor.

Senior medical staff, such as consultants, nurses and other professionals, should be legally prohibited from accepting gifts of more than nominal value, particularly from companies, or their representatives. This would bring them into line with other senior public servants, who are forbidden to accept presents of any substance. For decades, pharmaceutical corporations have cosied up to the medical profession without let or hindrance. Public safety demands that the intimacy of this relationship be curbed. Had it been more at arm's length, our superbugs today might be fewer and weaker. The Medical Council allows doctors to participate in sponsored junkets in the name of medical 'education'. The era of luxury all-expenses-paid weekends in Ireland's top hotels, champagne city breaks, French rugby internationals and holidays abroad—for two—needs to end. Such perks should be unlawful. Despite doctors' protestations to the contrary, there is some evidence that company representatives flog their wares in hospitals to good effect.

Regulations should also be introduced to protect health-care institutions, including hospitals, clinics, and surgeries, from being used by corporations to advertise, promote or distribute their products. Distributing 'gift' packs to pregnant women and new mothers reduces breastfeeding, regardless of whether or not the bags contain samples of formula milk.

Conflicts of interest will invariably arise where hospital consultants own shares in companies that manufacture or distribute pharmaceuticals, medical goods and devices that are used in hospitals. Doctors and other health professionals should, like Dáil deputies and senators, be legally obliged to declare any commercial interests they may hold. The tribunal on blood contamination revealed that one of the Blood Transfusion Board's senior employees ran his own blood business in tandem with his public duties. This kind of private enterprise in state boards, such as the Blood Transfusion Board, should be illegal. Medical consultants and other staff should be legally required to withdraw from hospital purchasing processes that involve decisions relating to products made or distributed by companies in which they hold a financial interest. Such abuse of insider positions should no longer be lawful. Where abuses persist, they should be exposed and prosecuted.

Almost half of patient advocacy groups in Ireland receive money and/or support in kind from the pharmaceutical industry, often for 'educational' purposes. We should have legislation obliging patient groups to disclose such funding publicly. The ban on advertising drugs directly to patients should be tightened; corporations are now using their alliances with patient groups to brand company names, if not company products. This kind of marketing should be unlawful.

In the US, the private health-care industry is one of the largest and the most corrupt. Now that the industry is set to grow in Ireland, we need specific protection in the fraud area; we have no whistleblowers' legislation, for example. We need legislation along the lines of the US False Claims Act, the benefits of which we saw in Chapter 12.

Finally, we need a ban on corporations advertising or promoting their products, or teaching courses or modules in schools and colleges. The integrity of the public teaching sphere needs to be protected from corporate intrusion. Abuses need to be investigated. In University College Dublin, for example, an infant-formula manufacturer was allowed to 'lecture' in 'nutrition' as part of a recognised public health nursing course. It should not be possible for college authorities to make their facilities available to corporations in this way, to promote their own interests. Nor is it appropriate, from a public interest perspective, for pharmaceutical corporations to sponsor chairs in health care; Ciba-Geigy, for example, currently funds a professorship in general medical practice at University College Dublin. While this is no reflection on the post-holder, it is exactly the kind of sponsorship you would expect to find in a developing country, not in a wealthy society such as Ireland's. University chairs should be publicly funded.

Chapter 16

Restoring the Republic

INTRODUCTION

Health is defined in terms of medicine, and medicine, increasingly, has become care that can be provided only under consultant control. Primary care—health promotion and disease prevention—is virtually non-existent. In some parts of the country, community health services are almost unknown. As a people, we are increasingly treated with contempt by a complacent government and an arrogant bureaucracy. Sick people are treated, of course, and many are treated extremely well. The public system continues to cope, despite everything, thanks to the determination and dedication of medical consultants, doctors in training, nurses, midwives and others.

But the role of the patient is to put up, and shut up. Information is jealously guarded; the culture is one of deep secrecy, as the many complaints to the Information Commissioner relating to health testify. Service users have systematically been shut out; everywhere you look, the democratic deficit warps the services.

A TWO-SPEED SERVICE

For over thirty years, the Government, the state, and the people had not the slightest influence in deciding how hospital care should be developed, or where specialist services should be located. That power was given to hospital specialists themselves. Successive governments and the Department of Health fully supported this ludicrous state of affairs. Most of the problems in the health service derive not from the way it is financed, but from the way in which it has encouraged the growth of medical fiefdoms. Except for the occasional political stroke here and there—the building of a new hospital in Tullamore, for example, within a radius of two hospitals 20 miles away (both now slated to close)—our health system is not politically driven: it is consultant-controlled.

Many of the problems we have today originated in the 1970 Health Act. It set up the Hospitals' Council. Few knew who Comhairle was, or what it did. Medical consultants, guaranteed a majority by law, made up the bulk of its members. Comhairle's function was not to advise, but to *regulate* consultant and senior medical staff in public hospitals. Since the service follows the consultant, this was tantamount to controlling hospital activities. The Act enabled Comhairle to act as a cartel, controlling the supply of specialist medical services in the public sector, creating jobs that were tailored to the needs of the colleges as well as the hospitals. It should not be forgotten that these were jobs where public salaries could be doubled, trebled, and even, later, quadrupled by private fees. From 1972 to 2005, Comhairle pursued an unwavering policy of centralisation, implementing the *FitzGerald Report* by stealth, starving smaller hospitals of medical consultants and fattening larger ones, mainly in Dublin but also in Cork and Galway, to supermac size.

In maternity care, for example, from 1973 to 2003, a staggering 83 per cent of the Republic's maternity facilities closed. In Bantry as in Brittany, the protests of local communities went unheard, falling on the deaf ears of technocrats, just as they did in 2003, when, sitting in conclave in Kildare Street, the Institute of Obstetricians and Gynaecologists, a scion of the Royal College of Physicians, decided to close eleven of the country's maternity units, with immediate effect in Monaghan and Dundalk Hospitals. Comhairle constructed its prototype unit from the Institute's blueprint, based on a line speed of three women per labour-ward bed per twenty-four hours. And, in promoting consultant management for all women in childbirth, as it did in 1976, Comhairle lawfully created a medical monopoly over the services for birth—services formerly provided by another profession.

As in France, a two-speed hospital service developed: one urban, high-status, high-cost, self-regarding and university-based; the other a non-urban, non-university hospital facility that was less prestigious, less costly—and more community-oriented. Today, with the collusion of the Government, the former threatens to destroy the latter, ostensibly in the name of 'safety'. Organised medicine has become increasingly corporatised: at the top, it behaves like a corporation, blindly pursuing its own objectives without the slightest regard for others. Like all corporations, it is incapable of empathy, devoid of the capacity to make moral judgements. All it knows is its own self-interest.

Over the years, the gap between the needs of the profession and the needs of society has widened. Sub-specialisation has made the staffing of smaller hospitals almost impossible; even bigger hospitals are in difficulty. The medical project needs empires; communities need care. This divergence now threatens the future of our second-level hospitals.

The medical technocrats who now run the system believe that the money being spent on smaller hospitals is wasted, because these hospitals do not promote specialisation. That money, Muiris FitzGerald believes, should be used to build the kind of empires in the regions that Comhairle created over the years in Dublin, Cork and Galway. No other sort of hospital should be allowed to exist. And people unfortunate enough to live in non-urban areas will, HSE chief Brendan Drumm says, just have to get used to it.

For imperially minded consultants, medicine is about specialisation. In large urban hospitals, particularly in Dublin where most of the city-centre hospitals were closed during the savage cuts of the 1980s, it is difficult to maintain any sense of a relationship with a local community. That thread, that connection, is broken. And when that happens, there is a danger that careerism and elitism may take over. Today, there is a new kind of blindness to the legitimate health needs of communities. Brendan Drumm memorably described those who articulate those needs, as having 'vested interests'. But this is a perversion of language: the real vested interests are those that now drive the system, those self-regarding, elitist, careerist empire-builders who now demand that the entire public hospital purse be put at the disposal of its micro-specialties.

However, as Joel Bakan points out, history humbles dominant institutions. It is unlikely that organised medicine will be the exception that proves the rule. Institutionalised greed is unattractive.

Today, the distortions of our health services threaten the future of rural communities. Large hospitals, both in Ireland and elsewhere, are the only ones properly suited to the needs of specialist medical consultants who require access to large swathes of patients to develop their specialties and sub-specialties. The same medical monopoly that has constricted the development of midwifery denies communities access to life-saving and maternity care; professional needs take precedence over those of communities. Officially, the notion that the function of a hospital is to serve the sick has become outmoded. Instead, the warped view that hospitals primarily exist to serve the interests of professionals has taken root among the medical technocrats who now, since the demise of local health boards, run our health services without the benefit—or the burden—of democratic controls. As HSE network manager Chris Lyons observed, it takes 200,000, at least, to sustain a hospital *properly*, as though it were a medical fattening station.

REVERSING CENTRALISATION
The Hanly-Teamwork template would see all urgent in-patient services centralised into enormous 1,000-bed industrial-style units; all human-scale hospitals, with the exception of for-profit entities, are to close. Ironically, one of the arguments used by the *Hanly Report* to close smaller hospitals was that Ireland had 'too many' of them, and that this was resulting in a 'costly duplication' of services. Now the Government plans to build at least ten new small hospitals on public sites; 'viability' for these hospitals has been set at eighty-plus beds. Arguments about hospital size are highly political, clearly.

This model treats people living in rural areas, in towns and villages, as though they were some unrepresentative and unimportant minority. Ireland is not near as urbanised as Britain, yet British population densities provided the basis for the Hanly-Teamwork hospital/ population ratios. Solutions that may be appropriate to high levels of urbanisation are utterly inappropriate when crudely applied, as they have been, to a much smaller population that is six times more dispersed.

As we saw earlier, the needs of health professionals, and, in particular, medical consultants, drive the services. Partly because specialists were first on the turf, they have always been much more powerful than general practitioners. One result is that hospital medicine in Ireland has been allowed to gobble up most of the cake, leaving little for primary care. Community services, in consequence, are seriously under-developed, as they are in most industrialised countries. Now, the medical elite who run our services have decided that second-level hospitals do not serve their needs. In any conflict between the professional needs of organised medicine and the health needs of local communities, people—those whom the profession exists, or should exist, to serve—have invariably lost out. In the case of Monaghan's maternity unit, for example, the community proved no match for the serried ranks of the medical training bodies, the local health board, the medical trade unions, and the Department of Health. *Their* combined efforts, not the insurers', closed the maternity unit.

If we look to other countries, we see that there *is* a commitment to providing even people who live in remote and rural areas with decent services. Here, however, there is none. Here, people who live in smaller towns, such as Monaghan, Ennis, Nenagh and Roscommon, are expected to accept the loss of life-and-death services on the spurious pretext of 'safety'.

The centralisation (and privatisation) of cancer services here has been presented as 'international best practice', a mantra which, increasingly, needs to be translated as 'international worst practice'. Yet cancer services in other countries are organised differently, as those making these decisions know very well. A Comhairle na n-Ospidéal report tells us that, for example, 'there are twenty-two radiotherapy units of various sizes in Holland.... Radiation oncologists and medical oncologists in the Netherlands visit peripheral hospitals for case conferences. Some satellite units have become *de facto* independent radiotherapy departments [emphasis added].' No one has ever mentioned the possibility of providing any form of decentralised cancer service here. It does not suit medical agendas.

Not enough attention has been paid to the costs of centralisation for patients, their families, and their communities. Here, both the Government and the HSE pretend that such costs do not exist, and, if they do, they are of no consequence. It is over twelve years now since researchers in Newcastle, England, called for more research into the avoidable deaths caused by delays in reaching hospital. There is a term of art for this: it is called *distance decay*. Here in Ireland, in Monaghan, distance decay has already contributed to at least seventeen needless deaths.

Patients living in the country spend an enormous amount of time—and money—travelling, both to access care for themselves and

to visit family and friends in hospital. A study of cancer patients in the
south-west of Scotland found that 13 per cent of their remaining time
on earth was spent travelling to a hospital. One 84-year-old described
having to make a one-way seven-and-a-half hour journey by
ambulance from Stranraer to Edinburgh for radiotherapy. Is this 'best
practice'?

The equity issues raised by the Hanly-Teamwork template are
enormous. Hardest hit, as always, will be the elderly, the less well off,
the disabled and those with little access to private transport.
Urban–rural inequalities in health are ugly. Research shows that
trauma deaths are higher in country areas, especially if there is no A&E
unit within striking distance. 'Dead on arrival' rates vary from 23 per
cent for city folk to 74 per cent for small-town dwellers. Country
patients are more likely to suffer from diabetes-induced blindness
than their urban counterparts. More people in remote areas die from
asthma. In a society that calls itself civilised, these inequalities are
intolerable.

And when you consider that non-urban communities are expected
to pay the same taxes as everyone else, and to accept, at the same time,
that their access to publicly funded hospital services is far less, the
unfairness begins to look unjust. Funding should be allocated fairly.
The NHS in England and Wales has been faulted for the way it
allocates resources: 'it effectively takes money from rural and poor
areas and gives it to the most affluent parts of the country.' The same
could be said about funding in Ireland. Scotland has now adopted an
equitable approach to health funding, following a fundamental
review, described in 'Fair Shares for All'. We should do the same.

Access to appropriate health care is a human right. We cannot, as a
society, deny this right to the hundreds of thousands of people who
live in non-urban areas. There are other ways of dealing with the
work-time directive, of maintaining clinical skills, even of providing
medical training. Countries whose governments have a commitment
to providing equitable hospital services have developed ways of providing bedrock services, such as A&E and maternity care. We should
retain our network of second-level hospitals, complete with 24/7 in-
patient A&E and maternity care. Acute surgery should form part of
urgent care; certain surgical procedures need to be available on an
emergency basis 24/7 to prevent avoidable deaths. A recent RCSI report
on managing severely ill patients actually admits that 'life-saving

surgery may be needed occasionally before transfer to a regional trauma unit'. Implementing the Hanly-Teamwork template would remove the possibility of access to that life-saving surgery.

There *is* a need to reorganise hospital services—in a way that prioritises community health needs *over* medical career-building. Specialised services, such as burns and neurosurgery, should, of course, continue to be provided in hospitals, such as St James's and Beaumont in Dublin. There is no reason why smaller hospitals cannot specialise in certain planned surgical procedures, just as private hospitals do. Liam McMullin, a surgeon at Roscommon Hospital, makes the point that his hospital has had spare capacity over the past eighteen months. 'Curiously enough, 50 miles away in private Galway hospitals, public patients are being treated by the NTPF scheme, services we could deliver here at Roscommon. Why such spectacular waste of public funds?' he asks. 'At a stroke, the Minister could dramatically reduce costs and increase our surgical throughput.' This offers a real solution to much of the attrition that has taken place in smaller hospitals: adopted nationally, this approach would help reduce public waiting lists in bigger hospitals and increase the cost-effectiveness of smaller institutions, while at the same time enabling them to provide sustainable 24/7 emergency services. Only vested interests prevent its implementation.

Specialties erect boundaries: specialisation has made practitioners think about skills in a rigid, compartmentalised way. Unions also erect and maintain demarcation lines. But specialist nurse practitioners have shown that it is possible to move successfully beyond traditional boundaries. The loss of general physicians and surgeons is one that can be remedied; tailoring the specifications for some consultant posts to fit the needs of smaller hospitals is one obvious solution. The royal colleges could conceivably develop a new and much-needed sub-specialty: a special interest in smaller hospitals. Not everyone in medicine, nursing or midwifery wishes to work in huge high-tech urban centres that have long ago been severed from their communal roots. Not everyone practising medicine today wishes to be a technocrat or a micro-specialist. If the colleges fail to act, the state should do so.

Only 5 per cent of patients need specialist care; why should the other 95 per cent be cared for—at much greater cost—in a third-level hospital? They suffer from the common or garden maladies that afflict everyone—heart failure, pneumonia, gall bladder and hernia, to name but a few. These currently account for 95 per cent of the work done in smaller hospitals. John Barton says that, for these conditions, smaller hospitals' results are as good as those of bigger units. 'A good clinician will get good results wherever he or she practises.' American research shows that outcomes in smaller hospitals are as good as those of bigger units. Of the 100 highest-ranking hospitals in the United States, for example, forty are small to medium-sized, with bed numbers ranging from twenty-five to 250. The vast bulk of surgery and medicine carried out in smaller hospitals does not require large numbers for good outcomes. Only larger hospitals do the kind of complex surgery that requires larger volumes for optimal results.

Chris Lyons asked the question: What can a local hospital provide to a road accident victim with a head trauma, other than 'delay the point at which the experts could work on the patient'? The 2003 RCSI report cited with interest an Irish study of accident victims in a 'peripheral' hospital; it undermines the doctrine of centralisation. The county hospital's results were indeed impressive: it managed 80 per cent of its 963 road-crash victims itself, transferring just 20 per cent to a regional centre, admitting 19 per cent and operating on 12 per cent of these in-patients. On the specific issue of head trauma, a large-scale study tracking over 1,500 head injuries in an Irish regional hospital concluded that 96 per cent of people with head injuries serious enough to warrant hospitalisation could *safely* be treated in a non-specialist setting, with CT scanning and telemedicine links to a specialist neurosurgical unit.

The same RCSI report actually advises ambulance personnel to get the very ill patient from the ambulance to 'definitive' care within one hour. (Definitive care is defined as an operating theatre, an ICU or a rehabilitation facility.) But if the Hanly-Teamwork model is applied, hundreds of thousands of people will live two hours' drive or more from definitive care. In addition, research shows that the vast bulk of casualty patients do not avail of ambulance services to get to A&E, although this fact has been conveniently glossed over. If 83 per cent of people transport themselves to A&E, what will they do when the nearest casualty unit is two hours' drive away?

In the light of the work-time directive and royal college training requirements, other countries, such as Scotland, England and Wales, are dealing with the issue of how to manage smaller general hospitals in a very different way. The work-time directive can be dealt with in a number of ways—by bringing in a public-only contract, for example, as discussed in the last chapter. Other work-time solutions include developing community and primary care, and making more use of information technology and work substitution—giving NCHDs, advanced nurse practitioners, certified nurse specialists, general nurses and other professionals a wider range of duties. Reorganising medical training, investing more money in medical education, would also help. Our investment in medical education is abysmally low by international standards: in Dublin, per head spending on medical students is €6,000–€7,000, compared with €28,000 in Edinburgh.

Telemedicine has a role to play in the viability of smaller hospitals in Ireland, as in Canada. The cost of technology is falling, not rising. ECGs and X-rays can now be reviewed by specialists remote from the patient. In Grampian, for example, video-linking between community A&E units and the main hospital in Aberdeen has cut referrals by up to 80 per cent

Finally, the training nexus needs to be addressed. The royal colleges have tended to view smaller hospitals negatively: the painting by numbers approach—three consultants or nothing—has led to hospitals losing their accreditation as training sites. But smaller hospitals offer training opportunities missed in larger centres, 'to deal with uncertainty, for doctors to think for themselves, to practise procedures and offer time for reflection'. In France, Professor Jean-Marie Clement has proposed that training accreditation should be based on individual specialists, not on hospitals. This innovative idea would, if implemented, see medical training revert to a former model—apprenticeship. Legal training, both for the Bar and for solicitors, is still based on this model. It has much to recommend it; in medicine, for example, it would ensure that students were exposed to clinical excellence, not bad practice. The current training model assumes that all doctors, clinically, are as good as each other and make equally good teachers. This is far from being the case. The *Harding Clark Report*, for instance, showed clearly that trainees in the Lourdes Hospital were learning bad habits. A culture of Caesarean hysterectomy developed in the obstetrics department; trainees showed signs of being too ready to resort to such a draconian remedy.

MIDWIFE-LED CARE

One area of centralisation that can be addressed is maternity care, where the specialist all but wiped out the generalist. Squaring the circle in maternity care is not too difficult; if obstetricians feel they must withdraw their labour from smaller maternity units, those units can very well be run by midwives. Midwifery is central to national systems of maternity care in the Netherlands, Germany, France, Denmark, Austria, Switzerland and Britain. Women in childbirth are best looked after by midwives, the World Health Organisation says. Research shows that care provided by midwives is as safe, or safer, than care provided by doctors.

Dutch obstetricians have testified to the safety of midwifery-based care. The Dutch system of maternity care, which is based on midwives, is acknowledged to be one of the best in the world. Midwives there are allowed to take private 'patients' in hospital, just like consultants. (Mind you, millionaire obstetricians are unlikely to enthuse about bringing in such a model here.) Midwifery-led maternity units are common in many of Britain's smaller hospitals, as they are in New Zealand. In Germany, a country with a system of health care we can only envy, births in birth centres run by midwives increased by 50 per cent from 1999 to 2002. There are now well over 7,500 'birth houses' in Germany.

Predictably, Comhairle rejected the idea of stand-alone midwife-led units. Monaghan Hospital, for example, was told it could have a midwifery-led unit, but only after such a service had been piloted and evaluated in Cavan and Dundalk. It was as though we needed to reinvent the wheel. But there is no good evidence for routinely involving obstetricians in the care of all women during pregnancy and childbirth. National maternity-care policy on this point is outdated, out of line with the evidence. It needs to be changed to reflect the needs of today's women, who increasingly look for alternatives to the standard model of obstetric care.

Institute of Obstetricians and Gynaecologists (IOG) plans to close nine of the country's maternity units will, if implemented, force women to travel longer and longer distances to have their babies in increasingly remote hospitals. Women have a right to local maternity services; centralised systems expose them and their babies to the risks of roadside births and needless deaths; medical inductions lead to Caesarean section and are also associated with autism. There is an urgent need for birth centres and maternity units run by midwives; home-birth services should be available for those who want them.

I visited remote and rural areas in Aquitaine, Midi-Pyrénées and Auvergne in south-west France in April 2006. When I asked how far the nearest maternity unit was for any childbearing woman in the region, I was invariably told, '*vingt, trente minutes à la rigueur* [20–30 minutes at the outside]'. From Le Puy-en-Velay to St-Jean-Pied-de-Port, no woman I spoke to had a concept that access to a maternity unit *could be* any longer.

POLITBUROS AND PATIENTS

Medicine is possibly the only profession in history that has had absolute power to shape the market to its needs. That absolute power must now be ended. Public safety—and sustainability—demand that the untramelled control of professional medical bodies over health care be dismantled.

Compared with Britain's, our level of democracy is low. There, extensive consultation is the norm on draft legislation: bills are widely circulated before being finalised. Here, this breadth of consultation is unusual. End-stage consultation is the norm, and this is usually confined to the professional insiders. Despite being in gestation for ten years, the upcoming Nurses' and Midwives' Bill, for example, has never been circulated to the professions or to service users for their comments. Consultation in health should be a legal requirement, as it is in Britain. By the time a bill gets to the Houses of the Oireachtas, it is far too late for, say, health advocacy groups to have more than a skeletal input into the legislation. In addition, the time available for debate is far less than it used to be. You have only to compare the passage of the 1970 Health Act through the Dáil with that of the 2004 Act to see how far levels of democracy have fallen in just a couple of decades. Today's Dáil and Seanad do not sit long enough to process properly the volume of legislation going through the Oireachtas. Moreover, the Government does not scruple to rush through critically important legislation; this is profoundly undemocratic. Like many another significant piece of legislation, the 2004 Health Act was rushed through the Dáil just before the Christmas recess. The calibrated stripping out of existing accountability and transparency mechanisms in our health services went largely unnoticed.

Lack of information is another barrier to democracy. Eyebrows were raised when the Secretary-General, Department of Health and Children, requested the Comptroller and Auditor General (whose job it is to ensure that we get value for money) not to disclose how much different hospitals charged for different procedures. Such disclosure should be mandatory; the NTPF is funded by taxpayers.

Information is like gold in a culture that retains it. Dealing with the deficits of the Freedom of Information (FoI) Act is beyond our scope, however. Private non-profit hospitals, such as the Dublin maternity hospitals, were not brought into the FoI net until 2003, while, in yet another illustration of their power, bodies such as the RCSI and An Bord Altranais were FoI-exempt until May 2006, ten years after the legislation had been introduced. Among the health bodies still not covered by the Act are the Office for Health Management and the National Ambulance Training Board. The FoI Act should now be extended to all health-care institutions, including private for-profit (as well as not-for-profit) nursing homes and hospitals; private for-profit health enterprises located on, say, university campuses; professional health practitioner bodies, including, for example, the long-established but mysterious Institute of Community Health Nursing, as well as emerging entities, such as the Health Information and Quality Authority.

The language of 'partnership' is ubiquitous, and nowhere more than in Ireland, whose model of 'social partnership' has attracted widespread interest abroad. Here, social partnership has been criticised for emasculating the unions, making a fetish of consensus and stifling dissent. Meanwhile, new control and surveillance systems are in the process of being developed; the language of 'governance' masks a new lust for power among bureaucrats. What oncologist John Crown wittily refers to as HACS (health administrators and civil servants) are now in the ascendancy over elected representatives.

Policy-making in health follows the beaten path of information retention and control. In recent years, managing by 'consensus' has become the norm; 'strategy' documents and 'mission' statements have been in vogue; and the rhetoric of 'key stakeholders' dominates. The art of managing the media through spin, of moulding public opinion through 'newspeak', of manufacturing consent through 'consultation' has never been higher. Reports, most of them unread even within the industry, multiply. Meanwhile, the citizen has never been more neutered.

There is little genuine commitment to public consultation, only lip service. Unrepresentative bodies, top-heavy with consultants and studded with bureaucrats, are the norm, as is pseudo-consultation. Expensive roadshows have become common: 'facilitators' are hired at enormous expense to manipulate an unsuspecting public through 'workshops' where the agenda is pre-set and the results pre-ordained. Lunch is obligatory, crèches rare.

Behind the rise of newspeak—the art of public lying—lies the growth of management. In 2005, for example, there were eighty-three organisations involved in regulating urgent care services in Ireland. What do they do? Produce an impenetrable thicket of language, for one thing. Take, for example, the following, from the Irish Health Services Accreditation Board: 'A Study of the Relationships between Hospitals: Governance/Management Structures and Patient Safety'. This examined whether or not a relationship existed between the governance/management structures of hospitals and their approach to patient safety. A potentially interesting topic, you might think. The findings, however, as posted on the website, were impenetrable: they suggested that 'organisations with traditional bureaucratic structures were slightly more compliant with care/service patient safety criteria than those with clinicians in management/clinical directorates structures. The opposite was the case for non care/service criteria'. In addition to this, 'health board hospitals were generally more compliant than voluntary with care/service patient safety criteria and again the reverse was the case for non care/service criteria'. This kind of jabberwocky is bad value for money; it is unlikely to contribute to patient safety.

Public safety demands a role for service users in health: the toothless 'consumer panels', established in Britain and now being replicated here, will not protect against the dry rot that permeates the system. These panels are little more than an exercise in optics, their sole purpose to give a veneer of consultation to decisions taken at a higher level. The regional forums established under the 2004 Act are very similar.

The Government has now erected a massive bureaucracy in an effort to remedy the defects in the health service—the inability to deliver a safe, timely, cost-effective service. The new bureaucratic monster that is the Health Service Executive has all of the disadvantages—and the dead wood—of the old regional health board system, with none of the advantages. Those halcyon days when dual membership of Fianna Fáil and Opus Dei was enough to guarantee swift promotion have left their legacy. The same people sit at the same chairs.

The monster of bureaucracy that is the HSE has resulted in far greater levels of centralisation, has reduced local control over health and personal social services, and has further diminished the quality of service. The bigger the bureaucracy, the more inefficient. Presided over by a *politburo* of six—under a praesidium of twelve—that includes the former CEO of Comhairle, and headed by a former chair of Comhairle who represents those very academic, specialist medical interests that now threaten the future of communities across Ireland, the new nomenklatura is utterly impervious to the public gaze.

Thanks to the 2004 Act, the Minister may now kick to touch in the Dáil: parliamentary questions are now referred to HSE except where they concern ministerial policy; these questions take that 145,000-strong body up to eight weeks or more to answer. (Parliamentary questions in other areas are usually answered within three days.) Accountability and transparency are now a thing of the past. The new Act shelters both the HSE and the medical profession to a degree that endangers public safety. The Act, for example, has made it impossible for anyone to get an answer to anything that can be interpreted as involving 'clinical judgement'. Since almost everything, with the possible exception of hotel services, involves patient decision-making, this throws a veil over patient care behind which you cannot look. All patient complaints, grievances and queries will in future be dealt with by the Medical Council—a body not known for its commitment to dealing with patient complaints—or not at all. This state of affairs—reminiscent of the old Soviet Union—is all the more extraordinary when you remember that, on average, the system logs 1,000 adverse incidents *every week*.

Today, after more than 250 years of self-regulation in the medical profession, that tradition may be drawing to an end. The heads of the new Medical Practitioners' Bill provide for a 50:50 medical/lay council, but, understandably, the profession has declared its opposition to this proposal. Opening up professional bodies to 'lay members'—non-members of the profession—is something that has been done in Britain in recent years. Following the Shipman and Bristol scandals, service users in Britain were given parity with health professionals, opening up regulatory and other boards in health. A 50:50 stake for lay members was introduced into bodies, such as the National Council for Nursing and Midwifery. We should do the same in our professional and regulatory bodies, including the colleges, if public protection is a priority and democracy a consideration.

The dated concept of 'representatives of the public interest' should be abandoned: it has always been a fig leaf for members of the party faithful to be given their just reward. The experience of the Blood Transfusion Board suggests that boards should no longer be in the gift of ministers, however. In boards in Britain and Northern Ireland, political patronage has largely been superseded by more democratic processes involving public advertisements and selection processes. We should follow their example. We need a new mind-set, one that believes in involving genuine health advocacy groups and patient organisations in the planning process and giving them representation on the authorities and structures that run the health services. Many of these associations have built up significant expertise over the years; while some are admittedly little more than vehicles for corporate interests, others are independent.

More widely, people must be given greater ownership over health policy-making and planning. In an ideal world, we would attempt to set limits to medicine, formally and rationally scrutinising every single piece of legislation that enshrines medical power. But this is unlikely to happen in the near future. For now, at a minimum, we should amend the eighteenth-century charters governing the royal colleges to provide for greater oversight from bodies such as the Department of Health. In addition, in the interests of transparency and accountability, the 50:50 lay/professional model should be applied to the colleges' governing bodies. In the case of the RCSI, its charitable status should be reviewed in light of its €91 million annual turnover, its property portfolio, and its health oases and pharmaceutical interests. For-profit subsidiaries of non-profit companies should be required to pay taxes, as they are in the US.

Communities must be empowered to take responsibility for their health. In a highly centralised system of health care, such as ours, there is a need to decentralise decision-making. Regional health boards—eliminated by the 2004 Health Act—represented the only countervailing power there was to the power of organised medicine. Centralising health administration was an expensive mistake. The corporate model adopted by the Government to administer our health services—a model that pays CEOs and their senior executives vast salaries augmented by beefed-up performance bonuses—has failed lamentably to deliver. It is a model that should be jettisoned. The HSE should be abolished and the regional health boards restored but with the significant de-layering of bureaucracy and redeployment of staff from middle management to frontline health care. This is the only way to reverse the double democratic deficit, to rebalance the power of medical technocrats with that of elected representatives, to restore the democratic balance between the centre and the regions.

Right now, we are standing at a crossroads, on the cusp of centralisation, at the pass of privatisation. A brave new world beckons, one that will deny many people in non-urban areas, or on low incomes, access to services. This is a model of care derived from the British royal colleges, driven by medical technocracy: one that will industrialise care in hypermarket hospitals, and that will see hospital corporations gobble up precious resources. But there is still time, time to remind ourselves that we are a republic, time to say no: no to vested interests, and private enrichment; no to McMedicine. A health-care system we have confidence in, hospitals that can be relied upon, a public system that is accessible—these things await us.

References

PROLOGUE

page xv

'*adverse event*': Cornelia Stewart and Irene O'Hanlon 2002 'A review of a clinical adverse event in December 2002 in which a pregnant patient attended Monaghan General Hospital and was transferred to Cavan General Hospital'. 16 Dec [Online] Available: http://www.dohc.ie/publications/pdf/monagh1.pdf? direct=1 [Accessed 31 Jan 2007]; *Report of the Independent Review Panel to the Minister for Health and Children concerning the birth of Baby Bronagh Livingstone on 11 December* 20 Dec [Online] Available: http://www.dohc.ie/publications/pdf/ monagh2.pdf?direct=1 [Accessed 31 Jan 2007].

Baby Bronagh: *Evening Herald* 12 Dec 2002; *Irish Times* 12, 13, 14 Dec 2002; *Sunday Independent* 15 Dec 2002; *Northern Standard* 19 Dec 2002; Marie O'Connor 2003 *Northern Standard* 9, 16 Jan.

1: MEDICAL FIEFDOMS

page 2

Dublin Barbers' Guild: John Fleetwood 1983 *The History of Medicine in Ireland*. The Skellig Press, Dublin, 19. A fascinating, if segmented, account, written by a practitioner.

'*empiricks, impudent quacks, women*': ibid, 67.

'*sauce for the goose*': Anne Witz 1992 *Professions and Patriarchy*. Routledge, London, 106. Shows how class and gender have interacted in complex ways to produce hierarchies of power and prestige in professional work.

page 3

struggled with male doctors: ibid, 104–27.

'*ignorant and illiterate persons*': Fleetwood op cit, 33.

page 4

herbs to heal: ibid, 33–4.

to train doctors: ibid, 36.

Surgeons came into being: ibid, 69.

page 5

warehouse the dead: ibid, 204.

page 6

'*clinical material*': ibid, 214.

'*[bodies] for teaching purposes*': ibid, 217.

page 7
'*regarded as dawdling*': ibid, 142.

2: WORLD-CLASS CHAOS
page 11
'*Patients come first*': Mary Harney TD Tánaiste and Minister for Health 2005 *Irish Times* 11 Apr. Leader's speech to a Progressive Democrats conference in Cork.
'*open-heart surgery*': Paul Carson 2006 *Irish Times* 16 May.
'*leave him at night*': Paul Walsh 2004 quoted by Christine Newman 2004 *Irish Times* 13 Nov.

page 12
A&E *plan*: Maev-Ann Wren 2003 *Unhealthy State: anatomy of a sick society*. New Island, Dublin. Indispensable.
in Manhattan: Martin Wall 2004 *Irish Times* 10 Nov.
went into examinership (bankruptcy protection): [Online] Available: http://www.nytimes.com/2005/07/06/nyregion/06hospital.html?ex=1278302400&en=fc4024 8628e49b85&ei=5090&partner=rssuserland&emc=rss [Accessed 3 Jan 2007]
'*highly dysfunctional*': unnamed contributor 2005 'Opinion' *Irish Times* 14 Jan.
'*where to look*': Denise Deegan 2005 *Irish Times*, 8 Mar.

page 13
'*a terrible scandal*': Dr Jerry Cowley TD 2005 quoted by Eithne Donnellan 2005 *Irish Times* 5 Apr.
brother John: Annie Talbot 2005 quoted by Martin Wall 2005 *Irish Times* 28 Apr.
'*every action*': Mary Harney 2005 *Irish Times* 11 Apr, op cit.
'*crying with pain*': from a constituent's letter to Jim O'Keeffe TD quoted by Michael O'Regan 2005 *Irish Times* 23 Oct.
'*On the radio*': Anne Enright 2005 *Irish Times* 5 Nov.
woman with a clot: Bernadette Higgins 2006 quoted by Fiona Gartland and Eithne Donnellan 2006 *Irish Times*, 19 Jan.

page 14
forty-seven others: ibid.
scaled new heights: Eithne Donnellan 2006 Irish Times 15 Feb.
INO: ibid.
'*3.30 a.m.*': Miriam Donohue 2006 *Irish Times* 21 Feb.

page 15
waiting on trolleys: Christine Newman 2006 *Irish Times* 9 Mar.
inquest: Ali Bracken 2006 *Irish Times* 11 Mar.
€55: 2002 *Irish Times* 28 Feb.
'*wait years for treatments*': Wren op cit, 17.

page 16
'*an acceptable waiting list*': Surgeon Frank Cunningham 1997 quoted by Alison O'Connor 1997 *Irish Times* 29 Sept.

the High Court: Wren op cit, 140–1. Janette Byrne 2006 *If It Were Just Cancer: a battle for dignity and life*, Veritas, Dublin, 127.
developed gangrene: ibid, 141.

page 17
'rung of the ladder': ibid, 142.
In the Dáil: Eithne Donnellan 2006 *Irish Times* 31 Mar.
Brendan Drumm: ibid.
over a year: Wren op cit, 146.
Peter Sheridan: ibid, 141.
over 20,000: Eithne Donnellan 2005 *Irish Times* 28 Dec.
almost 22,000: ibid.
Róisín Ruddle: ibid.

page 18
National Treatment Purchase Fund: ibid.
'catalogue of human misery': Dave Hughes INO Deputy General Secretary 2005 quoted by Eithne Donnellan 2005 *Irish Times* 4 Feb.
Janette Byrne: op cit, 120–8.
Patients Together: Eithne Donnellan 2004 *Irish Times* 6 Nov.
Brendan Drumm: quoted by Eithne Donnellan 2006 *Irish Times* 21 Mar.

page 19
'worse than Baghdad': Dr Gerry Lane emergency consultant 2006 quoted by Eithne Donnellan 2006 *Irish Times* 25 Mar.
underspent its capital allocation: Eithne Donnellan 2006 *Irish Times* 31 Mar.
'national emergency': Mary Harney 2006 quoted by Eithne Donnellan 2006 *Irish Times* 29 Mar.
'go' to the private sector: Eithne Donnellan 2006 *Irish Times* 16 May.
Dublin Fire Brigade: Tony McDonnell SIPTU 2005 quoted by Elaine Edwards *Irish Times* 2005 19 Apr.
'things like bed-pans': Martin Wall 2005 *Irish Times* 28 Apr.
Two nurses: Olivia Kelleher 2005 *Irish Times* 23 May.

page 20
trolley population had doubled: Michael O'Regan 2005 *Irish Times* 26 Oct.
200 people lay down: Leah McBride 2006 *Irish Times* 15 Apr.
'excess mortality': Drs James Binchy and Gerry Lane 2006 quoted by Alison Healy 2006 *Irish Times* 28 Apr.

page 21
'Persistent cries': Dr Aidan Gleeson 2006 *Irish Times* 24 May.
'Patient care': Mary Harney 2005 *Irish Times* 11 Apr.
deck on the Titanic: Martin Wall 2005 *Irish Times* 13 June.

page 22
significant funding: Eithne Donnellan 2005 *Irish Times* 22 June.

not seen a penny: Peadar McNamara 2006 Ennis General Hospital Development
Committee, personal communication.

flagged in March: Eithne Donnellan 2006 Irish Times 12 May.

a carrot: Martin Wall 2006 *Irish Times* 14 Aug.

'admission lounges': Eithne Donnellan 2006 *Irish Times* 29 Aug.

page 23

extra deck: Martin Wall 2006 *Irish Times* 2 May.

'management condones': Dr Paul O'Connor consultant anaesthetist 2006, personal
communication.

spend on health: A. Dale Tussing and Maev-Ann Wren 2006 *How Ireland Cares: the
case for health care reform*. New Island, Dublin, 56. A study commissioned by the
Irish Congress of Trade Unions in the run-up to the Social Partnership talks in
Nov 2005.

page 24

less than half: ibid, 58.

a guesstimate: ibid, 68.

less than 90 per cent: ibid, 54.

'battled and bewildered': Dave Hughes 2005 quoted by Eithne Donnellan 2005 *Irish
Times* 4 Feb.

page 25

'rabbit': Dr Sean Murphy consultant physician 2006 quoted by Kitty Holland 2006
Irish Times 5 Jan.

legacy of these cutbacks: Triba Secta unpublished quoted by Martin Wall 2006 *Irish
Times* 21 Mar. Obtained under the Freedom of Information Act.

pulmonary disease: ibid. quoted by Eithne Donnellan 2006 *Irish Times* 21 Apr.

endoscopy units: Dr Paul O'Connor 2006, personal communication.

page 26

only 44 per cent: Tussing and Wren op cit, 76.

amount of bureaucracy: Triba Secta op cit, quoted by Eithne Donnellan 2006 *Irish
Times* 21 Apr.

during the 1990s: Tussing and Wren op cit, 182.

the month of August: ibid, 183.

half the quota: ibid, 182.

over-equipped: Dr Brendan Drumm Health Service Executive (HSE) CEO 2006
quoted by Eithne Donnellan 2006 *Irish Times* 28 Mar.

page 27

€1 million each: Mary Harney 2006 quoted by Eithne Donnellan 2006 *Irish Times* 31
Mar.

the Programme for Government issued: Department of Health and Children 2001 *Quality
and Fairness: a health system for you—Health Strategy*. Stationery Office, Dublin

new public beds: Eithne Donnellan 2005 *Irish Times* 15 July.

more apparent than real: Tussing and Wren op cit, 195.

lie down, or otherwise recover: ibid.

dying cancer patients: Dr O'Reilly medical oncologist 2005 quoted by Michael O'Regan 2005 *Irish Times* 23 Nov.

'a higher elite': Muiris FitzGerald Dean School of Medicine University College Dublin 2002. In Ray Kinsella *Acute Healthcare in Transition in Ireland: Change, Cutbacks and Challenges*. Oak Tree Press, Dublin, 57.

page 28

short of hospital specialists: Dr John Barton consultant physician, Portiuncula Hospital, Ballinasloe, Co. Galway, 2006, personal communication.

31 per cent more likely: Madeleine Speirs President Irish Nurses' Organisation (INO) 2005 *Irish Times* 7 Oct.

rose by only 0.6 per cent: Tussing and Wren op cit, 276.

page 29

3,000 Irish-trained nurses: Eithne Donnellan 2004 *Irish Times* 5 Nov.

'limited supply of nurses': Department of Health and Children 2000 *The Nursing and Midwifery Resource Interim Report of the Steering Group*. Sept Government Publications, Dublin, 53.

left unfilled: Maureen Flynn 2002, speaking on 11 Sept at launch of *The Nursing and Midwifery Resource Final Report of the Steering Group Towards Workforce Planning*. July Nursing Policy Division Department of Health and Children. The lack of demand for these places continues.

25 per cent: FÁS 2005 *Healthcare Skills Monitoring Report*. In Tussing and Wren 2006 op cit, 285.

worked full-time: Department of Health and Children 2000 op cit, 65.

annual turnover among nurses: Professor Geraldine McCarthy et al 2002 *National Study of Turnover in Nursing and Midwifery*. Department of Health and Children, Dublin. The study found an average turnover of 12 per cent across all services in 1999 and 2000: it ranged from a high of 44 per cent at St Vincent's Hospital Dublin to a low of 1 per cent in Cavan General.

'nurses from abroad': Department of Health and Children 2000 op cit, 71.

page 30

not need more midwives: FÁS 2005 op cit. In Tussing and Wren 2006 op cit, 281.

16 per cent: from a national survey of hospital staff conducted by the INO, based on the total number of midwives registered with An Bord Altranais, who must pay an annual fee to retain their registration. Mary Higgins Secretary Midwives' Section INO 2005, personal communication.

3: THE KILLING WARDS

page 31

'unless you're really ill': Mary Harney 2005 Interview *Marian Finucane Show* RTÉ Radio One 21 June.

St Vincent's Hospital: Eithne Donnellan 2006 *Irish Times* 15 Mar.

'a complex caseload': Professor Hilary Humphreys consultant microbiologist, Beaumont Hospital, 2005 *Irish Times* 14 Oct.

page 32

'stop the norovirus': Professor Martin Cormican President Irish Society of Clinical Microbiologists 2006, quoted by Eithne Donnellan *Irish Times* 15 Mar.

15 million: Andrew Nikiforuk 2006 *Globe and Mail* Toronto 30 Sept. Andrew Nikiforuk is the author of *Pandemonium: bird flu, mad cow and other biological plagues of the 21st century*. Penguin.

'formidable hospital invader': ibid.

resistant to ampicillin: J.F.A. Murphy 2005 'Ireland Has Lessons to Learn' *Irish Medical Journal* June 98 (6) [Online]. Available: www.imj.ie [Accessed 15 Oct 2005].

clostridium difficile: Brendan Drumm 2006 quoted by Eithne Donnellan *Irish Times* 31 Mar. Andrew Nikiforuk says that, over 2003–4, this bug killed almost 2,000 elderly patients in Quebec hospitals. Hospital infections sicken 90,000 annually in the province, killing 4,500.

'mother of all super-bugs': Florence Horsman-Hogan 2006 *Irish Times* 1 May.

VRE: [Online] Available: http://www.ndsc.ie/hpsc/A-Z/MicrobiologyAntimicrobial Resistance/EuropeanAntimicrobialResistanceSurveillanceSystemEARSS/Entero cocciVRE/ReferenceandEducationalResourceMaterial/File,2015,en.pdf [Accessed 15 Jan 2007].

page 33

42 per cent: J.F.A. Murphy 2005 op cit. MRSA has proliferated alarmingly: in 1998, for example, just 31 per cent of S. aureus bugs were methicillin-resistant.

more and more antibiotics: Strategy for the Control of Antimicrobial Resistance (SARI) 2005: 121–5 [Online] Available: http://www.ndsc.ie/hpsc/AboutHPSC/ AnnualReports/File,2141,en.pdf [Accessed 15 Jan 2007].

medical-card holders: those entitled to reimbursement—30 per cent of the population—accounts for 60 per cent of the national spend on antibiotics. In 2005, the bill amounted to €51.7 million. Ibid.

chemist with a mission: Strategy for the Control of Antimicrobial Resistance in Ireland (SARI) 2005 *Annual Report*, 35 [Online] Available: http://www. ndsc.ie/hpsc/A-Z/MicrobiologyAntimicrobialResistance/Strategyforthecontrol ofAntimicrobialResistanceinIrelandSARI/OverviewandKeyDocuments/File,1771 ,en.pdf [Accessed 23 Jan 2007].

the bill dropped: ibid.

page 34

compare badly: J.F.A. Murphy 2005 op cit. 'Narrow spectrum' penicillin accounts for just 10 per cent of prescribing here, compared with 80 per cent in Scandinavian countries.

Marsha Hunt: Kate Holmquist 2005 *Irish Times* 11 Oct. Having moved from St Vincent's Hospital to the Blackrock Clinic, Hunt discovered that her wound had been infected with MRSA. [Online] Available: http://www.canceractive.com/ page.php?n=991 [Accessed 31 Jan 2007].

See also Marsha Hunt 2005 *Undefeated*. Mainstream, Edinburgh. Preliminary results from the Hospital Infection Society HCAI Prevalence survey (Robert

Cunney 2006) indicate that the bigger the hospital, the greater the risk to the patient. [Online] Available: http://www.ndsc.ie/hpsc/A-Z/Microbiology AntimicrobialResistance/StrategyforthecontrolofAntimicrobialResistancein IrelandSARI/SARIandAMRAPSARIAnnualConferences/2006AMRAPSARIConf erence/File,2102,en.pdf [Accessed 30 Jan 2007]

limbs amputated: Interview *Prime Time* 2006 RTÉ television 30 Nov.

fifteen-fold: C. Griffiths et al 2004. 'Trends in MRSA in England and Wales: an analsysis of morbidity and mortality data for 1993–2002'. *Health Statistics Quarterly*, Spring 21:15–22.

168 deaths: ibid.

might frighten people: Dr Brendan Drumm 2006 quoted by Eithne Donnellan *Irish Times* 31 Mar.

page 35

'afraid of MRSA': Dr Teresa Graham 2005 quoted by Eithne Donnellan *Irish Times* 27 Dec.

550 people: By the end of 2006, this figure had risen to nearly 600, according to Dr Robert Cunney consultant microbiologist at the National Health Protection Surveillance Centre 2006, quoted by Eithne Donnellan 2006 *Irish Times* 6 Nov. Comparing the number of bloodstream infections in Denmark (11) and Norway (4) with Ireland's, Dr Cunney said that these countries had more isolation facilities, less hospital overcrowding, more infection control staff, aggressive screening policies and less use of antibiotics. Norway has a population of 4.6 million. 'Healthcare associated' bloodstream infections carry a death rate of 25 per cent. [Online] Available: http://www.ndsc.ie/hpsc/A-Z/MicrobiologyAntimicrobial Resistance/StrategyforthecontrolofAntimicrobialResistanceinIrelandSARI/Anti bioticStewardship/File,1065,en.pdf [Accessed 31 Jan 2007].

nine out of ten: Department of Health and Children 2000 *North/South Study of MRSA in Ireland 1999*. Department of Health and Children, Dublin, 34.

'a water-slide for germs': Andrew Nikiforuk 2006 op cit.

29.1 per 1,000 beds: Department of Health and Children 2000 op cit, 26.

page 36

'private patients': Healthcare Risk Resources International 2001 *Report on Our Lady of Lourdes Hospital Drogheda*. Commissioned by the North-Eastern Health Board in the wake of the Caesarean hysterectomy scandal at that hospital.

paper guidelines: Department of Health 1995 Guidelines for the control of methicillin resistant *Staphylococcus aureus* [MRSA] in acute hospital wards, including specialist units. Department of Health, Dublin.

out with its hands up: Martin Wall 2006 *Irish Times* 22 Aug.

page 37

'no toilet paper': posting on irishhealth.com [Online] Available: irishhealth.com [Accessed 1 Dec 2006].

a cloth: *Late Late Show* Interview RTÉ television 23 Sept 2005.

hands are washed: J.F.A. Murphy 2004 'Handwashing: a personal responsibility'. *Irish Medical Journal* June 97 (6).

page 38

Poor patient–nurse ratios: Professor Hilary Humphreys 2006 'Overcrowding, under-staffing and infection in hospitals'. *Irish Medical Journal*, Apr 99 (4).

'heavy and bed-ridden': Florence Hogan Horsman 2006 op cit.

Even in intensive care: Dr Paul O'Connor 2006, personal communication.

'a serious impediment': Hilary Humphreys 2005 op cit.

a fifth bed: ibid.

page 39

over-occupancy of beds: Mary Harney 2005 op cit.

85 per cent: Professor Martin Cormican 2006 op cit.

'one isolation room': Hilary Humphreys 2005 op cit.

$42–59 million: Andrew Nikiforuk 2006 op cit.

'piece of meat': Eoin Reynolds 2006 *Evening Herald* 8 Sept.

4: PRINCIPALITIES AND POLITBUROS

page 40

'I was very unwell': Interview with Maria Maguire 2006 (not her real name).

page 45

the nuns: Commission on Nursing 1998 *A Blueprint for the Future*. Stationery Office, Dublin, 35.

'semi-militaristic': ibid, 137

page 46

'command and control': Commission on Nursing 1998 op cit, 125

'entire hospital wards': Muiris Houston 2000 *Irish Times* 22 Jan.

'Mickey Mouse': Dr Bill Tormey 2003 *A Cure for the Crisis: Irish healthcare in context*. Blackwater Press, Dublin, 3.

'checks and balances': ibid, 5.

'The next army': ibid, 3.

page 48

twenty-nine years: Dr Cormac Muldoon 1999 quoted in *Irish Times* 24 Dec.

'tension': Muiris Houston 2000 op cit.

'ultimate responsibility': Dr Cormac Muldoon 1999 op cit.

'carrying a shotgun': Finbarr Fitzpatrick 2000 quoted by Nuala Haughey 2000 *Irish Times* 22 Jan.

page 49

'within the norms': Dr Ambrose McLoughlin 2000 quoted in *Irish Times*, 8 Jan.

'Doctors' decisions': Dr Cormac Muldoon 2000 quoted by Nuala Haughey 2000 op cit.

died waiting: Dr Cormac Muldoon 2000 quoted by Nuala Haughey 2000 op cit.

backing the health board: 2000 *Irish Times* 16 Jan.

between nurses: Commission on Nursing 1998 op cit, 181.

page 50

'major source of stress': Dr S. Cheema 2005 'Bullying of junior doctors prevails in Irish health system: a bitter reality'. *Irish Medical Journal* Oct 98 (9).

'Persistent offensive': ibid.

30 per cent: ibid.

50 per cent are non-nationals: Medical Council [Online] Available: [Accessed 14 Dec 2006].

a London consultancy: Healthcare Risk Resources International 2001 Report on Our Lady of Lourdes Hospital Drogheda unpublished

page 51

32 per cent: Alison O'Connor 1997 *Irish Times* 29 Sept.

'40,000': this is very likely to be an underestimation, as it refers to a period when the health services employed 100,000. It has not been possible to establish just how many of the 145,000 (see below) work in administration. In 2000, just 52 per cent of all staff employed in the health services were directly involved in patient care (Department of Health and Children 2002 The Nursing and Midwifery Resource, 68).

'Absolutely chaotic': a medical source who wishes not to be named, personal communication 2006.

the Secretary-General: Fergus O'Ferrall 2000 *Citizenship and Public Service: voluntary and statutory relationships in Irish healthcare.* Dundalgan Press, Dundalk, 50.

145,000: figure supplied by Taoiseach Bertie Ahern quoted by Dr Maurice Neligan (see above).

'palpably inadequate': Maurice Neligan 2006 *Irish Times* 11 Oct.

eighty-three bodies: Irish Health Services Accreditation Board 2006: 7 [Online] Available: http://www.ihsab.ie/documents/IHSABAugust2006Newsletter-Final.pdf [Accessed 5 Jan 2007].

page 52

'an open system': Commission on Nursing 1998 op cit, 125.

'protecting' and 'enhancing': Madeleine Speirs INO President 2006 *Irish Times* 7 Oct.

highly inflated salaries: are a noticeable feature of the politburo. CEO Brendan Drumm was appointed at a basic salary—excluding overtime and expenses—of €400,000 per annum, on a 5–8 year contract (Donnellan 2005 *Irish Times* 17 June). His five advisors are paid at a rate of €200,000 each; these salaries are further boosted by a daily overtime rate of €1,200, in addition, presumably, to the normal public service expenses.

'€1.7 million': John Gormley TD Green Party Spokesperson on Health 2006 quoted by Eithne Donnellan *Irish Times* 29 Aug.

parents from Co. Meath: On Friday 5 March 2005, gardaí and social workers arrived at the home of Pádraig and Mary O'Hara with a care order committing their five children. The O'Haras told *The Irish Times* (5 Mar 2005) that they had been fighting for basic services for their children for several years. More than 100 people, many of them parents of children with autism, subsequently protested outside the HSE headquarters in Kells. 'The fear provoked by the State's response on that Friday night is still resonating among parents of autistic children' (Carol O'Brien *Irish Times* 12 Mar 2005). 'Parents are literally scared stiff,' said Seamus Greene, Chair of the National Parents' and Siblings' Alliance. The Department of Education was then facing 110 legal actions from the parents of children with special needs.

Mikola Goureng, mother of a child with a disability and a neighbour of the O'Haras, said: 'you don't have to be found guilty of anything. That's the most frightening thing of all' (*Irish Times* 12 Mar 2006). Judge David Anderson subsequently dismissed the interim order secured by the HSE against the O'Haras.

It later emerged that the HSE had also taken another special-needs child into care. In December 2004, Jacqueline Mohan contacted the HSE to say that she needed additional supports for her 13-year-old son, whom she had fostered for thirteen years. On 3 December, her son went to his special school; he never returned home. That day, his mother got a call from the HSE to say that a social worker would call around to collect his things. 'We are being punished for asking for help,' Mrs Mohan told *The Irish Times* (24 Mar 2005).

Fetal rights: John Seymour *Childbirth and the Law*. Oxford University Press, Oxford, 135–88.

page 53

a fully conscious Jehovah's Witness: *Irish Times* 22 Sept 2006. The substantive case against the mother, who is from the Democratic Republic of the Congo, is due to be heard in the High Court: two women, also Jehovah's Witnesses, are due to give birth at the same hospital in 2007, *The Irish Times* reported (8 Dec 2006).

Paul O'Beirne: Carol O'Brien 2004 *Irish Times* 12 Oct.

bodily integrity: Marie O'Connor 2006 'Conjuring choice while subverting autonomy: medical technocracy and home birth in Ireland'. In Andrew Symons (ed) *Risk and Choice in Maternity Care*. Churchill Livingstone Elsevier, Edinburgh, 109–22.

5: THE LAST WALTZ

page 54

lung and liver cancer: Eithne Donnellan 2005 *Irish Times* 27 Dec.

11 per cent: Charles Vincent et al 2001 'Adverse events in British hospitals: preliminary retrospective record review' [Online] Available: http://www.bmj.com/cgi/content/full/322/7285/517 [Accessed 29 Jan 2007]. About half of these events were preventable, the study showed; the potential cost to the NHS, in terms of additional bed days, was estimated at £1 billion annually.

30,000 patients: Harvard Medical Practice Study 1990 *Patients, Doctors and Lawyers: medical injury, malpractice litigation and patient compensation in New York. The Report of the Harvard Medical Study to the State of New York*. Harvard University, Boston.

14,000: Interview *Prime Time* 2003 RTÉ television 15 Dec.

page 55

Only Britain: Sheelagh Bonham 2005 *Report on Perinatal Statistics for 2002*. Economic and Social Research Institute Dublin, 15–16. 'Ireland's perinatal mortality rate is among the highest recorded,' the report notes, at 7.6 per 1,000, 'with only the United Kingdom and a number of new member states including Hungary, Latvia, Lithuania and Estonia showing higher rates.'

Catherine Dunne: Jo Murphy-Lawless 1998 *Reading Birth and Death: a history of obstetric thinking.* Cork University Press, Cork, 218.

page 56

'frivolous claims': J.F.A. Murphy 2006 'Making sense of medical litigation' *Irish Medical Journal* June 99 (6)

'closed ranks': Colm MacGeehin 2006, personal communication.

seven types of injury: MDU Ireland 1998 *Lessons in Litigation—Irish Obstetric Claims.* MDU Ireland, Dublin.

page 57

vaginal dilator: Eithne Donnellan 2005 *Irish Times* 27 Dec.

'ambulance-chasing' solicitors: Finbarr Fitzpatrick [Online] Available: http://archives.tcm.ie/businesspost/2006/01/15/story11038.asp [Accessed 31 Jan 2007].

'sub-standard care': Ann O'Driscoll claims manager St Paul's 2002 Interview RTÉ radio 18 Feb.

'separate fact from fiction': Michael Boylan 2004, interview.

myth: Medical Defence Union Ltd 1992. Press release, London. 6 Jan. Announcing its 1992 subscription package, MDU warned that tort reform was urgently needed, claiming that, among countries with MDU subscribers, the frequency of litigation and the level of awards in Ireland were 'the highest'.

only 10 per cent: Harvard Medical Practice Study Investigators 2000 op cit.

eight times: Ralph Nader 2002 17 Oct [Online] Available: http://www.nader.org/interest/101702.html [Accessed 4 Jan 2006].

page 58

around 1,000: Michael Boylan 2004 op cit.

only 620 claims: Prime Time 2003 RTÉ television 15 Dec.

70 per cent: Michael Boylan 2004 op cit.

risk pools: Ralph Nader 2002 op cit.

High-risk specialties: consultants in obstetrics, neurosurgery and orthopaedic (spinal) surgery have to insure themselves for just €500,000, a modest amount in the context of specialties that carry a risk of brain damage. The State Claims Agency says that legal fees or awards in excess of this amount will be paid by the state.

page 59

pay-outs in Irish courts: Michael Boylan 2004 op cit.

claims have rocketed: Dr Rick Porter consultant obstetrician Director Bath and West Wiltshire Maternity Services England 2005, personal communication.

page 60

'confined to obstetrics': Medicine Weekly 2004 19 Feb.

MDU claimed: Catherine Shanahan 2004 *Irish Examiner* 14 Jan.
indecent assault: *Irish Independent* 2004 8 Oct.
a technicality: *Irish Times* 2005 17 June.

page 61
200 babies with cerebral palsy: Eithne Donnellan 2003 *Irish Times* 31 Jan: research
   shows that only a minority of parents claim. A cohort study done in England by
   the National Perinatal Epidemiological Unit shows that only one-fifth of cerebral palsy babies—excluding multiple births and postnatal cerebral palsy—born
   between 1984 and 1993 in the former Oxfordshire Health Authority were the subject of a claim. Of the twenty-seven claims made, twelve were discontinued, eight
   were settled and seven remained in active litigation (Catherine Greenwood et al
   2003 'Cerebral palsy and clinical negligence litigation: a cohort study'. *British
   Journal of Obstetrics and Gynaecology* 110 (1): 6–11 [Online] Available:
   http://www.blackwell-ynergy.com/doi/abs/10.1046/j.1471-0528.2003.02095.x
   [Accessed 27 Jan 2007].
'a potential litigant': Eithne Donnellan 2003 op cit.
'a deadly dance': Marie O'Connor 1995 *Birth Tides: turning towards home birth*.
   Pandora, London, 287.

page 62
over 28 per cent: In 2003, the national Caesarean rate was 24.2 per cent (Bonham op
   cit, 2). Allowing for an annual rise of 1 per cent, this gives a rate of 28.2 per cent
   in 2007. This may be an underestimation, however: from 2000 to 2003 the
   Caesarean rate rose by 1.8 per cent (ibid). Colin Francombe and Wendy Savage
   1993 'Caesarean section in Britain and the United States: 12 or 24 per cent, is
   either the right rate?' *Social Science and Medicine* 37 (10).
death and injury: MDU Ireland 1998 op cit.
29 per cent: Dermot Condon 2000 *Report of the Review Group on the Maternity
   Services in the North-Eastern Health Board*, 10.
two out of every five: Our Lady of Lourdes Hospital Drogheda 2002 *Annual Report*.
five-year study: A. Clarke et al 1992 'Intrapartum asphyxia in term and post-term
   infants'. *Irish Medical Journal* 85 (3): 97–100. An extensive review of 28,655 births
   at the Rotunda Hospital. [Online] Available: http://www.imj.ie//Archive/
   Intrapartum%20asphyxia%20in%20term%20and%20post%20term.pdf
   [Accessed 31 Jan 2007].

page 63
new technologies: MDU Ireland 1998 op cit.
'dog food': Ralph Nader 2003 [Online] Available: counterpunch.org/nader01072003.
   htm.7Jan [Accessed 31 Jan 2007].
'legally exposed': J.F.A. Murphy 2006 op cit.

6: HEART OF DARKNESS
page 64
'as severe a test': Dr Arthur Barry quoted by Jacqueline Morrissey 1999 *Irish Times* 6
   Sept. This was a case of major 'disproportion': symphysiotomy failed the test. Its

head 'deeply impacted' in its mother's pelvis, the baby became profoundly distressed. Doctors failed to revive the infant.

page 65

'*some African countries*': Margaret Myles 1975 *Textbook for Midwives* 8th edn. Churchill Livingstone, Edinburgh, 581.

1777: Jo Murphy-Lawless *Reading Birth and Death: a history of obstetric thinking*. Cork University Press, Cork, 99.

'*disability in walking*': Margaret Myles 1975 op cit, 581.

May 2002: Launch of Survivors of Symphysiotomy (SOS), sponsored by the National Women's Council. John Gormley TD made the point that he had called for a full investigation of this 'callous and barbaric practice' in the Dáil in May 2001. Senator Mary Henry MD recalled how she had seen women with urinary incontinence following symphysiotomy, attending Dr Peter Denham's gynaecological clinic. 'Later, in Professor George Fegan's varicose vein clinic in Sir Patrick Dun's, I saw some women with dilated veins up to their abdomens who, I believe, also had this operation.'

page 66

'*darker times*': Jacqueline Morrissey 1999 *Irish Times* 6 Sept. Her doctoral thesis, then in preparation, was on the influence of Catholic ethics on Irish medicine.

'*against the weight*': Dr Alex Spain quoted by Jacqueline Morrissey 1999 op cit.

Luke, Cosmos and Damian: John Cooney 2003 *Irish Times* 19 Sept.

page 67

'*contrary to moral law*': ibid.

'*cut the symphysis*': Dr Arthur Barry quoted by John Cooney 2003 op cit

165 symphysiotomies: Jacqueline Morrissey 1999 op cit.

twelve babies: Arthur Barry National Maternity Hospital *Annual Clinical Report* 1962 quoted in ibid.

'*horrified*': Professor T.N. Jeffcote 1950 quoted in ibid. He pointed out that, in many cases, the babies were already distressed by the time of the operation and that Caesarean section (unlike symphysiotomy) would have offered them certain and immediate relief.

page 68

fatally: Professor Chassar Moir 1951 quoted in ibid. 'Is it then your policy to sacrifice the first-born baby and to use its head or dying body as nothing more than a battering ram to stretch its mother's pelvis?' he asked.

'*not ours*': Dr Donal Browne 1951 quoted in ibid

a 'mote': Dr Kieran O'Driscoll 1966 quoted in ibid, speaking at a Royal Academy meeting. None of the four was suitable for symphysiotomy, he pointed out.

'*The real harvest*': Dr Kevin Feeney 1953 quoted in ibid.

Lourdes Hospital: Maureen Harding Clark 2006 *The Lourdes Hospital Inquiry: an Inquiry into peripartum hysterectomy at Our Lady of Lourdes Hospital, Drogheda*. The Stationery Office, Dublin, 233–4. One consultant member at the Lourdes who was allegedly influenced by Arthur Barry was Dr Connolly (now deceased), a 'firm believer' in symphysiotomy, who had worked at the Medical Missionaries of Mary's hospitals in Africa, in Anua (p 62).

page 69

Archbishop Montini: John Cooney 2003 op cit.

tight wiring: Seamus O'Friel 2004 Letter *Irish Times* 22 July.

a Swedish doctor: Peter Boylan 2003 Letter *Irish Times* 17 June.

Dr Bjorklund: Kenneth Bjorklund 2002 'Minimally invasive surgery for obstructed labour: a review of symphysiotomy during the twentieth century (including 5,000 cases)'. *British Journal of Obstetrics and Gynaecology* 109 (3): 236–48.

page 70

a bucket: Maureen Harding Clark 2006 op cit, 223. The consultant was Dr Michael Neary.

vertical cuts: ibid, 226, 230.

untouchable: ibid, 189.

50 per cent: ibid, 188

respect: ibid, 231.

page 71

obstetric disasters: ibid, 238.

Twenty women: ibid, 237.

maternal deaths: ibid, 215–6.

if they were allowed: ibid, 230.

'third world despots': ibid, 232.

stranded beetles: ibid, 144, 188 and 271.

episiotomies were standard: ibid. An incision widening the opening of the birth canal, episiotomies are frequently performed without good reason, although in recent years, efforts have been made to reduce the rates. Other outmoded obstetric practices which continued at the Lourdes until 1996, apparently, included genital shaving and enemas ('prepping'); and rectal examinations during labour.

twenty-four hours: ibid, 158–9. No one, apparently, could recall this death: the mother died in intensive care following an emergency Caesarean section having been left on an oxytocin drip—a failed induction—for twenty-four hours. Although classified medically as a maternal death, the Inquiry was told 'she was not considered as a death in the maternity unit'.

4 to 27 per cent: ibid, 60.

eight birth-related hysterectomies on average: ibid, 40. For every seventeen Caesarean sections he performed, Michael Neary did one hysterectomy, the Inquiry calculated.

twenty times the average: ibid, 82.

page 72

voiced no concern: ibid, 33. The 'strangest' finding made by the Inquiry was that, until the late 1990s, 'no one had any worries, concerns, apprehensions, unease or disquiet' (317). The judge concluded that, given similar circumstances, what happened in the Lourdes Hospital could happen again elsewhere.

double operations: ibid, 31.

A patient complained: ibid, 32–33.

a first baby: ibid, 71–2. One victim was 19 years of age, the other 29.

their wombs removed: ibid, 104.

ovaries: ibid, 159

repeatedly accredited: ibid, 264–71.

page 73

methodically and systematically: ibid, 147. The registers were removed by 'one or more persons working in the hospital who had an intimate knowledge of the recording and filing system,' the judge concluded. See also p 289.

declined to give evidence: ibid, 52

not investigated: Colm MacGeehin 2006, personal communication. The Inquiry's terms of reference did not extend to these complaints.

page 74

anaesthetists: Maureen Harding Clark 2006 op cit, 213–2.8

'concerned and alarmed': ibid, 47.

postnatal ward daybook: ibid, 132.

page 75

two *women*: ibid, 158.

'Unquestioning submission': ibid, 29.

page 76

'time had elapsed': ibid, 50.

risked his career prospects: ibid, 165.

lunching: ibid, 269. Although the practice had been exposed in October 1998, the Institute of Obstetricians and Gynaecologists did not inspect the maternity unit until 2004.

'caring obstetrician': ibid, 6.

page 77

'Quite the contrary': ibid, 4

41 per cent: Mary Raftery 2006 *Irish Times* 7 Dec.

'irrelevant to them': ibid.

'a systems failure': J.F.A. Murphy *Irish Medical Journal*. It was also a failure of peer review: were it not for the fact that the North-Eastern Health Board sought an external review of Michael Neary's practice from Dr Michael Maresh, an obstetrician in Manchester, the vogue for Caesarean hysterectomy at the Lourdes Hospital might have continued. Reviewing the same cases reviewed by three eminent obstetricians in Ireland, Dr Maresh expressed 'major concerns' about Dr Neary's continuing to practise as a consultant obstetrician (Maureen Harding Clark 2006 op cit, 7).

7: HIGH KINGS WITHOUT OPPOSITION

page 81

'champagne': Dr Michael Cox c. 1900. In John Fleetwood 1983 *The History of Medicine in Ireland*. Skellig Press, Dublin, 84.

Henry VI's charter: ibid, 65.

page 82

'jack-of-all-trades': ibid, 148.

'following local inspection': Comhairle na n-Ospidéal *Seventh Report 1992–95* Aug–June Comhairle na n-Ospidéal, Dublin, 39.

page 83

poor quality: Richard Smith 2006 *The Trouble with Medical Journals*. Royal Society of Medicine, London, 71–81. Smith, a former editor of a leading journal, the *British Medical Journal*, argues that medical journals often contain poor science. Among the problems he identifies as contributing to spurious results are: bias, debasement, dishonesty, industry sponsorship and methodological flaws.

page 84

most senior: [Online] Available: http://www.ucd.ie/president/team.htm [Accessed 29 Jan 2007]. Medical influence in Irish universities may be set to grow. Another member of the medical profession was appointed as President of University College Cork in 2006.

women were barred: Anne Witz 1992 *Professions and Patriarchy*. Routledge, London, 75, 83 and 99.

midwifery into medicine: ibid, 104–27.

page 85

'know their own ignorance': HMSO 1892 *Report from the Select Committee on the Registration of Midwives* House of Commons. In Witz 1992 op cit, 113.

Medical men dominated: L. Park 2005 'Who's regulating whom?' *Midwifery Matters* summer 9–12.

'handywomen': Brenda Knox 1992 'The role of the midwife in primary health care in Ireland'. Thesis (bachelor's), Institute of Public Administration, Dublin, 7.

death rate: A. Susan Williams 1997 *Women and Childbirth in the Twentieth Century: a history of the National Birthday Trust Fund 1828–1992*. Sutton Publishing, Stroud, 57–8.

borne fruit: Marie O'Connor 1995 *Birth Tides: turning towards home birth*. Pandora, London, 9.

'the changing of sheets': HMSO 1892 op cit. In Anne Witz 1992 op cit, 110–111.

page 87

'socialisation of medicine': Noël Browne 1986 *Against the Tide*. Gill and Macmillan, Dublin, 160.

'best troops': Maev-Ann Wren 1993 *Unhealthy State: anatomy of a sick society*. New Island, Dublin, 41.

upper-income women: Peter McQuillan 1994 *Report of the Maternity and Infant Care Scheme Review Group*. Department of Health, Dublin, 9.
'free visits': Noël Browne 1986 op cit, 156.

page 88
district medical officers: Maev-Ann Wren 1993 op cit, 36.
qualified nurses: Department of Health and Children 2004 *The Nursing and Midwifery Resource*. Stationery Office, Dublin, 23.

page 89
senior registrars: Comhairle na n-Ospidéal 1992–95 op cit, 39.

page 90
eighteen months: Comhairle na n-Ospidéal *8th Report 1995–2000*. Dec–Dec Comhairle na n-Ospidéal, Dublin, 45. Note: 'a voluntary hospital is free to advertise and fill a post without recourse to the Department or the LAC or any other body.'
one in every three: Feidhmeannacht na Seirbhíse Sláinte/Health Service Executive 2005 *Consultant Staffing*. Jan National Hospitals Office/Comhairle, Dublin, 22.
professorial jobs: Particulars of these are given in ibid.

page 91
47 per cent: Feidhmeannacht na Seirbhíse Sláinte/Health Service Executive 2005 op cit, 10.

page 92
over the graveyard: Fleetwood 1983 op cit, 73.
€91 million: Claire Shoesmith 2006 *Irish Times* 23 June.
'The concept from Bahrain': RCSI CEO Michael Horgan ibid.
'Court of Patrons': [Online] Available: http://www.rcsi.ie/development/patrons. asp?id=272&pid=272&jid=31&jpid=272 [Accessed 29 Jan 2007].
wealthiest landlords: According to Shoesmith, just two of the College's leased buildings are worth around €150 million.
Keating Investments: Neil Callanan 2003 *Sunday Business Post* 20 Apr [Online] Available: http://archives.tcm.ie/businesspost/2003/04/20/story515482657.asp [Accessed 29 Jan 2007].

page 93
'no regulation': Charitable Donations and Bequests Office 2005.
6 per cent: Claire Shoesmith 2006 op cit.
More than 75 per cent: ibid. This is a proportion that has remained unchanged since the 1950s.

page 94
1839: John Fleetwood 1983 op cit, 296.
the biggest gift: Common contract for consultant medical staff 1981. It had universal appeal: consultants in heath board hospitals got the private practice rights long enjoyed by their colleagues in the voluntary sector, in addition to their public

salaries; while doctors in the private sector got a state salary with all the trimmings, such as expenses and pensions, to featherbed their private practices.

page 95

'Clinical independence': Common contract for consultant medical staff 1997.

streptomycin: John Fleetwood 1983 op cit, 277–8.

ninety specialists: Wren 2003 op cit, 101.

1997: This step was taken on foot of Report No 32 to the Minister for Finance on Hospital Consultants—Review Body on Higher Remuneration within the Public Sector. In Maev-Ann Wren op cit, 93. Talks on a new contract began in 2006, after two-and-a-half years (Pat Leahy 2006 *Sun Business Post* 6 Aug) of delay. The state failed to get agreement on a public-only contract (Eithne Donnellan 2006 *Irish Times* 5 Jan), reportedly priced at over €250,000 Ed Micheau 2006 *Sun Business Post* 22 Jan). Consultant earnings then averaged €170,000. The HSE's decision to abolish Category II contracts, together with its intention to introduce a public only contract, raised hackles. Talks stalled from February until October 2006 (Eithne Donnellan 2006 *Irish Times* 7 Oct). Once more, the Government capitulated to consultant demands. On 12 Nov 2006, the HSE Employers' Agency signalled its willingness to discuss private practice, including in the proposed co-located hospitals. In February 2007, the Government set 27 March 2007 as the final date for conclusion of these negotiations.

page 96

Today's contract: Common contract for consultant medical staff 1997.

up to €250,000: Martin Wall 2006 *Irish Times* Health Supplement 11 July. Figures released by the HSE showed that, in many cases, medical and nursing salaries were significantly supplemented by overtime, on call and other allowances. A consultant radiologist in Mullingar Hospital, for example, earned €253,029 in 2005, including on call and other payments. Overtime payments may double or treble the salaries of non-consultant hospital doctors: a specialist registrar, for example, at Our Lady's Hospital Crumlin on a salary of around €71,000 earned €205,000 in 2005.

around 50 per cent: Martin Wall 2005 *Irish Times,* 9 June.

page 97

The Brennan Report: Report of the Commission of Financial Management and Control Systems in the Health Service (The Brennan Report) 2003. The Stationery Office, 92.

'No other group': Michael Clifford 2004 *Sunday Tribune* 15 Feb.

'I could not believe': Professor Niamh Brennan 2003 quoted in *The Irish Times,* 19 June.

One legal source: In 1997, Martin Wall reported in the *Tribune* (2 Mar) that VHI was paying up to six hospital consultants £500,000 annually. VHI described some billing practices as 'outrageous', with surgeons in some private hospitals reportedly billing for two or three procedures performed 'simultaneously' that involved registrars opening and closing the surgery. The insurer also said it had told

medical oncologists it would no longer pay for chemotherapy which was admin-
istered almost solely by nurses.

Private maternity fees: The total number of births registered in 2004 was 61,684
([Online] Available: www.cso.ie/statistics/bthsdthsmarriages.htm [Accessed 29
Jan 2007]); 23,913 mothers gave birth in Dublin hospitals. Half of all mothers opt
for private obstetric services at the National Maternity Hospital; approximately
50 per cent of these choose semi-private care (Fionnuala Byrne, personal communication). A similar ratio applies in the other big Dublin maternity hospitals
and has been applied nationally: over half of the population holds private health
insurance and nineteen of the country's twenty-two maternity facilities have
semi-private beds. The total number of obstetricians employed in 2004 was 104;
forty-five were in Dublin ([Online] Available: www.comh-n-nosp.ie/pdf.
ConsultantStaff2005.pdf [Accessed 29 Jan 2007]). VHI, the main private insurer,
pays a flat semi-private fee of £790 and this has been applied nationally. With
private fees averaging an estimated £3,000 in Dublin, and a total of 5,978 private
and 5,978 semi-private 'patients', the market for private obstetrics is worth
£22,657,370, yielding an average per-head income, annually, of £503,497. Outside
Dublin, private fees are estimated at £2,000, the market is valued at £26,345,470,
giving an average annual income of £446,533 each.

page 98
John Fielding: Maev-Ann Wren 2003 op cit, 80.
industrial action: Alison O'Connor 1997 *Irish Times* 29 Sept.
an 'absolute rebellion': Finbarr Fitzpatrick 2004 quoted in *Irish Times* 2 Jan.

page 99
'clinical independence': Colm Quigley 2003 quoted by Muiris Houston *Irish Times* 24
    Feb.
jump ship: Eilis O'Regan 2003 *Irish Independent* 25 June.
seven years: Marie O'Connor 2003 *Northern Standard* 9 Oct.
€50 million: Eilis O'Regan ibid.

page 100
'well-heeled': Stephen Collins 2003 *Sunday Tribune* 23 Feb.
consultants' continuing angst: leader 2004 *Medicine Weekly* 12 Feb.

page 101
'faces ruin': IHCA advertisement 2004 *Irish Times* 11 Feb.
27,000 babies: Dr Conor Carr 2004 Interview. *Five Seven Live* RTÉ Radio One 12 Feb.
'ethical responsibility': Martin Wall and Martin Frawley 2004 *Sunday Tribune* 15 Feb.
a 'curtailment': Martin Wall 2004 *Sunday Tribune* 15 Feb.
interview panels: Martin Wall 2004 *Sunday Tribune* 15 Feb.
all non-emergency patients: Finbarr Fitzpatrick 2004 Letter *Irish Times* 21 Feb.

page 102
eight obstetricians: Eithne Donnellan 2004 *Irish Times* 16 Sept.
loomed again: Eithne Donnellan 2004 *Irish Times* 18 Mar.

refusing to enter: Eithne Donnellan 2004 *Irish Times* 7 Oct.

89 per cent: Martin Wall 2005 Irish Times 5 Feb

public outpatients: Eithne Donnellan 2005 *Irish Times* 24 Feb.

'a medical mishap': Martin Wall 2005 *Irish Times* 26 Feb.

against the MDU: Muiris Houston 2005 *Irish Times* 19 Mar.

boycotted: Martin Wall 2004 *Irish Times* 25, 26 Dec.

the cap: Karl Hanlon 2005 *Irish Times* 8 Oct.

page 105

parliamentary questions: 10 per cent of the parliamentary questions referred by the
    Minister since the beginning of 2006 remained to be answered by the end of the
    year (Martin Wall 2006 Irish Times 11 Dec).

page 106

Ombudsman: The 2004 Health Act provides for non-clinical complaints against the
    HSE and health service providers to be made to the Ombudsman. In late 2006,
    Emily O'Reilly (Eithne Donnellan 2006 *Irish Times* 6 Oct) announced that, as the
    HSE had still not published the necessary guidelines, she would take complaints
    from the public from 1 Jan 2007.

    Her office had dealt solely with health board hospitals; she now proposed to take
    complaints against the Dublin private non-profit hospitals, such as the Mater
    and Tallaght, and against HSE-funded agencies in fields such as disability.

'360-degree audit': Eithne Donnellan 2006 *Irish Times* 21 Feb.

average 235 complaints: Eithne Donnellan 2006 *Irish Times* 14 Feb.

8: THE INDUSTRIAL REVOLUTION

page 112

'discussion document': Comhairle na n-Ospidéal 1976 *Development of hospital mater-
    nity services: a discussion document.* Comhairle na n-Ospidéal, Dublin

Peel Report: A. Susan Williams 1997 *Women and Childbirth in the Twentieth Century:
    a history of the National Birthday Trust Fund.* Sutton Publishing, Stroud, 231–2.

an assumption: ibid, 231

page 113

Private nursing homes: John Fleetwood 1983 *The History of Medicine in Ireland.* The
    Skellig Press, Dublin, 148.

page 114

The new system: Kieran O'Driscoll, Declan Meagher and Peter Boylan 1993 *Active
    Management of Labour: the Dublin experience*, 3rd edn. Mosby, London, 114.
    Kieran O'Driscoll was the architect of 'active management': he implemented the
    blueprint with military precision during his 'Mastership' at the National
    Maternity Hospital, Holles Street. The manual is replete with references to
    industry: the labour ward, for example, is referred to as the *shop floor* (p 97).
    Elsewhere it becomes the *bottleneck* (p 114) through which all must pass. The
    speed of the line? One centimetre per hour: this was the rate at which women

were required to dilate. Hourly internal examinations measured their 'progress' (p 44): rectal examinations were still the norm at the National Maternity during the early 1980s. Oxytocin ensured that the speed of the *production line* (p 42) was uniform. A naturally occurring hormone, oxytocin has been synthesised as Syntocinon (Pitocin in the US).

animals' feed: Michel Odent 2002 *The Farmer and the Obstetrician*. Free Association Books, London, 31.

units of production: Kieran O'Driscoll pointed out that in five comparable units in 'the British Isles', 'the unit cost of production, relating salaries paid to nurses to number of babies born, was three times higher' than it was at the National Maternity.

page 115

In 1966: Department of Health 1980 *Health Care for Mothers and Infants: a review of the Maternity and Infant Care Scheme*. Department of Health, Dublin, 66.

externalities: See Joel Bakan 2004 *The Corporation: the pathological pursuit of profit and power*. Constable, London, 60–84.

Susan Lawlor: Marie O'Connor 1995 *Birth Tides: turning towards home birth*. Pandora, London, 12.

108: Comhairle na n-Ospidéal 1976 op cit.

Australia: Sheila Kitzinger (ed) 1988 *The Midwife Challenge* 2nd edn. Pandora, London.

91 per cent: Marie O'Connor 1995 op cit, 13.

page 116

4,000 babies: Sheelagh Bonham 2005 *Report on Perinatal Statistics for 2002*. Economic and Social Research Institute, Dublin, 67. The figure was 44 per cent in 2002. The closure of three smaller maternity units in Cork City in 2007 and the opening of the new maternity unit at Cork University Hospital brings the total number of women giving birth in Ireland in units of 4,000-plus to an estimated 52 per cent.

half of all mothers: ibid, 111.

9: SERFS AND EMPERORS

page 117

'United Kingdom': Comhairle na n-Ospidéal 1989–92 *Sixth Report 20th Anniversary Edn*. July–June Comhairle na n-Ospidéal, Dublin, 37–8.

T.J.D. Lane: John Fleetwood 1983 *The History of Medicine in Ireland* 2nd edn. The Skellig Press, Dublin, 210–11.

page 118

300 beds: *Outline of the Future Hospital System: Report of the Consultative Council on the General Hospital Services* 1968. Stationery Office, Dublin, 23. The need for specialisation in medicine is the governing principle cited by FitzGerald: he sees medicine in terms of surgery. His ambition is to 'add even a small quantum to the pool of new knowledge' (p 19). Only large hospitals can provide the complex facilities the profession requires, although 'the majority of hospital patients will not require such complicated care,' he admits.

a single article: R Milnes-Walker (1968) *Annal of the Royal College of Surgeons in England* 42: 161–2. In ibid, 24.

a Lancet *leader:* Leader 1967 *The Lancet* 199 (1).

Sean Flanagan: Minister for Health *Dáil Debates* Col 1664 Vol 239 23 Apr 1969.

'*rationalising*': John Fleetwood 1983 op cit, 280.

page 119

'*concentration*': Comhairle na n-Ospidéal 1992–95 *Seventh Report.* Aug–June Comhairle na n-Ospidéal, Dublin, 31.

'*modern standards of medical specialisation*': Comhairle na n-Ospidéal 1992–95 op cit, 20

'*professional viewpoint*': ibid, 16.

St Vincent's: ibid July 1994 Appendix D 'Framework for a Joint Department of Surgery in South East Dublin', 73–6.

'*further sub-specialisation*': ibid, 75.

ad hoc training: Comhairle na n-Ospidéal 1989–92 *Sixth Report 20th Anniversary Edn.* Comhairle na n-Ospidéal, Dublin, 38.

page 120

'*mono-specialist pathologists*': ibid, 37

the biggest propagator: Comhairle na n-Ospidéal 1992–95 op cit, 40.

general *general surgeons:* Comhairle na n-Ospidéal 1995–2000 *Eighth Report.* Comhairle na n-Ospidéal, Dublin, 54. This classification has now been dropped: in 2005, *all* general surgeons were classified by 'sub-specialty interest' (Feidhmeannacht na Seirbhíse Sláinte/Health Service Executive 2005 *Consultant Staffing.* National Hospitals Office/Comhairle, Dublin, 4–5).

'*service problems*': Comhairle na n-Ospidéal 1989–92, op cit, 37. In a section entitled 'Trend towards more specialisation', reiterated in Comhairle's 1992–95 Report (37–38).

'*up to date*': Comhairle na n-Ospidéal 1992–5, op cit, 38.

'*a wider range of skills*': Comhairle na n-Ospidéal 1989–92 op cit, 37.

page 121

Arthur Tanner: 2003 *Irish Times* 6 Jan.

'*very minor virtues*': Muiris FitzGerald Dean School of Medicine University College Dublin 2002. In Ray Kinsella 2003 *Acute Healthcare in Transition in Ireland: change, cutbacks and challenges.* Oak Tree Press, Dublin, 59.

'*reasonable competence*': ibid, 61.

'*generalist model*': ibid, 61.

page 122

'*complex surgery*': ibid, 62.

'*India/Pakistan*': ibid.

Hanly Report: Report of the National Task Force on Medical Staffing 2003, which became known as the *Hanly Report* (after the group's Chair, David Hanly).

Because reaction to the report was negative in communities scheduled to lose their hospitals, public servants were later instructed to refer to the document solely by its original title.

work-time directive: Irish Medical Journal 2004 Mar 97 (3).

page 123

'a first cousin': Deputy Philip Burton 1969 *Dáil Debates* on the health bill later enacted as the 1970 Health Act. Col 359 Vol 240 1 May 1969.

46 million: National Coalition on Health Care 2004 *Health Insurance Coverage*. In 2004, 46 million Americans—15.7 per cent of the population—were uninsured. From 2000 to 2004, the numbers of uninsured people rose by 6 million. 19 per cent of all working adults hold no health insurance. [Online] Available: http://www.nchc.org/facts/coverage.shtml [Accessed 29 Jan 2007].

page 124

medical men: Joe Robins, Department of Health, acted as Secretary: he was the only non-medic.

'purely': Sir Anthony Esmonde TD *Dáil Debates* Col 1755 Vol 239 23 Apr 1969.

'lop-sided': Brendan Corish TD *Dáil Debates* Col 270 Vol 240 30 Apr 1969.

'professional men': Patrick Reynolds TD *Dáil Debates* Col 343 Vol 240 30 Apr 1969.

non-involvement: Mark Clinton TD *Dáil Debates* Col 2087 Vol 242 27 Nov 1969.

'40 miles': Brendan Corish TD *Dáil Debates* Col 270 Vol 240 30 Apr 1969.

page 125

Nenagh Hospital Report: Nenagh Hospital Action Committee 2006 *Small Hospital, Big Service. Working Proposal for the Future of Nenagh Hospital: the way forward for the smaller acute general hospitals in Ireland*, Nenagh Hospital Action Committee, Nenagh, 18–19.

10 per cent: James Dillon TD *Dáil Debates* Vol 239 23 Apr 1969.

dying: Joan Burke TD *Dáil Debates* Col 2087 Vol 242 27 Nov 1969.

Health Services Action Group: a national coalition of hospital action and health advocacy groups, the Health Services Action Group was formed in 2004 to campaign against government policy closing the country's general (second-level) hospitals (as per the *Hanly* (2004) and *Teamwork* (2006) *Reports*).

'digits': Sean Treacy TD *Dáil Debates* Col 303 Vol 240 30 Apr 1969.

'getting lost in the system': T.E. Getzen 1997 'Health Economics: fundamentals and flow of funds', 191. In Catherine McNamara 2004 *The Hanly Report: a critique*, 10 [Online] Available: http://www.saveourhospital.com/ [Accessed 29 Jan 2007].

page 126

'Bellevue Hospital': Oliver J. Flanagan TD *Dáil Debates* Col 2102–2103 Vol 239 23 Apr 1969.

Portiuncula: Brigid Hogan-O'Higgins TD *Dáil Debates* Col 271-6 Vol 240 30 Apr 1969.

live in poverty: Almost a fifth of people (19 per cent) in Ireland are at risk of poverty: 7 per cent live in continuing poverty [Online] Available: *http://www.cpa.ie/*

povertyinireland/facts.htm [Accessed 29 Jan 2007]. Poorer people die disproportionately where hospital care is centralised, New Zealand evidence shows. See M.
Mc Kee and J. Healy 2000 'The role of the hospital in a changing environment'.
Bulletin of the World Health Organisation 78 (6). In Catherine McNamara 2004
op cit, 13.

Peadar McMahon: Chair Health Services Action Group. Presentation to the Joint
Oireachtas Committee on Health 24 Mar 2005.

page 127

mollified: Hugh Gibbons TD *Dáil Debates* Col 924–5 Vol 243 10 Dec 1969. By then, a
general election had intervened and Erskine Childers had replaced Sean
Flanagan as Minister for Health.

deep misgivings: Sean Flanagan TD Minister for Health *Dáil Debates* Col 520 Vol 240
6 May 1969.

'doing wrong': Dr Maurice Gueret 2002 Letter *Irish Times* 12 Dec. He blamed med-
ical specialisation for the death of baby Bronagh Livingstone. The premature
baby, born in an ambulance on the side of the road between Monaghan and
Cavan, died shortly after her mother had been turned away from Monaghan
General, which had lost its maternity unit a few months earlier. See also the
Prologue in this book.

body parts: Marilyn French 1998 *A Season in Hell: a Memoir.* Virago Press, London,
165.

elder sibling: The *Harding Clark Report* (2006) gives one indication of the close ties
that exist between the siblings. Until 1992, at least, the London-based Royal College
of Obstetrics and Gynaecology inspected Irish maternity units (for training purposes); several such inspections took place at the Lourdes Hospital (p 309).

page 128

elitist and inequitable: Jean-Marie Clement 1998 *Reflexions pour l'hôpital: proximité,
cooperation, pouvoirs.* Les Etudes Hospitalières, Bordeaux.

more than double: Comhairle na n-Ospidéal 1992–95 op cit, 30.

beckoned in psychiatry: Comhairle na n-Ospidéal ibid, 69–70. These sub-specialisms
were in addition to child psychiatry, which was further sub-divided into 'mental
handicap', a sub-specialty.

page 129

bankruptcy: Jean-Marie Clement 1998 op cit, 43, 49–50.

page 130

'medical admissions units': Comhairle na n-Ospidéal 1995–2000 op cit, 55.

not even exist in 1989: David Tomkin and Patrick Hanafin 1995 *Irish Medical Law.*
The Round Hall Press, Dublin, 281.

page 131

Alan O'Gorman: Eithne Donnellan 2006 *Irish Times,* 12 Dec. His tissue samples got
mixed up with those of a 70-year-old cancer patient. From 2002 to 2006, Alan

O'Gorman tried to take his own life four times. He told *The Irish Times* he was now adjusting to the consequences of the surgery: chronic pain and discomfort, inability to eat normally and low energy that precludes full-time work. He is 26 years of age.

page 132

hyper-specialisation: Catherine McNamara 2004 op cit, 4–5.

'a direct attack': Ennis General Hospital Development Committee 2004 *A Response to the Report of the National Task Force on Medical Staffing*. Ennis General Hospital Development Committee, Ennis, 37.

page 133

a quarter: Total number of obstetric beds (2005): 1,109. Hospitals expected to lose their obstetric units under the *Hanly/Teamwork* template include Mullingar (30) Portlaoise (26) Cavan (30) Clonmel (26) Kilkenny (32) Wexford (23) and Ballinasloe (34). Total bed loss: 201, or 19 per cent of the total. These are minimum figures. *Hanly* also recommended closing single-specialism hospitals, 'relocating' the three main Dublin maternity hospitals onto acute hospital sites.

'lack of capacity': Health Services Action Group (HSAG) 2005 'Conditions set to worsen in A&E units'. Media release. 1 June. HSAG was responding to the publication of a report by the Health and Safety Authority on A&E units.

slashed by 29 per cent: Wren 2003 op cit.

'downsizing': ibid.

350–500,000 people: *Report of the National Task Force on Medical Staffing* (*Hanly Report*) 2003 Stationery Office, Dublin

sufficient population numbers: Conor Teljeur 2004 Letter *Irish Medical Journal* Dec 97 (10).

'totally unsuited': Catherine MacNamara 2004 op cit, 5. British thinking is beginning to move beyond centralisation: 'the mindset that "biggest is best" that has underpinned many of the changes in the NHS in the last few years needs to change. The continued concentration of acute hospital services without sustaining local access to acute care runs the danger of making services increasingly remote from many local communities.' Department of Health (UK) 2003 *Keeping the NHS Local–A New Direction of Travel*, Department of Health Publications.

page 134

'the golden hour': Dr Conor Teljeur 2004 op cit.

30 per cent: D.D. Trunkey (1983) 'Trauma', *Scientific American*; 249: 28–35. In Catherine McNamara 2004 op cit, 13.

trauma care: Emergency consultant Conor Egleston 2005 'Focus on: the golden hour'. *Modern Medicine* Mar.

twenty deaths: Peadar McNamara Chair Ennis General Hospital Development Committee told the Joint Oireachtas Committee on Health 24 Mar 2005. This is a minimum figure, derived from a conservative analysis of hospital records at Ennis General: actual deaths are likely to be higher.

82 per cent: C. Teljeur, J. Barry and A. Kelly 2004 'The potential impact on travel times of closure and redistribution of A&E units in Ireland'. *Irish Medical Journal*

June [Online] Available: http://www.imj.ie//Issue_detail.aspx?issueid=+&pid =315&type=Papers [Accessed 29 Jan 2007].

Northwick Park: Healthcare Commission 2006 Investigation into ten maternal deaths at, or following delivery at, Northwick Park Hospital, North West London Hospitals NHS Trust, between April 2002 and April 2005. Aug. The Central Middlesex Hospital closed in 2002, 'transferring' its maternity services to Northwick Park, then under refurbishment. This led to 'a temporary reduction' in the number of beds in the labour ward. [Online] Available: http://www.healthcarecommission.org.uk /_db/_documents/Northwick_tagged.pdf [Accessed 21 Jan 2007].

Here, there has been a 40 per cent rise in the number of births at Our Lady of Lourdes Hospital, due mainly to the closure of the maternity units in Dundalk and Monaghan; no additional beds or staff have been provided (Maureen Harding Clark 2006 *The Lourdes Hospital Inquiry.* The Stationery Office, Dublin).

further from hospital casualty units: 'One study in England and Wales covering 100,692 deaths found increased mortality when patients were a greater distance from the nearest hospital. The conditions for which this was significant were diabetes mellitus, asthma, mortality in the first 28 days of life, and road traffic accidents.' A.P. Jones 1996 *Health Service Accessibility and Health Outcomes,* University of East Anglia. In Catherine McNamara 2004 op cit, 13.

page 135

Quebec: 'A study in a semi-rural area of Quebec found a significantly higher rate of deaths of children under 5 years from acute medical post neonatal syndromes (including respiratory, gastro-intestinal, meningitis and other acute medical) when these children were more distant from the nearest hospital.' A. Kelly and L. Muran 1974 'Epidemiological patterns of childhood mortality and their relation to distance from medical care', *Social Science and Medicine* (8): 363–7. In ibid, 3.

Montreal: 'A study in Montreal of 360 severely injured patients showed that patients not reaching hospital within one hour of the injury had a 3-fold increase in the risk of dying within 6 days of admission compared with those who reached hospital within the hour.' J.S. Sampalis et al 1993 'Impact of on-site care, pre-hospital time, and level of in-hospital care on survival in severely injured patients'. *Journal of Trauma* 34: 252–61. In ibid, 14.

'*A pestilential odour*': Michelle Bressand 2006 *Infirmière: la passion de l'hopital.* Robert Laffont, Paris, 23 [Translated by the author].

'*medical, surgical*': Peadar McMahon Chair Health Services Action Group, presentation to Joint Oireachtas Committee on Health and Children 24 Mar 2005.

page 136

urban/rural inequalities: Dr Tom Nolan Secretary Health Services Action Group, to the Joint Oireachtas Committee on Health and Children 24 Mar 2005.

Trinity College: C. Teljeur, J. Barry and A. Kelly 2004 op cit.

81–82 per cent: These figures are derived from the Teljeur study: they are based on two scenarios, a literal application of *Hanly* and a non-literal one (adjusted for geography); and have been calculated for two groups, road traffic accident victims and heart-attack sufferers.

Clontibret woman: Northern Standard 2002 19 Dec.
Phillip Courtenay: Patsy McArdle 2005 *Northern Standard* 12 May.
Bennie McCullagh: Eithne Donnellan 2004 *Irish Times* 28 Oct.

page 137

Take Clare: Ennis General Hospital Development Committee 2004 op cit, 58–61.
national study: N. Breen et al 2000 'A national census of ambulance response times
    to emergency calls in Ireland'. *Journal of Accident and Emergency Medicine* 17:
    392–5. The census found 'inappropriately delayed responses to critical incidents'.
poor, geographically: D. Moore and A.W. Murphy 2002 *Spatial analysis of road traffic
    accidents in the Western and North-Western Health Boards.* Report by
    McCutcheon Hogan & Department of General Practice, NUI Galway. Feb.
    Analysing ambulance services in relation to road traffic accidents in the west and
    north-west, they found the spatial coverage poor. The ambulance services were
    unable to get to significant areas within a twenty-five-minute response time
    (leaving a fifty-minute return time to hospital, the target time set by the study).
    Even the state recognises that 'rural communities are disadvantaged in accessing
    the links in the "chain of survival".... The regions in Ireland which are disadvan-
    taged include the North Western, Western and South Western seaboards, the
    peninsulas and their inhabited islands.' (Department of Health and Children
    2006 *Reducing the Risk: A Strategic Approach The Report of the Task Force on
    Sudden Cardiac Arrest.* Department of Health and Children, Dublin, 95.)
sparsely populated region: Ennis General Hospital Development Committee 2004 op cit
Gaps in cover: fewer A&E units will mean longer travel times to those units. Longer
    travel times for ambulances will reduce emergency cover, with crews in transit for
    extended periods. The current stock of ambulances and the staff manning those
    vehicles will be inadequate to maintain existing standards of service provision,
    according to the Pre-Hospital Emergency Care Council (PHECC) 2003. See 'A&E
    Regionalisation: implications for pre-hospital emergency care' Discussion paper.
    [Online] Available: http://www.phecc.ie/Papers%2005%20-%20A%20&%20E%20
    Regionalisation%20(May%202003).pdf [Accessed 20 Jan 2007]. PHECC also identi-
    fies other problems in transporting patients to remote A&E units, such as cross-
    infection and hypothermia (p 16). 'Basic airway management may not be sufficient,
    increasing the potential for hypoxia and cardiac arrest: one of the critical factors in
    delayed admission to an A&E facility is the potential for exacerbation of the patient's
    condition due to hypoxia.' Advanced airway management will need to become
    routine, PHECC says, 'to reduce preventable pre-hospital mortality'. But advanced
    airway management requires EMT–A training.
only just begun: the first ever EMT–A exam was held in May 2005: [Online] Available:
    http://www.phecc.ie/PHECC%20VOICE%20March%202005%20Pg02.pdf
    [Accessed 20 Jan 2007]. The first national examination for emergency medical
    technicians (EMTs) in Ireland was held in October 2002 [Online] Available:
    http://www.phecc.ie/PROpeningAddress.htm [Accessed 20 Jan 2007].
3 per cent: twenty-nine had completed the EMT–A course by June 2006, out of a total
    of 1,822 EMTs, the number on the PHECC database (this may not cover all ambu-
    lance personnel). For a summary of the HSE plans for ambulance services, see

Teamwork Management Services Limited 2006 *Improving Safety and Achieving Better Standards: an action plan for health services in the North East.* Teamwork Management Services Ltd Bolton, 39.

'eventually': Teamwork 2006, op cit.

6,000: Kay McIntosh 2005 *Guardian* 29 June. This, the Staffordshire result, topped the league in terms of what can be achieved by paramedics: the figure comes from a survey on ambulance response times carried out by *Health Which* (part of the Which consumer organisation) in 2002 and 2003: Kay McIntosh was then the magazine's editor. She derived the figure of 6,000 by extrapolating the Staffordshire figures to the rest of England.

McIntosh explores a paradox: how ambulance response times are getting better—on paper—yet heart-attack survival rates remain the same. Ambulance trusts are measured on how many of their crews reach at least 75 per cent of their most urgent calls within eight minutes—the time limit set for cardiac arrest treatment. But, as McIntosh points out, 'you can delay the clock "start" … you can fiddle the clock "stop", or you can decide, like Berkshire, that only 8 per cent of calls are life-threatening.' Following the survey, *Health Which* gave evidence to the public administration select committee of the House of Commons and briefed the Healthcare Commission; the Commission subsequently found that one-third of ambulance trusts had altered their response times to make themselves look good.

page 138

acceptable level of mortality: Peter West Director of York Health Economics Consortium University of York 2003 *Irish Medical Times* 28 Nov.

'touted': Dr Tom Nolan 2005 op cit. On paramedic death rates, see: M. Mc Kee and J. Healy (eds) 2002 *Hospitals in a Changing Europe.* Open University Press: 63. Also J. Nicholl et al 1998 'The costs and benefits of paramedic skill in pre-hospital trauma care'. *Health Technology Assessment* 2: 1–67.

Other studies evidence even higher paramedic death rates. Emergency consultant Conor Egleston (op cit 2005) discusses a meta-analysis (Silverman Mulder and Sampalis) of fifteen different studies comparing advanced life support (including intubation, putting up a drip and giving fluids and drugs) and basic life support (including maintaining the airway, giving oxygen and stemming haemorrhage) in severe trauma. Crucially controlling for the severity of the injuries sustained, the researchers found that those receiving advanced life support were almost three times (2.92) more likely to die than those in receipt of basic life support. Advanced life support is associated with 'longer on-scene times'—delay in getting the patient to hospital. Basic life support—which gets the patient to hospital as quickly as possible — is key. Dr Egleston concludes: 'it is logical that a wider range of therapeutic interventions and investigations can be carried out in an appropriate hospital than in the back of an ambulance or at the side of the road.'

acute coronaries: Frank Doyle 2005 *Biomed Central Journal* 11 Feb. Cited by Dr Tom Nolan 2005 op cit.

Peadar McMahon: Rural Link National Conference address, 11 May 2006.

page 139

thousands of women's lives: Dr John Gallagher 2003 quoted by Mary Dundon *Irish Examiner* 21 Feb. Up to twelve maternity units faced closure, Dundon reported; the draft *Hanly Report* proposed to close six. Tralee, Clonmel, Kilkenny, Wexford, Ballinasloe, Portlaoise and Mullingar were named as being particularly at risk. 'There would be World War III,' Dr Gallagher said, 'if the Government tried to close any of those maternity hospitals [in the south-east] because each of them is already full to capacity and there is nowhere to send the 1,500 women who have babies in them every year.'

eight times higher: Rhona Campbell et al 1984 'Home births in England and Wales: perinatal mortality according to intended place of delivery'. *British Medical Journal* 289: 721–4. This is the only national survey of its kind, as far as I know, that established mortality rates for both intentional and non-intentional out-of-hospital births. The first group consists of home-birth mothers giving birth at home intentionally, generally with midwives to support them. The second group includes roadside births: within a centralised system of care, some mothers intending to give birth in hospital whose labours are short will find themselves giving birth in a setting not of their choosing without professional help. Half of all out-of-hospital births here are unplanned (Marie O'Connor 1995 *Birth Tides*) compared with only one-third in England and Wales (Campbell et al 1984).

labours induced: Since the maternity unit closed in Monaghan, concern has been expressed by the INO about the number of Monaghan mothers having inductions, forceps and Caesarean births *Northern Standard* 31 July 2003.

oxytocin: a naturally occurring hormone produced in synthetic form (Syntocinon or, in the US, Pitocin). Many midwives believe oxytocin should not be used routinely in the labour ward. In cases of genuinely prolonged labour, however, particularly where an epidural has slowed the birth, oxytocin can be invaluable.

infant brain damage: R Taylor 1988 'Quick birth drug can kill babies' *Observer* 19 Apr. No conclusive research on oxytocin appears to exist; very large studies would be required to examine its effects. An extensive review of 28,655 births at the Rotunda Hospital found thirteen deaths in full-term babies associated with asphyxia, and thirty-two surviving infants had asphyxial seizures. Nineteen per cent of those who fitted subsequently developed cerebral palsy. Syntocinon was used in 44 per cent of the infants who seized and 31 per cent of those who died. See A. Clarke et al 1992 'Intrapartum asphyxia in term and post-term infants'. *Irish Medical Journal* 85 (3): 97–100) [Online] Available: http://www.imj.ie// Archive/Intrapartum%20asphyxia%20in%20term%20and%20post%20term. pdf [Accessed 31 Jan 2007]. According to King Pharmaceuticals, 'maternal deaths due to hypertensive episodes, subarachnoid haemorrhage, rupture of the uterus, and fetal deaths due to various causes have been reported associated with the use of parental oxytocic drugs for induction of labour or for augmentation in the first and second stages of labour.' [Online] Available: http://www. kingpharm.com/kingpharm/uploads/pdf_inserts/PitocinWebPI.pdf [Accessed 31 Jan 2007]. Permanent brain or central nervous system damage to the baby is also listed by the manufacturer, Merck, as being among the adverse reactions to the drug. See: [Online] Available: http://www.merck.com/mmpe/lexicomp/oxytocin.html [Accessed 31 Jan 2007].

multi-million euro awards: In 2003, RTÉ reported the largest settlement of a personal injuries case in the history of the state, to Haya Shiri Kraft. The settlement of €4.5 million made by the National Maternity Hospital was without an admission of liability. Senior Counsel Paul Sreenan said that his client's case was that Mrs Kraft had had her waters punctured and her labour accelerated with oxytocin: all the evidence on behalf of the child would have said that this was the wrong thing to do. The heart monitor recorded extreme variations after the oxytocin drip had been put up, the baby needed to be resuscitated and suffered cerebral palsy in consequence. [Online] Available: http://www.rte.ie/news2/2003/0225/krafth.html [Accessed 31 Jan 2007].

In a more recent action, an award of €4 million, plus costs, was made in 2006 against John Monaghan and the Western Health Board. Seamus Dywer was born at 41 weeks on 24 March 1999: the use of oxytocin left him quadriplegic and suffering from cerebral palsy. [Online] Available: http://209.85.135.104/search?q=cache:xwqKs5LYN2YJ:www.augustuscullen.ie/pdfs/news_items/Med_Neg_August_2006.doc+oxytocin+cerebral+palsy+awards&hl=en&gl=ie&ct=clnk&cd=1 [Accessed 31 Jan 2007].

page 140

trebles your chances: Our Lady of Lourdes Hospital Drogheda 2002 *Maternity Unit Annual Report*. North-Eastern Health Board, Drogheda, 8. In 2002, 31 per cent of all mothers pregnant with their first child, who were induced at thirty-seven weeks or over, had a Caesarean section.

nearly four times: C. Deneux-Tharaux et al 2006 'Postpartum maternal mortality and Caesarean delivery'. *Journal of Obstetrics and Gynaecology* vol 108 (3): 541–8. Women who give birth by Caesarean are 3.6 times more likely to die following the operation than those who give birth vaginally.

two young mothers: In 1999, a 34-year-old woman, described as having 'no risk factors other than a Caesarean section', died in the National Maternity Hospital when her heart stopped after a clot developed in her lung. Her death, the hospital report commented, highlights 'the increased risk of thromboembolic disease following abdominal delivery' (*Annual Clinical Report* 1999: 51). Also in that year, a 28-year-old mother, who suffered from congenital heart disease, died at the Coombe Hospital, following 'an uneventful elective Caesarean section': she suffered a cardiac arrest after losing a moderate amount of blood (*Annual Clinical Report* 1999: 17).

likely to be ill: J Griffiths et al 2005 'Surgical site infection following elective Caesarean section: a case-control study of post-discharge surveillance'. *Journal of Obstetrics and Gynaecology* Canada 27 (4): 340–4. Ten per cent of women in this study developed a wound infection; in another study (D.K. Creedy and D.L. Noy 2001 'PostDischarge surveillance after caesarean section' *Birth* Dec 28 (4): 264–9) 17 per cent of mothers did so. See also: E. M. Hillan 1995 'Postoperative morbidity following Caesarean delivery'. *Journal of Advanced Nursing* Dec 22 (6): 1035–42. Indices of sickness included wound, womb, urinary tract and chest infections, elevated temperatures, need for a urinary catheter and postnatal blood transfusion. Nine women in ten suffered some form of morbidity after the operation.

twice as likely: Marian F. MacDorman et al 2006 'Infant and neonatal mortality for primary Caesarean and vaginal births to women with "no indicated risk" United States 1998–2001 Birth Cohorts'. *Birth* 33 (3): 175–82. Babies born by voluntary Caesarean section—where there are no clinical reasons for the operation—are more than twice as likely to die as those born vaginally.

intensive care: T. Rohininath 2005 Workload and short-term outcome of babies weighing 2,500g or more at birth admitted to the paediatric unit of the Rotunda Hospital. *Journal of Maternal-Foetal and Neonatal Medicine* Feb 17 (2): 139–43. Infants born by Caesarean section are twice as likely to be admitted to intensive care as babies born vaginally.

stillborn: C. Gordon et al 2003 'Caesarean section and risk of unexplained stillbirth in subsequent pregnancy'. *The Lancet* Nov 362: 1779–84.

impact negatively: D.J. Murphy et al 2002 'The relationship between Caesarean section and subfertility in a population-based sample of 14,541 pregnancies. *Human Reproduction* July 17 (7): 1914–7.

St George's: D.A. Gould et al 1999 'Emergency obstetric hysterectomy—an increasing incidence'. *Journal of Obstetrics and Gynaecology* Nov 19 (6): 580–3.

misapplied: Catherine McNamara 2004 op cit, 7. Professor Barbara Starfield, professor of health policy management at Johns Hopkins University, also said that Hanly appeared to have used research linking high volumes of care with better outcomes 'inappropriately'. 'Because research linking volume to outcome is procedure orientated, it is questionable whether this relationship is really valid,' she said. Quoted in Muiris Houston 2004 *Irish Times* 26 May.

page 141

Only five procedures: ibid, 7–9.

'*competently*': Muiris FitzGerald 2002 op cit, 61.

'*common conditions*': Dr John Barton, personal communication, 2005. Irish research corroborates this. Ennis General, for example, deals with more than 95 per cent of its admissions itself (Ennis General Hospital Development Committee 2004 op cit, 26); while in Nenagh Hospital, just 3 per cent of patients require transfer to more specialised care (Nenagh Hospital Action Committee 2006 op cit, 18).

'*better results*': One reason why smaller hospitals get better results may be that bigger hospitals tend to be more infectious. Preliminary results from a 2006 North-South study indicate that smaller hospitals are associated with lower levels of hospital-acquired infection. [Online] Available: http://www.ndsc.ie/hpsc/A-Z/MicrobiologyAntimicrobialResistance/StrategyforthecontrolofAntimicrobialResistanceinIrelandSARI/SARIandAMRAPSARIAnnualConferences/2006AMRAPSARIConference/File,2102,en.pdf [Accessed 20 Jan 2007]. Recent jurisprudence in France also shows that smaller hospitals are less infectious than larger institutions. Moreover, smaller maternity hospitals get better results than larger ones: maternal sickness rates and perinatal mortality rates there are substantially lower (Jean-Marie Clement 1998 op cit, 83).

page 142

Department of Health figures: Department of Health and Children 2003 Health Statistics [Online] Available: http://www.dohc.ie/publications/pdf/stats05_acute.pdf?direct=1 [Accessed 20 Jan 2007].

less costly to run: Poor management information systems here make it very difficult to compare costs accurately. But dividing total hospital expenditure by bed days used, an in-patient bed costs €711 per day in Nenagh Hospital, €956 in Limerick Regional and €1,153 in Beaumont Hospital (Nenagh Hospital Action Committee 2006 op cit, 69). In Limerick Regional, in 2001 and 2002, allowing for differences in facilities and in categories of patients treated, the cost per patient was 50 per cent higher than it was in Ennis General (Ennis General Hospital Development Committee 2004 op cit, 49). National figures in other European Union countries bear out this trend: French university hospitals, with only 20 per cent of public beds, account for 41 per cent of public hospital expenditure; while regional centres, with 25 per cent of the beds, account for 48 per cent of total hospital costs (Jean-Marie Clement 1998 op cit, 45).

'waste' money: Muiris Fitzgerald 2003 op cit, 61.

'properly sustain': Chris Lyons 2006 *Northern Standard* 19 Jan.

'deep and abiding': Fintan O'Toole 2004 *Irish Times* 18 May.

10: WAR

page 144

'medical imperatives': Dr Finbarr Lennon 2000 letter to Dr Jim Kiely chief medical officer Department of Health 6 Dec.

page 145

the FitzGerald Report: *Outline of the Future Hospital System: Report of the Consultative Council on the General Hospital Services* 1968. Stationery Office, Dublin.

1994: Comhairle na n-Ospidéal 1994 *Report on Paediatric and Adolescent Services in Dublin* June Comhairle na n-Ospidéal, Dublin.

page 146

Tierney Report: Department of Health, Comhairle na n-Osp307 idéal and the Postgraduate Medical and Dental Board 1993 *Medical Manpower in Acute Hospitals—a discussion document*. June.

a health strategy: Department of Health 1994 *Shaping a Healthier Future—a strategy for effective healthcare in the 1990s*. Stationery Office, Dublin.

Forum on Medical Manpower: Department of Health and Children 2001 *Report of the Forum on Medical Manpower*.

task force: Department of Health and Children 2003 *Report of the National Task Force on Medical Staffing (Hanly Report)*.

page 147

a blizzard of letters: given to the author by a member of the former North-Eastern Health Board and summarised in the *Northern Standard* 19 Dec 2002.

page 149
November 2000: Dermot Condon 2000 *Report of the Review Group on Maternity Services in the North-Eastern Health Board.*

page 154
Barry Desmond: Maev-Ann Wren 2003 op cit, 184.
Antoinette Doocey: Loose Talk LMFM 2001 22 June.

page 155
'phased opening': Patrick Kinder 2001 *Report of the Maternity Services Review Group to the North-Eastern Health Board* Sept 2001: 36.
Montréal: Hélène Vadeboncoeur 2003 Letter to the National Birth Alliance.

page 156
declared its opposition: Marie O'Connor 2003 *Northern Standard* 3 Sept.
the council later rejected: ibid.
'at risk': Institute of Obstetricians and Gynaecologists 2003 quoted by Eithne Donnellan 2003 *Irish Times* 20 May. Released under FOI to *The Irish Times.*

page 157
politics should be 'removed': Maev-Ann Wren 2003 op cit, 196.
a strategic approach: Eithne McCord Chair South Tyrone Action Committee 2001 'Despite one of the largest hospitals campaigns in the UK,' she told the Border Counties Maternity Services Forum on 28 June, 'there is now no maternity unit between Enniskillen and Craigavon.'

page 159
'immediate surgery': Dr John Barton 2005, personal communication.
dread the day: Downpatrick Hospital staff member 2005, personal communication.
a bleeding duodenal ulcer: Eithne Donnellan 2006 *Irish Times* 8 Sept.
Carey Report: *Report into the death of Mr Patrick J. Walsh*: an independent private inquiry conducted by Mr Declan Carey Belfast City Hospital and Professor John R T Monson University of Hull Aug 2006 [Online] Available: http://www.hse.ie /en/Publications/PatrickJoeWalsReport/FiletoUpload,3616,en.pdf [Accessed 29 Jan 2007].

page 161
'clinical redesign projects': Teamwork Management Services Limited 2006 *Improving Safety and Achieving Better Standards: an action plan for health services in the North East.* Teamwork Management Services Limited, Bolton.
'clinical networks': ibid.

page 162
Eilis McGovern: Sean McMahon 2006 *Anglo Celt* 4 Jan.
100,000: Bernie O'Halloran 2005, personal communication.
Birth Alliance: Annette O'Meara 2003 *Star*, 2 Apr.

page 164
Aindrias Ó Caoimh: *Irish Times* 2004 10 July.
'Report warned' Eithne Donnellan 2004 *Irish Times* 10 July.
did not breach: *Irish Times* 2004 30 July.

page 165
Brenda McAnespie: *Northern Standard* 2004 5 Aug.
promising: *Northern Standard* 2004 30 Sept; Eithne Donnellan 2004 *Irish Times* 29
    Sept.

11: CORPORATE LOVE AFFAIR

page 169
Ms Harney: Martin Wall (2004 *Irish Times* 10 Nov) announced the impending visit.
Memorial Sloan-Kettering: [Online] Available: *http://www.mskcc.org/mskcc/html
    /511.cfm* [Accessed 31 Jan 2007].

page 170
Reiki: [Online] Available: http://www.mskcc.org/mskcc_resources/sidebar/index.
    cfm?WWWROOT=/mskcc/&MainSrc=http%3A//www.mskcc.org/mskcc/html/
    457.cfm&SidebarType=Contents [Accessed 31 Jan 2007].
managed health care: [Online] Available: http://www.mskcc.org/mskcc/html
    /11851.cfm [Accessed 31 Jan 2007].

page 171
'Denied Coverage': [Online] Available: http://www.mskcc.org/mskcc/html/
    62752.cfm [Accessed 31 Jan 2007].

page 172
Royalty Pharma: [Online] Available: http://www.mskcc.org/mskcc_resources/side-
    bar/index.cfm?WWWROOT=/mskcc/&MainSrc=http%3A//www.mskcc.org/m
    skcc/html/457.cfm&SidebarType=Contents [Accessed 31 Jan 2007].
Neupogen: ibid.
$1 billion: [Online] Available: http://www.mskcc.org/mskcc/html/15937.cfm [Accessed
    31 Jan 2007].
canines: 'We felt it was useful to see if immunotherapy might help these very sick
    dogs with advanced melanoma since the response rates for standard chemother-
    apy were extremely poor with no evidence of improved survival.' [Online]
    Available: http://www.mskcc.org/mskcc/html/13199.cfm [Accessed 31 Jan 2007].
travelling the world: Marilyn French 1998 *A Season in Hell: a Memoir*. Virago Press,
    London, 114.
bad food: ibid, 58. French generalises about hospital food ('they cook the food into
    oblivion'); she appears to extend this judgement to Sloan Kettering.

page 173
no apology: ibid, 159.
half a heart: ibid, 224.

into walls: ibid, 233.
getting through: ibid, 60.
'their bit': ibid, 165.
$2,000: ibid, 50.

page 174
neo-liberalism: Joel Bakan 2005 *The Corporation: the pathological pursuit of profit and power*. Constable, London, 21.
'punishing financial penalties': ibid, 22.
an Israeli trial: Debbi Gedal-Beer 2006 *Midwifery Matters* 24: 110.
synthetic hormones: Joel Bakan 2005 op cit, 24.

page 175
'fundamental needs': ibid, 112.
genes, airports: ibid, 113.
'Our foundation hospitals': Professor Allyson Pollack 2005 'Ireland's Healthcare Reforms—for people or for profit? Health Services Action Group Conference Liberty Hall 26 Nov.
American chains: ibid.
WTO: Joel Bakan 2005 op cit, 23.
WHO's budget: Diana Melrose *Bitter Pills*. Oxfam, 163. In Joan Donley 2002 'UN/WHO Bureaucracy'. Extract from work then in progress, personal communication.

page 176
North Africa: Lesley Doyel 1981 *The Political Economy of Health*. Pluto Press, 273–88. In ibid (Donley).
Africa: Jared Diamond 1997 *Guns, Germs and Steel*. Vintage. In ibid.
American imports: Lesley Doyel. In ibid.
'World Bank': ibid.
Jakarta: ibid.
'private sector partnerships': ibid.
Depo-Provera: ibid.

page 177
FIGO: ibid.
Caesarean section rates in Britain: Colin Francombe and Wendy Savage 1993 'Caesarean section in Britain and the United States: 12 or 24 per cent, is either the right rate?' *Social Science and Medicine* 37 (10).
44 per cent: Orla O'Donovan 2006 'Corporate colonization of health activism? Irish advocacy organizations' modes of engagement with pharmaceutical corporations' *International Journal of Health Sciences* [In press].
Industry links: Richard Smith 2006 *The Trouble with Medical Journals*. Royal Society of Medicine, London, 71–81. The author is concerned that 'much of what medical journals do is ethically weak'. Most authors, he says, have conflicts of interest, 'particularly in their financial relations with pharmaceutical companies (p 9). Until very recently, journals—themselves closely tied to pharmaceutical

companies—did not even ask authors to declare these relationships. Yet, as Dr Smith underlines, in some cases, '[drug] studies linked to the manufacturers reach completely different conclusions than those that are not' (p 10).

page 178
Novartis: Dr Peadar O'Grady 2005 'Why is the Irish Health Service in Crisis?' Pamphlet. Socialist Workers' Party, Dublin, 23.
Pfizer: ibid.
WHO *code*: *Interim Report of the National Committee on Breastfeeding* May 2003. Health Promotion Unit, Dublin, 19.
Tazocin: Strategy for the Control of Antimicrobial Resistance in Ireland (SARI) 2005 Annual Report, 35 [Online] Available: http://www.ndsc.ie/hpsc/A-Z/ MicrobiologyAntimicrobialResistance/StrategyforthecontrolofAntimicrobialRe sistanceinIrelandSARI/OverviewandKeyDocuments/File,1771,en.pdf [Accessed 23 Jan 2007].

page 179
pituitary glands: *Irish Times* 2004 23 Aug.
'friends and allies': Orla O'Donovan 2006 op cit

page 180
'Citizenship and Birth': 'Naissance et citoyenneté', a conference organised by a mid-wifery journal, *Les dossiers de l'obstetrique*, 4 May 2000, Nantes, France.
'battle plan': C. Medawar and A. Hardon 2004 *Medicines Out of Control? Antidepressants and the Conspiracy of Goodwill*. Aksant, Amsterdam, 121. In Orla O'Donovan 2006 op cit.
chestnut: Joel Bakan 2005 op cit, 27.
a secret location: It later emerged that the conference, dedicated to 'the partnerships involving businesses and citizens' organisations in Europe', had been held in Frascati, Italy. ACN claimed that the seminar had been attended by 160 representatives from twenty-one countries. Participants included Novartis, Schering-Plough Spa, Astrazeneca, Eli Lilly Italia and Pfizer Italia. [Online] Available: http://www.activecitizenship.net/documenti/Participants_List_Frascati.pdf [Accessed 31 Jan 2007].

page 181
Berlusconi-backed group: CittadinanzAttiva supported a Forza Italia candidate, Letizia Moratti, who was elected mayor of Milan on 28 May 2006 (Roxane Poggi 2007, personal communication).
biggest corporations: [Online] Available: http://www.activecitizenship.net/spon-sors.htm [Accessed 31 Jan 2007].
7 September: [Online] Available http://www.activecitizenship.net/health/euro-pean_charter.pdf [Accessed 31 Jan 2007].
Merck Sharp: [Online] Available: http://www.dcu.ie/nursing/healthcare_ rights. shtml [Accessed 31 Jan 2007].
Mary Harney: [Online] Available: http://www.irishscientist.ie/2005/contents.asp? contentxml=05p71b.xml&contentxsl=iso5pages.xsl [Accessed 31 Jan 2007].

'*Chronically Ill*': [Online] Available: http://www.activecitizenship.net/public_poli-cies/health/informed_patient.htm [Accessed 31 Jan 2007]. Another campaign listed on the ACN Web Site, the Cancer United Campaign, ran into difficulties on the eve of its Brussels launch on 19 Oct 2006, when it emerged that the campaign was funded solely by Roche, a leading manufacturer of cancer drugs; British MPS withdrew from the board and its planned launch in the European Parliament was aborted. The Cancer United Campaign reputedly relies on a report from the Karolinska Institute—funded by Roche—linking cancer survival rates in Europe with cancer drug spending by governments [Online] Available: http://society.guardian.co.uk/health/story/0,,1924747,00.html [Accessed 31 Jan 2007].

page 182

Its tactics include: Marie O'Connor 2006 *Northern Standard* 11 May. This informa-tion is still accessible on ACN's website.

'*an enrichment*': [Online] Available: http://www.activecitizenship.net/documenti/rethinking%20final%20report.pdf [Accessed 31 Jan 2007].

European Charter: Drafted, presumably, in English, the Charter has been translated into Italian, French, Spanish, Portuguese, Greek and Bulgarian. Age Action Ireland is reportedly monitoring the Charter in Ireland. [Online] Available: http://www.activecitizenship.net/projects/project_europe_chart.htm [Accessed 31 Jan 2007].

'*Active European Citizenship*': In 2005, the European Parliament approved the new programme on active European citizenship for 2007–14 [Online] Available: http://ec.europa.eu/dgs/education_culture/activecitizenship/citizens_en.html [Accessed 31 Jan 2007].

12: MCMEDICINE
page 183

Neiman Marcus: *Repertoire* Oct 2001 9 (10) interviews John O'Malley [Online] Available: http://www.medicaldistribution.com/repnew/viewarticle.asp?arti-cleno=1086&issueid=99 [Accessed 31 Jan 2007].

page 184

'*Soft volumes*': Jason Gurda. [Online] Available: http://www.smartmoney.com/bn/ON/index.cfm?story=ON-20060724-00729-1640 [Accessed 31 Jan 2007].

50 per cent: Triad annual reports (see below).

page 185

OECD *average*: A. Dale Tussing and Maev-Ann Wren *How Ireland Cares: the case for health care reform*. New Island, Dublin 2006, 61.

page 186

Staggeringly high: national research commissioned by the California Nurses' Association. Institute for Health and Socio-Economic Policy 2004. *The Second Annual IHSP Hospital 200: Hospitals, Big Pharma, HMOs and the Health Care War Economy*. An informative and incisive study of the drivers of US health-care costs today that is relevant to Ireland. [Online] Available: http://www.calnurses.org/research/pdfs/IHSP-Hospital-200.pdf [Accessed 31 Jan 2007]. The IHSP study was repeated in 2005. *The Third Annual IHSP Hospital 200: The Nation's Most— and Least—Expensive Hospitals Fiscal Year 2003/4.* [Online] Available: http://www.hospitalpricegouging.org/update1_012306.pdf [Accessed 31 Jan 2007].

blatant overcharging: ibid. This is set to intensify: as in Australia, the trend in the US hospital industry is towards consolidation, with fewer companies owning and/or operating more health-care facilities. In 1999, for example, at least half of all California's hospitals were associated with large hospital corporations; six of the biggest operated over one-third of all facilities. In 'Who Owns California's Hospitals?', a study by the Public Policy Institute of California. [Online] Available: http://www.ppic.org/content/pubs/rb/RB_1099JSRB.pdf [Accessed 31 Jan 2007].

TAP: [Online] Available: http://www.taf.org/top20.htm [Accessed 31 Jan 2007].

page 187

$18 billion: According to a a Justice Department report, Medicare overpayments amounted to $12.6 billion in 1998, down from $20.3 billion in 1997 [Online] Available: http://www.usdoj.gov/dag/pubdoc/health98.htm [Accessed 31 Jan 2007].

Two sisters: Phillips and Cohen's website gives extensive references for *qui tam* lawsuits [Online] Available: http://www.phillipsandcohen.com/CM/False ClaimsAct/FalseClaimsAct163.asp: [Accessed 31 Jan 2007].

New York radiologist: ibid.

page 188

Scrushy: Andrew Ward 2005 *Irish Times* 29 June.

November 2006: [Online] Available: http://www.cfo.com/article.cfm/8369793/c_8352537?f=archives&origin=archive [Accessed 20 Jan 2007].

page 189

465 defendants: [Online] Available: http://www.usdoj.gov/dag/pubdoc/hipaao1fe19.htm [Accessed 20 Jan 2007].

Dr Thomas Frist: A Brisbane surgeon, Michael Wynne, documented the Columbia/HCA fraud saga in detail in 2003. [Online] Available: http://www.uow.edu.au/arts/sts/bmartin/dissent/documents/health/columb_2003.html [Accessed 20 Jan 2007].

Kentucky Fried: [Online] Available: http://www.corp-research.org/archives/jan03.htm20060724-000729-1640 [Accessed 20 Jan 2007].

'economic dinosaurs': Michael Wynne 2003 op cit.

page 190

quietly terminated: ibid.

leviathan: [Online] Available: http://www.corp-research.org/archives/jan03.htm 20060724-000729-1640 [Accessed 31 Jan 2007].

cherry-picking: Michael Wynne 2003 op cit.

page 191

illegal kickbacks: ibid.

'*upcoding*': ibid. See also the report of the Office of the Inspector General. [Online] Available: http://oig.hhs.gov/reading/hcfac /HCFAC%20Annual%20Report%20 FY%202001.htm [Accessed 31 Jan 2007].

first fraud settlement: Michael Wynne 2003 op cit.

Montana: from the US Justice Department, this statement of James Alderson's case (1999) sets out very clearly the substantive whistleblower action taken against HCA and Quorum. [Online] Available: http://www.usdoj.gov/civil/cases/alder-son/complain.pdf [Accessed 31 Jan 2007].

non-allowable expenses: Michael Wynne 2003 op cit.

New York Times: For articles on Columbia/HCA, see the *New York Times* and the *Wall Street Journal*, 24–29 Mar 1997. See also Robert Kuttner 1996 'Columbia/HCA and the Resurgence of the For-Profit Hospital Business' *New England Journal of Medicine* 1 Aug (335: 363), 48 and also 8 Aug (335: 446); and Bruce Japsen 1997 'Columbia's highs and lows'. *Modern Healthcare* 28 July, 3. In Michael Wynne 2003 op cit.

page 192

walked away: Steffi Woolhander and David U Himmelstein 2004 'The high costs of for-profit care'. *Canadian Medical Association Journal* 8 June 170 (12): 1814–5

French chain: ibid.

'*fraudulent billing*': Triad's quarterly (to June) 2002 *Report to the Securities and Exchange Commission (SEC)*, 17. [Online] Available: http://www.getfilings.com/ 00000930661-02-002774.html [Accessed 31 Jan 2007].

page 193

'*reserve' accounts*: James Alderson. See Montana, 1999 op cit

200-plus hospitals: ibid. Appended to the draft settlement between HCA and the Justice Department. [Online] Available: http://contracts.onecle.com/hca/us.set-tle.2003.06.26.shtml [Accessed 31 Jan 2007].

December 1999: Michael Wynne 2003 op cit.

'*the baby Columbias*': Robert Neil 2001 'Shopping Spree'. *Repertoire* May 9 (5) [Online] Available: http://www.medicaldistribution.com/repnew/viewarticle. asp?articleno=957&issueid=94 [Accessed 31 Jan 2007].

HealthTrust: In 2000, its annual purchasing volume was $4.2 billion. [Online] Available: http://www.medicaldistribution.com/repnew/viewarticle.asp?arti-cleno=926&issueid=93 [Accessed 31 Jan 2007].

December 2000: Phillips and Cohen op cit. See also the Office of the Inspector General. [Online] Available: http://oig.hhs.gov/reading/hcfac/HCFAC%20 Annual%20Report%20FY%202001.htm [Accessed 31 Jan 2007].

criminal counts: The Office of the Inspector General (op cit) reported that two of HCA's subsidiaries 'pleaded guilty to several charges involving a wide range of criminal conduct'.

Jack Bovender: Michael Wynne 2003 op cit.

page 194

twelve whistleblower actions: [Online] Available: http://contracts.onecle.com/hca/us.settle.2003.06.26.shtml [Accessed 31 Jan 2007].

corporate integrity: see the Office of the Inspector General op cit.

$631 million: [Online] Available: http://www.ffhsj.com/quitam/fcaset.htm [Accessed 31 Jan 2007].

$1.7 billion: the Office of the Inspector General included the settlement for the fiscal year of 2001.

'anti-fraud': Triad's quarterly (to June 2002) *2002 Report to the Securities and Exchange Commission (SEC)*, 17. [Online] Available: Triad SEC 2002 http://www.getfilings.com/o0000930661-02-002774.html [Accessed 31 Jan 2007].

Olsten: ibid, 17.

page 195

Wall Street Journal: Dennis K. Berman et al 2006 *Wall Street Journal*, syndicated in the *Globe and Mail* (Toronto) 25 July.

KPMG: Michael Wynne op cit.

Public Citizen: [Online] Available: http://www.citizenshealthcare.gov/recommendations/appendix_e.pdfPDF] Appendix E–Health Care Presentations—updated June 1 2006 [Accessed 31 Jan 2007].

former HCA: See Triad website. [Online] Available: http://www.triadhospitals.com/custompage.asp?guidcustomcontentid={689ED35B-C4AF-11D4-81F5-00508B1249D5. http://www.allaboutquitam.org/cgi-local/quitam/articles.pl?s=press&a=Oct2Quorum [Accessed 31 Jan 2007].

CMS: Triad 2002 op cit, 16.

page 196

QHR: a wholly owned subsidiary of Triad, it is responsible for the liabilities of HCA Management Company, as well as being its successor in interest. Its parent company QHG (formed to buy HCA Management Company) no longer exists. See also: [Online] Available: http://sec.edgar-online.com/2003/03/27/0000930661-03-001250/Section2.asp [Accessed 31 Jan 2007].

Burke Whitman: Interview 2001 [Online] Available: http://www.ceocfointerviews.com/interviews/TriadHosp.htm [Accessed 31 Jan 2007].

two segments: see Triad 2005 *Report to the Securities and Exchange Commission (SEC)* setting out details of the whistleblower lawsuits against it. [Online] Available: http://library.corporate-ir.net/library/11/115/115178/items/186915/tri_2005_10K.pdf [Accessed 31 Jan 2007].

$95.5 million: see Phillips and Cohen [Online] Available: http://www.allaboutquitam.org/cgi-local/quitam/articles.pl?s=press&a =Oct2Quorum [Accessed 31 Jan 2007].

$87.5 million: see the Office of the Inspector General op cit.

two qui tam: Triad 2002 op cit, 16.

$427,500: ibid.

page 197

materially inflating: Triad 2005 op cit, 30–1.

Mississippi hospital: Triad 2005 op cit.

Georgia hospitals: Triad 2005 op cit. See also [Online] Available: http://www.arent-fox.com/legal_updates/content1162.pdf [Accessed 31 Jan 2007].

Pennsylvania: detailed plaintiff's statement setting out the amended *qui tam* action against Quorum (QHR), Tyrone Hospital, in Johnstown, Pennsylvania, and up to seven doctors. [Online] Available: http://www.altoonamirror.com/ ForThe Record/Documents/tcomplaint.pdf [Accessed 31 Jan 2007].

Ohio Valley: Paula Reed Ward 2006 20 Jan. *Report on the us Government case against a Quorum-managed hospital in Pittsburgh.* [Online] Available: http://www.post-gazette.com/pg/06020/641256.stm [Accessed 31 Jan 2007].

disallowed deductions: Triad 2005 op cit.

page 198

fifty-three hospitals: [Online] Available: http://contracts.onecle.com/hca/us.set-tle.2003.06.26.shtml [Accessed 31 Jan 2007].

Mission Bay: On 11 July 2003, the *East Bay Business Times* reported that Triad had closed San Diego's Mission Bay Hospital; San Leandro was also cited as a Triad hospital. [Online] Available: http://www.bizjournals.com/eastbay/stories/2003 /07/14/smallb2.html.
http://www.corporate-ir.net/ireye/ir_site.zhtml?ticker=TRI&script=410&lay-out=-6&item_id=801755 [Accessed 31 Jan 2007].

13: HEALTH FOR SALE?

page 199

'allocation of risk': Gemma Lynch 2006 'The Business of Health'. Berkeley Court Hotel Dublin 5 Apr. An investornet conference.

page 200

'strategic control': Barry Lynch 2006 ibid

the Republic: the 'ROI deal' involving four oncology units and two satellite centres is costing taxpayers in excess of €400 million. [Online] Available http://www.pri-vatehealth.ie/UB2.pdf [Accessed 15 Jan 2007].

the Hudson River: Joel Bakan *The Corporation: the pathological pursuit of profit and power*. Constable, London, 75–9.

page 201

image the heart: Dan O'Connor 2006 'The Business of Health'. Berkeley Court Hotel op cit.

'future-proofing': Paul Morton 2006 ibid.

page 202

'will cost': Vincent Sheridan 2006 ibid.

'Compressed morbidity': Joseph Hoban 2006 ibid.

'pushback': Jerry Mansmann 2006 ibid.

page 203

$2.6 million: [Online] Available: http://www.ffhsj.com/quitam/fcaset.htm [Accessed 15 Jan 2007].

UPMC: in partnership with the Whitfield Cancer Centre, Waterford. [Online] Available: http://www.whitfieldclinic.ie/CancerCentre/About.htm [Accessed 15 Jan 2007]. In 2003, Dr Susan A. Silver, a senior pathologist at UPMC, filed a whistleblower lawsuit against UPMC for allegedly falsifying hundreds of thousands of Pap smear tests and subjecting cancer patients to unnecessary testing (Andrew Conte 2003 *Pittsburgh Tribune Review*, 21 Dec). [Online] Available: http://www.pittsburghlive.com/x/pittsburghtrib/s_171110.html [Accessed 15 Jan 2007]. Five years earlier, the US Justice Department reported that UPMC had agreed to pay $14 million to Medicare, plus $3 to Medicaid for false billing. [Online] Available: http://www.usdoj.gov/dag/pubdoc/health98.htm [Accessed 15 Jan 2007].

page 206

74 per cent: Emmet Oliver 2005 *Irish Times* 30 May.

€147 million: ibid.

'*I lobbied him*': Jimmy Sheehan 2006 'Ireland's Health Service: For People or for Profit?' Auburn Lodge Hotel, Ennis, Co. Clare 8 May. Organised by the Ennis General Hospital Development Committee.

tax concessions: Maev-Ann Wren 2003 *Unhealthy State: anatomy of a sick society*. New Island, Dublin, 281.

page 207

'*business entities*': ibid, 283.

'*madness*': Vincent Sheridan 2006 'The Business of Health'. Berkeley Court Hotel op cit.

HCA: Maev-Ann Wren 2003 op cit, 291.

John Clarke: ibid, 292.

427: Barry O'Halloran 2005 *Irish Times* 19 July.

Golden Meadows: ibid.

Mowlam: ibid.

the Cooley Mountains: 'Ballymascanlon Clinic: delivering healthcare solutions for the North East'. Prospectus.

page 208

'*a million*': Dr Mary Grehan 2006 'Ireland's Health Service: For People or for Profit?' op cit.

'*devoid*': Ballymascanlon Clinic op cit, 7.

eleven private hospitals: A. Dale Tussing and Maev-Ann Wren 2006 *How Ireland Cares: the case for health care reform*. New Island, Dublin, 181.

page 209

36 per cent: Comptroller and Auditor General 2004 *Annual Report* Stationery Office, Dublin, 135.

staggering range: For several of the most common procedures, the highest price exceeded the lowest by over 200 per cent: ibid, 136–7.

page 211
'a perverse incentive': Dr John Barton, Chair, Health Services Action Group 2005 Press release.
60 per cent: Mary Harney 2006 *Irish Times* 4 May. Of the 13,255 beds in public hospitals, 2,500 are officially designated as private. But if only 1,000 of these beds are redesignated as public, that will still leave, according to the Minister's own figures, 1,500 private beds—or 60 per cent of the total—in public hospitals. These figures, moreover, under-represent the actual number of private beds in the public sector. The Minister acknowledges that the proportion of private activity is 25 per cent; this suggests 3,318 private beds, not 2,500. Secondly, as the Minister underlines, private admissions in some public hospitals amount to over 40 per cent of all planned admissions.

page 212
Donal Duffy welcomed: Eithne Donnellan 2005 *Irish Times* 15 July.
the sole union: Mary Harney 2006 op cit.
would be staffed: Eithne Donnellan 2006 op cit.
Asam Ishtiaq: ibid.
2,000 existing beds: Martin Wall 2006 *Irish Times* 17 Nov.
'nice little number': Anne Counihan 2006 'The Business of Health'. Berkeley Court Hotel op cit.

page 213
a new bed: Eithne Donnellan 2005 *Irish Times* 15 July.
€1 million: Mary Harney 2006 op cit.
€125,000: Maev-Ann Wren op cit, 286.

page 214
€300,000: Eithne Donnellan 2005 op cit.
€400,000 Mary Harney 2006 op cit.
'bearing this cost': Eithne Donnellan 2005 op cit.
'open to the HSE': Mary Harney 2006 op cit.

page 215
'public work only': ibid.
'reduce pressure': John Barton 2005 (a) 'Global evidence highlights risk of Harney's private for profit hospitals' Opinion *Irish Times* 12 Sept.
'"mythical"': Canadian Health Services Research Foundation/Fondation canadienne de la recherche sur les services de santé 2005 'Myth: a parallel private system would reduce waiting times in the public system'. See: [Online] Available: www.chsrf.ca. [Accessed 31 Jan 2007]. In ibid.
'adverse effects': 'A major study of surgical waiting lists and their management published by the OECD in 2003 refers to the potential adverse effects of a parallel

private hospital system in countries where consultants are in short supply, as currently applies in Ireland, and where doctors are allowed to pursue private practice in a parallel private hospital system.' In ibid.

'*Australian research*': Stephen J. Duckett 2005 'Private care and public waiting'. *Australian Health Review* 29 (1): 87–93. Professor of Health Policy at La Trobe University, Melbourne, Duckett recommends solving public patient waiting lists by stepping up activity in public hospitals. His study, which included private sector treatment of public patients, as in the NTPF, demonstrates that 'more privately provided care means longer waiting times for public patients'. In ibid. See also: Carolyn De Coster, Leonard MacWilliam and Randy Walld 2000 *Waiting times for surgery 1997/98 and 1998/99: update* Nov, Manitoba Centre for Health Policy and Evaluation.

five OECD *countries*: Carolyn Hughes Tuohy et al 2004 'How does private finance affect public health care systems? Marshaling [sic] the evidence from OECD nations'. *Journal of Health Politics, Policy and Law* 29 (3) June. In John Barton 2005 (a) op cit.

page 216

71 per cent: Department of Health and Children 2005 Hospital In-Patient Enquiry (HIPE).

page 217

€520 million: Mary Harney 2006 op cit.

page 218

Buxton: Jerry Mansmann 2006 'The Business of Health'. Berkeley Court Hotel op cit.

42 per cent: The total number of acute or short-stay beds in Ireland is 15,055 (13,255 in public hospitals, 1,800 in private). With 2,200 new private beds coming on-stream, this is set to rise to 17,255. Taking the Minister's figures at face value, pegging private activity in the public sector at just 25 per cent gives a notional 3,314 private beds in public hospitals; adding to this the existing 1,800 plus the 2,200 being built gives a total of 7,314, or 42 per cent of the total. Bearing in mind the fact that private admissions in some public hospitals are running at 40–50 per cent, the actual figure is likely to be well in excess of 50 per cent.

page 219

six of the co-located hospitals: See Deputy John Gormley, Health Spokesperson Green Party, on public-private partnerships. *Dáil Debates*, 27 Sept 2006. [Online] Available:http://debates.oireachtas.ie/DDebate.aspx?F=DAL20060927.XML&Dail=29&Ex=All&Page=2 [Accessed 21 Jan 2007]. See also Caoimhghín O Caoláin Health Spokesperson Sinn Féin *Dáil Debates* (Private Members' Motion) 24, 25 Oct 2006 [Online] Available: http://debates.oireachtas.ie/DDebate.aspx?F=DAL20060927.XML&Dail=29&Ex=All&Page=2 [Accessed 21 Jan 2007]. See also *Sinn Fein News* 2006: Health inequality being paid for with the lives of our people—Ó Caoláin 26 Oct [Online] available: http://www.sinnfein.ie/news/detail/16479 [Accessed 21 Jan 2007].

parent company: Michael Cullen 2006 *Irish Examiner* 10 Nov. See also Triad 2005 *Report to the Securities and Exchange Commission (SEC)*: 1. [Online] Available: http://library.corporate-ir.net/library/11/115/115178/items/186915/ tri_2005_10K.pdf: 'Triad's healthcare service business previously comprised the Pacific Group business of HCA, Inc ("HCA"). On May 11 1999, HCA divested itself of its Pacific Group business to Triad through a spin-off to its shareholders. The spin-off was accomplished by a pro rata distribution of all outstanding shares of Triad common stock to the stockholders of HCA.' [Accessed 15 Oct 2006]. See also indymedia 2006: Patient Inc comes to Ireland. 4 Oct. [Online] Available: http://72.232.163.18/article/78814?condense_comments=true&fontsizeinc=0 [Accessed 31 Jan 2007].

a not-for-profit: In a letter to *The Irish Times* (31 Oct 2005) Mark Redmond wrote: 'Triad hospitals Inc, the operators of Beacon Hospital, is a publicly-traded company which has never paid its shareholders a dividend. Any profits are reinvested in its hospitals.' However, as Burke Whitman, Triad's former chief financial officer, explained in 2001, the intention is to pay a dividend: 'the majority of the projects in which we are investing capital are projects that we expect to generate an attractive return that meets our investment criteria. We are feeling very bullish about those.' [Online] Available: http://www.ceocfointerviews.com/interviews/TriadHosp.htm [Accessed 16 Jan 2007].

indebtedness covenants: see Triad 2005 *Report to the Securities and Exchange Commission (SEC)*. [Online] Available: http://library.corporate-ir.net/library/11/ 115/115178/items/186915/tri_2005_10K.pdf [Accessed 31 Jan 2007].

page 220

a sense of ownership: Burke Whitman 2001 op cit.

a percentage: Michael Cullen 2006 op cit. Triad is leasing Beacon Hospital in return for a share in the profits, capped at 50 per cent.

Mission Bay: [Online] Available: http://www.bizjournals.com/eastbay/stories/ 2003/07/14/smallb2.html [Accessed 16 Jan 2007].

San Leandro: a listing of political donations records one of $400 for Mark Hoffman San Leandro Hospital CFO dated 4 June 2004 [Online] Available: http://www. capweb.net/zip/94506 [Accessed 16 Jan 2007].

HCA: see Triad 2005 op cit

'*physician relationships*': Burke Whitman 2001 op cit.

financial inducements: Triad 2005 op cit.

page 221

'*other asset*': ibid.

$64.9 million: ibid.

'*educational and consulting services*': Johns Hopkins 2006 Media release. [Online] Available: http://www.hopkinsmedicine.org/Press_releases/2006/05_09_06.html [Accessed 22 Jan 2007].

€*180 million*: Michael Cullen 2006 op cit. The project is heavily leveraged: borrowings total €153 million.

after-tax losses: [Online] Available: http://www.corporate-ir.net/ireye/ir_site.zhtml?
ticker=TRI&script=410&layout=-6&item_id=801755 [Accessed 31 Jan 2007].

long-listed: widely reported in the national press. See also Ruadhán MacAodháin
2006 'American Corporation in bid for private wing at CUH'. UCC *Express* 17 Oct
[Online] Available: http://www.ucc.ie/en/SIN/Communications/UCCExpress/
ExpressOnline/UCCExpress0607/UCCExpressv103-171006/DocumentFile,
25229,en.pdf [Accessed 21 Jan 2007].

primary care 'market': Johns Hopkins 2006 op cit.

14: CORPORATE RAIDERS

page 223

'the "hotel services"': John O'Brien 2006 'The Business of Health'. Berkeley Court
Hotel Dublin 5 Apr.

'clinical support': Emma Thompson and Matthew Hensley 2002 'Public-Private
Partnerships in Healthcare' [Online] Available: www.ip3.org/pub/publica-
tion2002.013htm [Accessed on 13 May 2006].

€*550 million*: Anne Counihan 2006 'The Business of Health'. Berkeley Court Hotel
op cit.

page 224

fourth step: Emma Thompson and Matthew Hensley 2002 op cit.

'Sale of public hospital': ibid.

Canada: Syndicat Canadien de la Fonction Publique (SCFP): 2005 'L'Innovation
Denoncée: un inventaire en continu des principales initiatives de privatisation
dans le systeme canadien de soins de santé'. 1 sept 2004–21 juillet 2005. See
[Online] Available *http://www.scfp.ca* [Accessed 31 Jan 2007]. Privatisation varies
from province to province. In British Columbia, for example, all health services
are for sale. According to SCFP, the union of public sector workers—Canada's
biggest union—privatisation leads to a drop in quality, an increase in turnover,
a fall in competency, a deficit in training, a hike in charges, decreases in salary
and a loss of confidence in the public system. Those who are particularly affected
by the lay-offs and the wage cuts include women, recent immigrants and visible
minorities.

29 per cent: Lewis Grey 1999 'Private Hospitals and the Private Health Insurance
Conundrum 1998-99' [Online] Available: www.aph.gov.au?Library/pubs/RN/
1998-1999?99rn01.htm [Accessed 29 May 2006].

page 225

35 per cent: ibid. Total number of beds: 78,868, of which 51,461 are public and 27,407
private.

three in every ten: ibid.

corporate crime: Michael Wynne 2003 [Online] Available: http://www.uow.edu.au/
arts/sts/bmartin/dissent/documents/health/columb_2003.html [Accessed 17 Jan
2007].

45 per cent: Lewis Gray 1999 op cit.

Mowlam: Barry O'Halloran 2005 *Irish Times* 19 July.

Golden Meadows: ibid.

Silver Stream: ibid.

bad for patients: John Barton 2005 (b) 'Emphasis on private healthcare ill-advised'. 'Opinion' *Irish Times* 18 Apr.

Australian Senate: John Barton 2005 (a) 'Global evidence highlights risk of Harney's private for-profit hospitals'. 'Opinion' *Irish Times* 12 Sept. The Senate report found 'no evidence' that PPPs had consistently delivered better value for public patients than the public sector; and, 'in some cases, PPPs had been detrimental to government and the public'.

page 226

poorer quality health care: Charlene Harrington, Steffi Woolhander and Joseph Mullan 2001 'Does investor ownership of nursing homes compromise the quality of care?' *American Journal of Public Health* 91: 1452–5. Investor-owned nursing homes were cited for deficiencies 43 per cent more often than public ones. Chain ownership predicted additional shortcomings.

for-profit hospitals: P.J. Devereaux et al 2002 'A systematic review and meta-analysis of studies comparing mortality rates of private for-profit and private not-for-profit hospitals' *Canadian Medical Association Journal* 166 (11): 1399–406.

dialysis centres: P.J. Devereaux et al 2002 'Comparison of mortality between private for-profit and private not-for-profit haemodialysis centres: a systematic review and meta-analysis' *Journal of the American Medical Association* 288 (19): 2449–57.

skimp on nursing care: Charlene Harrington et al 2001 op cit. In John Barton 2005 (b) op cit.

beefed-up bonuses: Steffi Woolhander and David U. Himmelstein 2004 'The high costs of for-profit care' *Canadian Medical Association Journal* 170 (12) 8 June.

Dutch Board: Barrie Dowdeswell and Michael Heasman 2004 'Public Private Partnerships in Health: a comparative study. Report prepared for the Netherlands Board for Hospital Facilities' *Journal of Health Politics, Policy and Law* 29 (3) June. In John Barton (a) op cit.

stung: Mary Harney 2006 *Irish Times* 4 May.

American Senate: Michael Wynne 2003 op cit.

page 227

secretly filmed: *Prime Time* 2005 RTÉ television 22 May.

enforced move: John Downes 2005 *Irish Times* 22 June 8 July.

high number of deaths: Eithne Donnellan 2005 *Irish Times* 5 July.

subsequently: Eithne Donnellan 2006 *Irish Times* 30 Nov.

commissioned: Professor Desmond O'Neill 2006 'A review of the deaths at Leas Cross Nursing Home' Apr [Online] Available: http://www.hse.ie/en/Publications/HSEPublications/LeasCrossReport/FiletoUpload,4094,en.pdf [Accessed 31 Jan 2007]. Eithne Donnellan and Martin Wall 2006 *Irish Times* 11 Nov.

page 228

skimp: Charlene Harrington et al 2001 op cit In John Barton 2005 (b) op cit.

seven of the thirty: Eithne Donnellan 2005 *Irish Times* 28 June.
hygiene: Eithne Donnellan and Martin Wall 2005 *Irish Times* 12 Oct.
Tullybeg: Liam Horan and Eithne Donnellan 2005 *Irish Times* 30 June.
green bin: ibid.

page 229
Cathy Armstrong: Liam Horan 2005 *Irish Times* 2 and 5 July.
Village Care: Barry O'Halloran 2005 op cit.
'new conflicts': in addition to ethical problems, private for-profit hospitals lead
    to increased costs for taxpayers, a rise in health insurance premiums,
    cherry-picking by private hospitals, collateral neglect of the public system
    and social divisiveness. See Risteárd Mulcahy 2006 *Is the Health Service for
    Healing? A doctor's defence of medicine's Samaritan role*. Liberties Press, Dublin:
    40–1.

page 230
Obese people: Professor Allyson Pollack 2005 'Ireland's Healthcare Reforms—for
    people or for profit?' Health Services Action Group Conference Liberty Hall 26
    Nov.
waited longer: Stephen J. Duckett 2005 'Private care and public waiting' *Australian
    Health Review* 29 (1): 87–93.
cuts in hospital services: Allyson Pollack 2005 op cit.
More costs: Risteárd Mulcahy 2006 op cit discusses the 'semi-exponential increase in
    medical costs', and its drivers, the commercialisation of investigations, excessive
    medical testing—induced in part by the decline of clinical medicine and by
    fear of litigation—the over-supply of medical treatment and the over-use
    of drugs. 'Such abuses are at the basis of our current escalating health costs'
    (54–61).
71 per cent: Lewis Gray 1999 op cit.
20 per cent: ibid.
full economic cost: Eithne Donnellan 2005 *Irish Times* 15 July.
'bricks and mortar': Burke Whitman 2001 op cit [Online] Available: http://
    www.ceocfointerviews.com/interviews/TriadHosp.htm [Accessed 16 Jan 2007].
Mission Bay: [Online] Available: http://www.bizjournals.com/eastbay/stories/
    2003/07/14/smallb2.html [Accessed 16 Jan 2007].

page 231
every eighty years: Eric Schlosser 2002 *Fast Food Nation* 2nd edn. Penguin, London,
    179.
Iowa Beef Packers: ibid 180.
lied systematically: Kay McIntosh 2005 *The Guardian* 29 June.
'information asymmetry': Patrick Massey and Tony Shortall 1999: 10 'Competition
    and regulation in public utility industries' [Online] Available:
    http://www.tca.ie/PromotingCompetition/DiscussionPapers/DiscussionPapers.
    aspx [Accessed 21 Jan 2007].
Bridget Seepersad: Eithne Donnellan 2005 *Irish Times* 14 July.

39 and 38 per cent: Triad 2002 *Report to the Securities and Exchange Commission (SEC)*. [Online] Available: http://www.getfilings.com/00000930661-02-002774.html [Accessed 21 Jan 2007].

page 232

bed occupancy rates: Triad 2005 *Report to the Securities and Exchange Commission (SEC)*. [Online] Available: http://library.corporate-ir.net/library/11/115/115178 /items/186915/tri_2005_10K.pdf [Accessed 21 Jan 2007].

American research: Elaine M. Silverman, Jonathan S. Skinner and Elliott S. Fisher 1999 'The association between for-profit hospital ownership and increased Medicare spending' *New England Journal of Medicine* 341: 420–6. In John Barton 2005 (b) op cit. See also: P.J. Devereaux et al 2004 'Payments for care at private for-profit and private not-for-profit hospitals: a systematic review and meta-analysis' *Canadian Medical Association Journal* 170 (12): 1817–24. Care in for-profit facilities costs 19 per cent more.

'ludicrous': Allyson Pollack 2005 *Irish Times* 30 Aug.

'spiralled out of control': Allyson Pollack 2005 'Ireland's Healthcare Reforms—for people or for profit?' Health Services Action Group Conference Liberty Hall 26 Nov. See Allyson Pollack et al 2004 *NHS plc: the privatisation of our health care*. Verso, London. A seminal work demonstrating how the NHS has been dismantled and privatised under New Labour.

€75,000: John Barton 2005 (b) op cit.

almost 84 per cent: Emmet Oliver 2005 *Irish Times* 30 May.

Croft Nursing Home: ibid.

cherry-picking: Dr Christine O'Malley President Irish Medical Organisation 2005 'Ireland's Healthcare Reforms—for people or for profit?' Health Services Action Group Conference, Liberty Hall 26 Nov.

page 233

bed and breakfast: Evelyn Ring 2003 *Irish Examiner* 17 June reported that a semi-private room in the Mater Private cost €6,721–6,800 for one night—or twelve: VHI confirmed that the charge—agreed with the insurer—was based on an average stay of six days. The Blackrock Clinic was reported to charge a similar price.

cost of dialysis: Risteárd Mulcahy 2006 'Ireland's Health Service: For People or for Profit?' Auburn Lodge Hotel, Ennis, Co. Clare 8 May. Ennis General Hospital Development Committee Conference. In his 2006 essay (op cit), Dr Mulcahy says 'it is difficult to understand the policy of the authorities in the case of the dialysis service.' HSE policy is to outsource to the private sector, at an estimated cost of €70,000 per dialysis patient per annum, yet the same treatment in Germany costs only €28,000 (p 47).

'disintegration and fragmentation': Allyson Pollack 2005 op cit.

page 234

'opt out': Australian Government. [Online] Available: www.tga.gov.au [Accessed 29 May 2006].

19 per cent: Lewis Grey 1999 op cit.

'new entrants': Australian Government op cit.

'higher than any other': Vincent Sheridan 2006 'The Business of Health'. Berkeley Court Hotel Dublin 5 Apr.

67 per cent: ibid.

page 235

'Good Samaritan': Steffi Woolhander and David U. Himmelstein 2004 op cit.

'piranha fish': Congressman Pete Stark. In Michael Wynne 2003 [Online] Available: http://www.uow.edu.au/arts/sts/bmartin/dissent/documents/health/columb_20 03.html [Accessed 31 Jan 2007].

15: COUP D'ETAT
page 240

prayers: Medical Council 2004 *A guide to ethical conduct and behaviour* 6th edn: 35–6 [Online] Available: http://www.medicalcouncil.ie/_fileupload/standards/ Ethical_Guide_6th_Edition.pdf [Accessed 23 Jan 2007].

eleven years: it was mooted even before the 1997 establishment of the Commission on Nursing which itself set early 1999 as the target date for legislation amending the 1985 Nurses' Act. See *Report of the Commission on Nursing 1998 A Blueprint for the Future*. Stationery Office, Dublin, 7.

history of the state: From March 1996 to December 2004, there were 3,119 claims lodged with the Hepatitis C and HIV Compensation Tribunal. Lawyers believe the vast bulk of outstanding claims will succeed. [Online] Available: http:// www.hepccomptrib.com/HEPATITISC2004.pdf [Accessed 22 Jan 2007].

page 241

up to 500: estimated number of survivors of symphysiotomy today: Colm MacGeehin solicitor to Patient Focus 2006, personal communication. There were 347 symphysiotomies done in the Lourdes Hospital alone, hospital records show.

page 242

an investors' market: privatisation lies at the core of the Government's strategy for developing cancer care. The current 'ROI deal' involves four oncology units and two satellite centres. [Online] Available http://www.privatehealth.ie/UB2.pdf [Accessed 15 Jan 2007].

page 243

leading causes of litigation: MDU Ireland 1998 *Lessons in Litigation—Irish Obstetric Claims*. MDU Ireland, Dublin.

birth reporting scheme: the National Perinatal Reporting Scheme does not record either the induction or acceleration of labour, for example.

Sweden: The Swedish Medical Birth Register dates from 1973. Most women are identified by their PIN (personal identification number): this makes it possible to link various registers, including health. Since 1982, the register has distinguished between planned and unplanned Caesareans; it records induction, but not anaesthesia or acceleration of labour. [Online] Available: http://www.sos.se/full-text/112/2003-112-3/2003-112-3.pdf [Accessed 22 Jan 2007].

'semi-militaristic': Commission on Nursing 1998 op cit, 137.

absenteeism: MDU Ireland 1998 op cit.

Lack of supervision: ibid.

page 244

Cornwall: South West Peninsula NHS Eldercare project in Cornwall. [Online] Available: http://www.swpsha. NHS.uk/annualreport/longTermIllHealth/elder-care Project.shtml [Accessed 22 Jan 2007].

page 245

5 per cent: Martin Wall 2006 *Irish Times* 22 Aug.

up to €50 million: Hilary Humphreys 2005 *Irish Times* 14 Oct.

page 246

death rates by doctor: In January 2006, NHS Scotland published death rates within thirty days of surgery, by doctor, for selected planned procedures, from 31 Dec 1998 to 31 Dec 2004. [Online] Available: http://www.indicators.scot.nhs.uk/TrendsJan2006/Planned.htm [Accessed 28 Jan 2007].

California: Department of Health and Children 2000 *The Nursing and Midwifery Resource Interim Report of the Steering Group* Sept Department of Health and Children, 59. Safety concerns prompted legislation requiring safe hospital staffing. 'Minimum, specific and numerical registered nurse-to-patient ratios' for intensive care and operating theatres are now legally regulated in all hospitals. Californian legislation also prohibits the use of 'unlicensed minimally trained personnel' from carrying out a range of functions, including invasive procedures and drugs administration.

'professional practice review': [Online] Available: http://www.medicalcouncil.ie/performance_in_practice/default.asp?NCID=73 [Accessed 28 Jan 2007].

page 247

New Zealand College: for a detailed description of the standards review process, see New Zealand College of Midwives (Inc) *Midwifery Standards Review Committee Canterbury/West Coast Region* (nd). The New Zealand College of Midwives (NZCOM) has a professional obligation to ensure that midwifery practitioners uphold the NZCOM standards of practice. See New Zealand College of Midwives (Inc) 1993 *Midwives Handbook for Practice*. New Zealand College of Midwives, Christchurch.

IHCA: Eithne Donnellan 2003 *Irish Times* 31 Jan. See also J.F.A. Murphy 2006 'Making sense of medical litigation *Irish Medical Journal* June' 99 (6).

page 248

'egregious system': Dr John Barton 2005 'Opinion' *Irish Times* 12 Sept.

One consultant in every three: 31 per cent of consultants in public hospitals hold Category II contracts. The majority of specialists in Dublin public hospitals hold Category II contracts, including about 90 per cent of anaesthetists and surgeons.

Almost all (98 per cent) paediatricians, psychiatrists and physicians in emergency medicine hold Category I contracts. *National Hospitals Office/Comhairle Consultant Staffing 2005* Jan National Hospitals Office/Comhairle, Dublin, 23.

page 249

over 30 per cent more: this should be regarded as a minimum. The *Brennan Report* showed that, in major teaching hospitals, public subsidy in 2001 of private practice was 56 per cent. *Commission on Financial Management and Control Systems in the Health Services* 31 Jan Stationery Office, Dublin, 72

page 251

predominantly negative: Charlene Harrington, Steffi Woolhander and Joseph Mullan 2001 op cit. See also Barrie Dowdeswell and Michael Heasman 2004 'Public Private Partnerships in Health: a comparative study. Report prepared for the Netherlands Board for Hospital Facilities' *Journal of Health Politics, Policy and Law* 29 (3) June.

Death rates are higher: P.J. Devereaux et al 2002 'A systematic review and meta-analysis of studies comparing mortality rates of private for-profit and private not-for-profit hospitals *Canadian Medical Association Journal* 166 (11): 1399–406. See also P.J. Devereaux et al 2002 'Comparison of mortality between private for-profit and private not-for-profit haemodialysis centres: a systematic review and meta-analysis *Journal of the American Medical Association* 288 (19): 2449–57.

over-testing and over-treatment: Dr Risteárd Mulcahy (2006 *Is the Health Service for Healing? A doctor's defence of medicine's Samaritan role*. Liberties Press, Dublin, 38) cites the case of a major American chain, Tenet, fined by the US Justice Department for carrying out unnecessary heart surgery. He also discusses the 'commercialisation of investigations' (p 56–60) in the context of for-profit health care. See also Michael Wynne on evidence given to the US Senate [2003 Online] Available: http://www.uow.edu.au/arts/sts/bmartin/dissent/documents/health/columb_2003.html [Accessed 21 Jan 2007].

50 per cent: see Triad 2005 *Report to the Securities and Exchange Commission (SEC)* [Online] Available: http://library.corporate-ir.net/library/11/115/115178/items/186915/tri_2005_10K.pdf [Accessed 29 Jan 2007].

$3.6 billion: John Barton 2005 'Emphasis on private healthcare ill-advised' *Irish Times* 18 Apr.

Over sixty hospitals: Jo Revill 2006 *Observer* 17 Sept. Up to sixty casualty units, midwife-led maternity units and children's centres in smaller hospitals are slated to close, as the NHS faces a £512 million deficit. Towns with populations of less than 250,000 are particularly at risk of losing services. James Johnson, head of the British Medical Association said that 'political timidity' had stopped the creation of 'large multi-centres which have all the facilities'.

around €6,500: Evelyn Ring 2000 *Irish Examiner* op cit.

page 252

49 per cent: The total number of acute or short-stay beds in Ireland is 15,055 (13,255 in public hospitals, 1,800 in private). With 2,200 new private beds coming on-stream, this is set to rise to 17,255. Taking the Minister's figures at face value, pegging private activity in the public sector at just 25 per cent gives a notional 3,314 private beds in public hospitals. Add to this the existing 1,800, plus the 2,200 being built: this gives a total of 7,314, or 42 per cent of the total. With private admissions in some public hospitals running at 40–50 per cent, the actual proportion of private beds is likely to be higher.

July 2005: Anne Counihan 2006 'The Business of Health' Berkeley Court Hotel Dublin 5 Apr.

linear accelerators: ibid.

page 253

Public waiting lists will rise: Stephen J. Duckett 2005 'Private care and public waiting' *Australian Health Review* 29 (1): 87–93.

value for money: The Comptroller and Auditor General's office is the sole agency, outside the Department of Health, to have access to the prices paid for procedures by the NTPF. He acceded to a request from the Department's Accounting Officer not to disclose these prices on the grounds of 'commercial sensitivity'. See Comptroller and Auditor General 2004 *Annual Report* Stationery Office, Dublin, 135. The report reveals a staggering variation in the prices charged by different hospitals and different doctors for the eight most common procedures funded by the NTPF. Private hospitals are allowed to build capital costs and depreciation into their charges for procedures carried out under the fund (p 133).

page 254

privatisation of VHI: At time of writing (Jan 2007), a report was expected from the Competition Authority, advocating the break-up of VHI into 'competing' entities; the Government had previously declared its intention to put VHI onto a commercial footing. http://www.rte.ie/news/2006/1215/insurance.html?rss [Accessed 21 Jan 2007].

'this costly over-supply': John Barton, personal communication, 2007.

page 255

'within government's control': Joel Bakan 2004 *The Corporation: the pathological pursuit of profit and power*. Constable, London, 153.

Sir John Moore: John Fleetwood 1983 *The History of Medicine in Ireland*. The Skellig Press, Dublin, 148.

HIQA: [online] Available: http://www.dohc.ie/issues/health_bill_2006/ [Accessed 22 Jan 2007].

Aut Even: Maev-Ann Wren 2003 *Unhealthy State: anatomy of a sick society*. New Island, Dublin, 292.

page 257

reduces breastfeeding: *Interim Report of the National Committee on Breastfeeding* May 2003. Health Promotion Unit, Dublin, 19.

senior employees: Joe Humphreys 2000 *Irish Times* 12 July. The Blood Transfusion Service Board's former chief technical officer Seán Hanratty was named as the director of a commercial company, Acu-Science, which supplied pharmaceutical products to the Board. In evidence to the Haemophilia Tribunal, it was suggested that Mr Hanratty might have funded a BTSB project which could have prevented haemophiliacs from becoming infected and from which, if patented, he stood to gain. The research project was abandoned after three years without explanation, however.

patient advocacy groups: Orla O'Donovan 2006 'Corporate colonization of health activism? Irish advocacy organizations' modes of engagement with pharmaceutical corporations' *International Journal of Health Sciences* [In press].

infant-formula: Lionra (formerly Baby Milk Action) 'The Code Report: summary of findings' [Online] Available: http://www.cmn.ie/cmnsitenew/training/sinead/report.htm#system [Accessed 31 Jan 2007].

page 258

Ciba-Geigy: Institute of Public Administration 2004 *Administration Yearbook and Diary*. Institute of Public Administration, Dublin, 233. Ciba-Geigy endows UCD's sole chair in general practice.

16: RESTORING THE REPUBLIC
page 263

'twenty-two radiotherapy units': Comhairle na n-Ospidéal 2000 *Review of titles, roles, training pathways and qualifications of consultant medical oncologists and radiation oncologists (radiotherapists/clinical oncologists): report of the review group.* Comhairle na n-Ospidéal, Dublin, 9–10. In Scotland, specialist outpatient clinics are held in district hospitals in the catchment area of the Beatson Oncology Centre at the Western Infirmary, Glasgow.

Newcastle: N. Rousseau, E. McColl and M. Eccles 1994 *Primary health in rural areas: issues of equity and resource management—a literature review* Report no 66. Newcastle Centre for Health Services Research, University of Newcastle upon Tyne. In I.J. Munhall 2005 'Trend towards centralisation of hospital services, and its effect on access to care for rural and remote communities in the UK' *Rural and Remote Health* 5: 390.

page 264

remaining time on earth: A.G Baird. et al 2000 'Centralisation of cancer services in rural areas has disadvantages'. *British Medical Journal* 320: 717. In ibid.

'Dead on arrival': Royal College of Surgeons 1988 *Working party on the management of patients with major injuries.* Royal College of Surgeons, London. In ibid

diabetes-induced blindness: G.P. Leese et al 1993 'Use of mobile screening unit for diabetic retinopathy in rural and urban areas'. *British Medical Journal* 306: 187–9. In ibid.

die from asthma: J.M. Wilson 1984 'Asthma deaths in Scotland 1965–1980'. *Scottish Medical Journal* 29: 84–9. In ibid.

'money from rural': C. White 2001 *Who gets what where—and why? The NHS is failing rural and disadvantaged areas.* Countryside Agency, Cheltenham. In ibid.

'Fair Shares': J. Arbuthnott 1999 *Fair Shares for All: report of the national review of resource allocation for the NHS in Scotland.* Scottish Executive, Edinburgh.

A recent RCSI *report*: L.E. Luke 2003 *Initial management of the severely injured patient: clinical guidelines*. Royal College of Surgeons in Ireland, Dublin. Trauma is the leading cause of death and illness in Ireland in the under-45s. Contributing factors include: 'The relatively poor condition of the national road network, the large proportion of unqualified drivers, the under-developed culture of "health and safety" observance in the construction and marine industries and the high rate of young male suicide'. [Online] Available: http://www.rcsi.ie/documents/SEVERLYINJUREDGUIDELINES.pdf [Accessed 22 Jan 2007].

'life-saving surgery may be needed': ibid, 15.

page 265

'Curiously enough': Liam McMullin 2006 Letter *Irish Times* 20 Nov.

page 266

100 highest-ranking: John Barton *A critique of Hanly and alternative* 2004, 23. From a survey of 6,000 acute hospitals in the US, ranked on indicators such as quality of care and efficiency. [Online] Available: www.saveourhospital.com [Accessed 22 Jan 2007].

'delay the point': Chris Lyons 2006 *Northern Standard* 19 Jan.

a 'peripheral' hospital: J.T. Street et al 1999 'Trauma on rural roads: the role of a peripheral hospital'. *Injury* Jun 30 (5): 337–40. In L.E. Luke 2003 op cit. 'This 'peripheral' hospital was able to manage nearly 80 per cent of the trauma case load resulting from road crashes in its catchment area in one year (1996): approximately 18.5 per cent of the 963 cases were admitted to the county hospital (of whom 12 per cent had surgery there) while 20 per cent of the patients needed to be transferred to the regional 'trauma centre' (a tertiary teaching hospital).'

1,500 head injuries: S.M. Carroll and T.P.F. O'Connor 1996 'Trends in the aetiology of facial fractures in the south of Ireland (1975–1993)'. *Irish Medical Journal* Sept–Oct 89 (5): 88–9. In L.E. Luke 2003 op cit. 'A retrospective study of 1,564 head injuries presenting to a regional hospital in Ireland, over twelve months, found that 1 per cent died, 12 per cent were admitted and the remainder discharged after initial assessment. Forty-three patients (22 per cent) had a computed tomographic (CT) brain scan performed and eighteen of these were abnormal. These scans were transmitted electronically to a specialist neurosurgical unit (SNU) and, based on this, just six patients needed to be transferred. The authors concluded that 96 per cent of those with a head injury severe enough to warrant hospitalisation can be safely managed in a non-specialist unit with access to CT facilities and image link transmission to a SNU.' Telemedicine was likely to improve trauma care in Ireland significantly over the next decade, the RCSI concluded.

'definitive' care: L.E. Luke 2003 op cit.

83 per cent: ibid, Appendix 2. Only 17 per cent of those who attend an A&E unit, nationally, arrive by ambulance or other emergency service

page 267

€6,000–€7,000: Health Services Action Group 2005 'Hanly—regional self-sufficiency or local landmine? A summary of the Health Services Action Group position'. Presented to the Joint Oireachtas Committee on Health and Children 24 Mar.

Aberdeen: Department of Health 2003 'Keeping the NHS local—a new direction of travel' [Online] Available: http://www.dh.gov.uk/assetRoot/04/08/59/47/ 04085947.pdf [Accessed 29 Jan 2007].

individual specialists: Jean-Marie Clement 1998 *Reflexions pour l'hôpital: proximité, cooperation, pouvoirs*. Les Etudes Hospitalières, Bordeaux.

bad habits: Maureen Harding Clark 2006 *The Lourdes Hospital Inquiry: an Inquiry into peripartum hysterectomy at Our Lady of Lourdes Hospital, Drogheda*. The Stationery Office, Dublin, 226, 230.

page 268

the Netherlands: European Workgroup of Independent Midwives 2000 *Europe needs midwives: midwives and women for a healthier Europe*. European Workgroup of Independent Midwives, Epen.

World Health Organisation: World Health Organisation 1996 *Care in Normal Birth: a practical guide*. WHO/FRH/MSM/96.24 Division of Family and Reproductive Health, Geneva.

as safe, or safer: M. MacDorman and G. Singh 1998 'Midwifery care, social and medical risk factors and birth outcomes in the USA'. *Journal of Epidemiology and Community Health* 52: 310–17. A study of 4 million low-risk births that compared outcomes between doctor and midwife-attended births; it showed that midwives had significantly lower neonatal and infant death rates than doctors.

Dutch obstetricians: A number of studies exist. See, for example, T. Wiegers et al 1997 'Outcome of planned home and planned hospital births in low risk pregnancies: prospective study in midwifery practice in The Netherlands'. *British Medical Journal* 313: 1309–13. See also D. van Alten et al 1989 'Midwifery in The Netherlands: the Wormerveer study; selection, mode of delivery, perinatal mortality and infant morbidity'. *British Journal of Obstetrics and Gynaecology* June (6). A classic outcome-oriented study that tracked a midwifery practice in Amsterdam for a number of years.

'birth houses': Jennie James 2004 'The battle over birth'. *Time Magazine* 28 Mar [Online] Available: http://www.time.com/time/magazine/article/0,9171,605437-2,00.html [Accessed 29 Jan 2007].

no good evidence: Murray Enkin et al 1995 *A Guide to Effective Care in Pregnancy and Childbirth*. Oxford University Press, Oxford, 15. 'It is inherently unwise, and perhaps, unsafe for women with normal pregnancies to be cared for by obstetric specialists, even if the required personnel were available.'

medical inductions: Our Lady of Lourdes Hospital Drogheda 2002 *Maternity Unit Annual Report*. North-Eastern Health Board, Drogheda, 8. In 2002, 31 per cent of all mothers pregnant with their first child, who were induced at 37 weeks or over, had a Caesarean section.

autism: Michel Odent (Primal Health), who has a particular interest in the action of oxytocin, discusses the rise of two epidemics, autism and induction: no causal relationship between the two has yet been established. [Online] Available: http://www.birthpsychology.com/primalhealth/primal12.html [Accessed 29 Jan

2007]. For a wide-ranging discussion of induction, see Nancy Griffin 2001 'Let the baby decide: the case against inducing labour'. *Mothering* 105 Mar–Apr. Again, highlighting the need for empirical work in this area, Griffin cites Dr Eric Hollander of Mt Sinai Medical Center New York, who believes autism is linked to oxytocin-induced labours. [Online] Available: http://www.mothering.com/articles/pregnancy_birth/birth_preparation/inducing.html [Accessed 29 Jan 2007].

page 270
stifling dissent: Orla O'Donovan 2006 'Corporate colonization of health activism? Irish advocacy organizations' modes of engagement with pharmaceutical corporations'. *International Journal of Health Sciences* [In press].

page 271
eighty-three organisations: Irish Health Services Accreditation Board 2006: 7 [Online] Available: http://www.ihsab.ie/documents/IHSABAugust2006 Newsletter-Final.pdf [Accessed 25 Jan 2007].
regional forums: the 2004 Health Act prohibits the regional forums from considering any issue related to 'clinical judgement', that is, anything that can be traced back to a decision on patient care. The same prohibition applies to all complaints machinery set up under the Act.

page 273
a 50:50 stake: the Council consists of twelve representatives of the professions and eleven lay members, drawn from a variety of backgrounds, including education, employment and consumer groups, appointed by the NHS Appointments Commission. [Online] Available: http://www.nmc-uk.org/aSection.aspx? SectionID=38 [Accessed 25 Jan 2007].

Acknowledgements

This book has its origins in the highs and lows of campaigning, in the struggle for decent health services that meet the basic needs of individuals, families and communities throughout Ireland. Although the views expressed here are mine, *Emergency* has been fuelled in part by my friends and colleagues in the Health Services Action Group (HSAG) and its affiliates, the National Birth Alliance and the committed public representatives who have supported our campaigns, among them Deputies John Gormley, Caoimhghín Ó Caoláin, Paudge Connolly and Seymour Crawford, and MEPs Kathy Sinnott and Marian Harkin.

I owe a particular debt of gratitude to Dr John Barton, consultant physician/cardiologist at Portiuncula Hospital, Ballinasoe, and former chair of the HSAG, who deepened my understanding of health care issues and contributed relevant research. Likewise Peadar McMahon, chair of both the Monaghan Community Alliance and HSAG, whose energy and commitment to the cause remain a source of inspiration to all. Dr Tom Nolan, a general practitioner in Kilrush, my predecessor as national secretary of the HSAG, was also generous with his encouragement.

The late P.J. Turley and Martin Smyth, former and current editors, respectively, of *The Northern Standard*, gave me the space to hone my skills as a columnist. Their family-owned newspaper, in its 167th year of publication, is a true standard-bearer of fearless and independent comment among Irish media. It has been a privilege to write for both of them and for the indomitable people of Monaghan.

Over the years, I have been sustained by a wide network of colleagues and friends, too extensive to list here, in the Irish and international birth communities. Special thanks are due to midwife Philomena Canning, who read the manuscript attentively, for her enthusiasm, comradeship, support and advice; to friend and photographer Máire O'Regan, well known for her long and selfless campaigning in Cork for better maternity services, whose acute understanding of birth issues helped to sharpen mine; and to Professor Jean-Marie Clément, of Paris VIII University, for the depth and lucidity of his thought.

Books need advocates and I was delighted to have Faith O'Grady, literary agent with Lisa Richards, as mine. She smoothed the path towards publication, effortlessly. It is an honour to be published by Gill and Macmillan, and I deeply appreciate the faith in this book shown by publishing director Fergal Tobin. Managing editor D Rennison Kunz showed patience and forbearance with an author struggling to produce a complex and detailed work to a hugely challenging timetable.

In these circumstances, faith, hope, love, support and encouragement were what I needed most and those closest to me never failed me. My gratitude goes to Emer, whose determination to see me write another book was boundless, and whose faith never flagged; to Ruadhán, whose keen interest in politics and practical engagement with computers were a bonus at all times; to Colm, for a lifetime of affection, support, collaboration and wise counsel; and Paul, whose medical knowledge and clinical experience could always be relied upon, and who read the manuscript with care. Finally, Wally's commitment to this book was indispensable. His research and contacts were vital, his moral and practical support key. In the concluding stages, his tenacious engagement with what had by then become a joint enterprise was essential to the meeting of almost impossible deadlines.